Workers and Allies:

Female Participation in the American Trade Union Movement, 1824-1976

Exhibition Organized by Judith O'Sullivan

Catalog by Judith O'Sullivan and Rosemary Gallick

Published for the Smithsonian Institution
Traveling Exhibition Service
by the
Smithsonian Institution Press, Washington, D.C. 1975

In Acknowledgment:

The celebration of our nation's Bicentennial marks a time for reflection upon the people and events that made and shaped our heritage.

It is significant that many Americans are choosing this time to focus on individuals forgotten or omitted from our history books. In presenting this history of women's participation in the American trade union movement, the Smithsonian Institution Traveling Exhibition Service has taken the initiative by sponsoring research in women's history and trade union history—two areas only recently receiving attention from researchers and the public. The simultaneous appearance of this book and the exhibition marks the first time that available information on women in the trade union movement has been consolidated into a single theme.

The concept for the exhibition and later its research and organization were provided by Judith O'Sullivan. Historian and feminist, descended from a Pittsburgh labor family, Ms. O'Sullivan combined scholarship with enthusiasm to provide original material together with many previously unpublished images.

Our thanks go to Rosemary Gallick, whose extensive research provided the bulk of the information for the publication.

There are also others to thank, including Harry Amdur and Al Striano at Modernage Photographic Services, Inc., for producing under great pressure fine quality work for the exhibition; and Martin Stephen Moskof, designer of both exhibition and publication, for his energetic and sympathetic treatment of the materials.

Andrea P. Stevens
Lary Rosenblatt
Exhibition Coordinators

Library of Congress Cataloging in Publication Data

O'Sullivan, Judith.
  Workers and allies.

  Bibliography: p.
  Supt. of Docs. no.: SI 1.2 : W89/2
  1. Women in trade-unions—United States—History—
Exhibitions—Catalogs. 2. Women in trade-unions—United
States—Biography—Exhibitions—Catalogs. I. Gallick,
Rosemary, joint author. II. Smithsonian Institution.
Traveling Exhibition Service. III. Title.
HD6079.2.U5085   331.4   75-619279

CONTENTS

Representative Bella S. Abzug confers with union members.

4

INTRODUCTION

by Bella S. Abzug, Member of Congress

Attention must be paid, the truth must be known—even if it takes 200 years.

This Bicentennial exhibition on the contributions of women to the American labor movement is welcome because it focuses at last on an aspect of our nation's history known only to a very few, and known scarcely at all to women. In presenting this fascinating pictorial display, the Smithsonian tells us not only about our past but enriches our understanding of present struggles. Most of all, it helps to demolish the myths that still persist.

In most American history texts, women have been the "also rans," the incidental characters who seemed to play no essential role in the development of our society except as wives and mothers. Even today, when thirty-nine percent of the labor force consists of women, the impression is widespread that this is a fairly new development and that women's pampered place has traditionally been in the home.

The truth, of course, is that from the dawn of history women have worked, performing tasks that required the utmost skill as well as the most physical strength and endurance. From colonial times on in America, women worked. In their homes as wives, daughters, indentured servants, they had to weave, spin, sew, make soap, shoes, candles, furniture, cook, clean, and do repairs; they had to bear, nurse, and educate children; they had to work in the fields, and they did so without pay and with no claim to their men's earnings. In the towns they worked as seamstresses, milliners, cooks, laundresses, barmaids, teachers, printers, and at other crafts, and always they were paid less than men.

On the slave plantations they worked like beasts of burden, and no concern was shown for their presumably cherished femininity. As Sojourner Truth was to say: "Nobody ever helped me into carriages, or over mud puddles, or gives me any best place, and ain't I a woman? Look at me! Look at my arm! I have plowed, and planted, and gathered into barns, and no man could head me—and ain't I a woman?"

It was not until the New England mills and factories began to spring up in the early nineteenth century that women in large numbers—many of them very young girls—were drawn into wage labor. Almost inevitably with their employment came militancy, organization, and demands for equal pay and humane working conditions.

The women shoemakers who went on strike in Lynn, Massachusetts, in 1833, declaring, "American ladies will not be slaves," were the foremothers of hundreds of thousands of women who took part in the bitter and often bloody struggles that have marked the growth of American trade unions and the gains made by labor.

In looking at this exhibition, I come away with three main thoughts. First, women have been much more deeply involved in the building of the labor movement than even I as a former labor attorney had suspected. Second, as they fought for better working conditions and equal pay—demands that have yet to be fully won after almost two centuries of struggle—women were too often discriminated against in their own organizations and shut out of leadership. Thus, we still have the phenomenon today of unions composed almost exclusively of women workers and led almost exclusively by men. Finally, women's efforts to achieve economic equality depend in large part on the success of women's struggle for political equality.

This was recognized at the first Women's Rights Convention in Seneca Falls in 1848 when Elizabeth Stanton, later an active participant in the labor movement, said the time had come "for the question of women's wrongs to be laid before the public. . . . Woman herself must do this work; for women alone can understand the height, the depth, the length and the breadth of her degradation."

The message that woman must liberate herself is both old and new.

As one of the founders of the National Women's Political Caucus, I find particular satisfaction in the fact that many of my sisters who helped to organize the caucus went on to organize the Coalition of Labor Union Women, which is dedicated to winning equality for women on the job and in their unions.

Women draw strength from knowledge of their own past struggles and today, 200 years after the founding of our nation, they draw strength from each other as they join in a broad women's rights movement that encompasses their demand for equal rights economically, socially, politically . . . and totally.

Workers and Allies:
Female Participation in the
American Trade Union Movement

by Judith O'Sullivan

"The Shoemakers' Strike in Lynn, Massachusetts," *Frank Leslie's Illustrated Newspaper*, March 17, 1860. *(Courtesy Library of Congress)*

The fabric of American history is woven from the lives of countless citizens. Despite the vast contributions and numerical preponderance of working Americans, however, this supposedly silent majority remains unsung, its experience chronicled by only a handful of historians, novelists, and filmmakers. The saga of the American working woman has been doubly neglected, for prejudice against the laborer has been compounded by the dismissal of woman as a subject of no intrinsic interest.

Since colonial times women have participated in the American labor movement, first forming sisterly self-improvement societies, then organizing their own trade unions, and finally demanding full admission, rights, and responsibilities in the national assemblies of brother workers.

Individually, women have contributed as organizers, often unionizing men in occupations to which they themselves could not aspire; as union leaders, elected officials, and journalists, calling national attention to industrial abuses; as historians and archivists, documenting the struggle for economic justice; as wives, mothers, and daughters, forming auxiliaries and emergency brigades; and as benefactresses, filling picket lines and contributing money to strike-depleted union treasuries. On the occasion of America's Bicentennial and in recognition of the present renaissance in both the women's and labor movements, the Smithsonian Institution Traveling Exhibition Service presents this catalog. It provides a unique repository of previously scattered core information, including a chronology, bibliography, and dictionary of biography of past and present workers and allies.

> *As our fathers resisted unto*
> *blood the lordly avarice of*
> *the British ministry, so we,*
> *their daughters, never will*
> *wear the yoke which has been*
> *prepared for us.*
> *—declaration of striking textile*
> *workers in Lowell, Massachusetts,*
> *October 1836* [1]

During the colonial period women contributed to the family income by producing cloth. In the winter months the entire family participated in textile production, the father weaving yarn carded and spun by his wife and children. The success of the American Revolution led to the demise of this domestic system. Cut off from England, the source of many staples, America was forced to develop its own industry. Faced with a limited supply of labor, American industry eagerly recruited women and children, their labors receiving the endorsement of our Founding Fathers.

Impressed by the virtues of women workers during a visit to the Boston Duck Sail Manufactory in 1789, President George Washington described the spinners as "daughters of decayed families, and girls of character—none others are admitted." [2] In his *Report on Manufactures,* communicated to the House of Representatives on December 5, 1791, Secretary of the Treasury Alexander Hamilton praised the industry of women workers and child laborers, "rendered more useful, and the latter more early useful, by manufacturing establishments than they would otherwise be." [3]

As the size of factories increased and absentee ownership became common, industrial abuses multiplied. Common exploitative practices included: immediate and arbitrary wage reductions of up to twenty-five percent; the thirteen-hour workday and six-day workweek; arbitrary increases in the cost of room and board at company boardinghouses; inflated accounts and costs at the company store; crowded conditions in company boardinghouses, in which six or more workers might share a room; obligatory support of the company church, which was often not of the employee's faith; and prohibition against talking on the job.

Workers were further obliged to take an "iron-clad oath," according to which the employee bound himself to work for whatever wages "the company may see fit to pay and be subject to the fines imposed by the company" and to abstain from entering "any combination whereby the work may be impeded or the company's interest in any work injured; if we do, we agree to forfeit to the company the amount of wages that may be due to us at the time." [4]

Such oaths were enforced by the prosecution of unionists for conspiracy. In *Commonwealth v. Pullis* (1806), eight cordwainers belonging to the

Journeymen Boot and Shoemakers of Philadelphia were found guilty by the Mayor's Court of attempting "to increase and augment the wages paid them," and of "deceitfully forming themselves into a club to attain their ends, thus constituting . . . a criminal conspiracy." In *People v. Melvin* (1810), twenty-four journeymen cordwainers were found guilty by the New York City Court of General Sessions of conspiring to maintain a closed shop and fixed price scale. In *Commonwealth v. Moore, et al.* (1827), twenty-five Philadelphia journeymen tailors charged with "conspiring to raise their wages" were found guilty on one of eight counts; and in *People v. Fisher* (1835), journeymen shoemakers in Geneva, New York, were found guilty by Chief Justice Savage of the New York Supreme Court of conspiring to establish a wage scale.[5] Despite such prosecution for "combination," workers continued to organize, demonstrating their discontent by striking.

In 1824 Pawtucket, Rhode Island, became the site of the first organized protest by female factory employees. At a meeting "conducted . . . without noise, or scarcely a single speech," 102 female workers struck in support of brother weavers protesting both the reduction of wages and extension of the workday.[6] Although reviled by the press as harbingers of a "gynecocracy," early women workers repeatedly asserted their right to a living wage and reasonable workday.[7] In 1828 Paterson, New Jersey, textile workers struck in support of the ten-hour workday; Philadelphia and Manayunk, Pennsylvania, cotton spinners struck to protest a wage cut of twenty-five percent; and Dover, New Hampshire, millworkers struck against company fines for tardiness and talking on the job. In 1829 Taunton, Massachusetts, textile workers struck in protest of a wage reduction. In 1831, 1,600 members of the United Tailoresses Society of New York struck for a wage increase of 33⅓ percent. In 1833 the Baltimore Society of Tailoresses and Seamstresses struck for a wage increase, and the Female Society of Lynn (Massachusetts) and Vicinity led striking shoebinders in a fight for increased wages. Signaled by the wave of a sister organizer's bonnet, 2,000 textile workers in Lowell, Massachusetts, walked out in 1834, protesting the dismissal of a coworker and a wage reduction of fifteen percent, and asserting

that "none of us will go back unless they receive us all as one."[8] That same year Manayunk mill operatives struck to protest a wage cut of 25 percent, and Amesbury, Massachusetts, weavers walked out in response to a company proposal that they tend two looms rather than one with no increase in pay. Strikes continued in 1835, when workers in twenty Paterson, New Jersey, textile mills demanded that the workday be shortened from 13½ to 11 hours, and New York shoebinders struck for higher pay. In 1836, 2,500 members of the Lowell, Massachusetts, Factory Girls Association struck to protest a 12½ percent increase in the cost of room and board at company boarding houses, and Dover, New Hampshire, textile workers decried a wage reduction. In 1837, 1,600 members of the Tailoresses Society of New York City struck for a wage scale.[9] Despite the accelerated prosecution of such unionists, organized labor finally received judicial endorsement in 1842, when Lemuel Shaw, the prestigious Chief Justice of the Massachusetts Supreme Court, reversed the conviction of seven members of the Boston Journeymen Bootmakers' Society. In *Commonwealth v. Hunt*, Shaw ruled that "such agreement could not be pronounced a criminal conspiracy" and that unions "far from being criminal or unlawful . . . may be highly meritorious and public spirited."[10] His landmark decision ended the American application of the English law of criminal conspiracy to trade unions and provided a legal foundation for unionization.

The character of the courageous pioneer unionists was not unlike that of the Founding Fathers. Sharing the belief derived from Puritan ancestors that industry was morally elevating and idleness sinful, early female factory employees, despite scant leisure time, participated actively in the cultural life of New England. Although their workday averaged thirteen hours, textile workers in Lowell, Massachusetts, attended lectures by Ralph Waldo Emerson and John Quincy Adams regularly and read the works of Margaret Fuller and Nathaniel Hawthorne. The fruits of such self-improvement appeared in *The Lowell Offering*, a "repository of articles, entirely written by females actively employed in the Mills." Many of these workers were, in fact, well educated, and had entered the mills because of the relatively high rate of pay and the limited opportunity for female teachers, males dominating that profession until after the Civil War.[11]

The social commitment of the first women workers transcended their immediate social situation. Reflecting this commitment, many early working women's associations adopted resolutions urging an immediate end to slavery. (In the South, of course, slavery rendered paid labor superfluous. Employment opportunities were rare; both male and female labor organizations were nonexistent.)

Perhaps the most important of the early organizations of working women was the Female Labor Reform Association. Founded in New England in 1845, it immediately recognized the kinship of all workers, black and white, male and female. The Manchester, New Hampshire, branch quickly admitted men to membership, "seeing [as] they can do nothing without us and we cannot do much without them." Asserting that "American slavery must be uprooted before the elevation sought by the laboring classes can be effected," the Lowell Reform League annually circulated a petition to Congress urging immediate abolition of slavery in the District of Columbia.

The Lowell branch also agitated for immediate industrial reform through its journal, *The Voice of Industry,* and through testimony before the Massachusetts legislature. *The Voice of Industry* condemned recruitment policies, including false representation "to the girls that they can tend more machinery than is possible, and that the work is so very neat, and the wages such, that they can dress in silks and spend half their time reading." The *Voice* also opposed use of the notorious "slaver," a black wagon whose driver scoured Vermont and New Hampshire for the Lowell mills, and was "paid a dollar a head for all he brings to market, and more in proportion to the distance—if they bring bring them from such a distance that they cannot easily get back." Appearing before the Massachusetts legislature for the Female Labor Reform Association, Sarah G. Bagley condemned conditions in factories, company stores, and company boarding-houses. She also urged extension of the federal ten-hour workday, proclaimed by President Martin Van Buren in 1840, to private enterprise, reasoning that

denial of "time to cultivate their minds" was one of the chief evils inflicted on workers by the factory system. Responding to the paired entreaties of the Female Labor Reform Association and the Workingmen's Association, the Massachusetts legislature set up the first state committee to investigate industrial abuse. As a result of the demands of textile workers, a majority of whom were women, New Hampshire adopted the ten-hour workday in 1847; Pennsylvania followed in 1848; New Jersey in 1851.[12]

Assisting the working woman in her campaign for redress of industrial abuse was her feminist sister, who shared her ethnic background and ethical preoccupations. Declaring that "All men and women are created equal," Elizabeth Cady Stanton, a champion of female suffrage, and Lucretia Mott, a Quaker minister and militant abolitionist, opened the first feminist convention in Seneca Falls, New York, in 1848. Two years later Lucretia Mott and Elizabeth Oakes Smith helped to establish a cooperative sewing shop in Philadelphia, which they supported financially.[13]

Throughout the nineteenth and twentieth centuries the working woman continued to attract feminist allies. Among these were Louisa May Alcott, Charlotte Perkins Gilman, and Helen Keller, who wrote. "So long as I confine my activities to social service and the blind, they [newspapers] compliment me extravagantly, calling me 'archpriestess of the sightless,' 'wonder woman,' and 'a modern miracle'. . . but to advocate that all human beings should have leisure and comfort, the decencies and refinements of life, is a Utopian dream, and one who seriously contemplates its realization must indeed be deaf, dumb, and blind."[14]

The difficulties besetting such alliances, however, are best illustrated by the trade union career of Susan B. Anthony, who was seated along with Elizabeth Cady Stanton, despite male opposition, as a delegate to the 1868 convention of the National Labor Union. At its 1869 convention, however, the membership voted against seating her, charging that she had underpaid employees of her journal, *The Revolution,* encouraged female strikebreakers, and discharged a typographer, Augusta Lewis, from *The Revolution* because of her organizational activity.[15]

Because of such ambiguities, many female labor

leaders remained skeptical about feminist support. "You don't need a vote to raise hell," observed veteran United Mine Workers of America organizer Mother Mary Harris Jones.[16]

The winter of 1848-49 brought with it a depression, the effects of which were felt for a decade, during which a surplus labor force of German and Irish immigrants gradually replaced Anglo-American industrial workers, who moved westward.[17] On March 7, 1860, 800 female shoebinders in Lynn, Massachusetts, breaking a decade of silence on the part of women workers, joined 4,000 brother workers to march through a blinding snowstorm to demand higher wages. "American ladies will not be slaves," their banners proclaimed. "Give us a fair compensation and we labour cheerfully."[18]

Two days earlier the strikers had received the support of presidential candidate Abraham Lincoln. Addressing an enthusiastic crowd of supporters in Hartford, Connecticut, on March 5, 1860, Lincoln endorsed the shoemakers' strike and asserted his faith in unionization. "Thank God that we have a system of labor where there can be a strike," he declared. "Whatever the pressure, there is a point where the working man may stop."[19]

During the Civil War, as in all subsequent conflicts, women filled the void created by the departure of men for battle. With the encouragement of the government, female employees assumed the soldiers' places in the fields, heavy industry, and munitions factories, and as teachers and sales personnel. Inspired by the examples of Clara Barton and Varina Howell Davis (Mrs. Jefferson Davis), women of good families became nurses. Despite enormous industrial expansion, the position of women workers after the war was jeopardized by the return of the veterans, an influx of widows, now the sole support of their families, and a new wave of immigrants, recruited by a coalition of manufacturers, steamship companies, and railroads. While veterans and male immigrants replaced female employees in heavy industry, women retained their places as teachers and salesclerks, and continued to work as nurses and farmhands.[20] This pattern of industrial opportunity during war and the ensuing displacement during peace continued through World Wars I and II and the Vietnamese conflict.

Impoverished, often unable to speak English, the new European immigrants and their children were ruthlessly exploited by unscrupulous employers. In the East, this exploitation was most often found in the clothing trades, in which foreign labor was predominant. There, men, women, and children toiled in crowded, airless quarters under a system of subcontracted labor which earned the name "sweatshop." Since workers were not paid salaries, but according to the number of items produced ("piece work"), hours were interminable and homework common. This was not only injurious to the worker but harmful to the consumer. Garments intended for market often provided makeshift beds for tubercular child laborers.

In Chicago the exploitation of the sweatshop was rivaled by the shame of the stockyards. The documentation of unsanitary conditions in the meatpacking industry in Upton Sinclair's *The Jungle* (1906), an exposé of the abuse of immigrants, shocked the American consumer. "I aimed at the public's heart," observed Sinclair, "and by accident I hit it in the stomach." Notwithstanding lack of educational and economic opportunity, immigrants flocked to the numerous postbellum labor organizations, which flourished despite the surplus labor market.

Among the many postbellum workers' associations were the National Labor Union, founded in 1866, which, transcending the self-interest of male workers, pledged "individual and undivided support to the sewing women, factory operatives, and daughters of toil"; the Knights of Labor, established in 1869, its membership open to blacks and females, among its goals "To secure for both sexes equal pay for equal work"; the Daughters of St. Crispin, the first national organization of trade union women, which held its first convention in Lynn, Massachusetts, on July 28, 1869; the Working Women's Protective Union, founded in 1866, empowered to collect back wages from recalcitrant employers; and the National Colored Labor Union, established in 1869.[21] The postbellum organizations were the first labor associations to enter the political arena. Among their achievements was the proclamation of an eight-hour federal workday on June 25, 1868.

The financial panic of 1873 was followed by a

Marjory Collins, *Women Workers Leaving Republic Steel, Buffalo, New York, 1943. (Courtesy Library of Congress)*

Lemuel Shaw (1781-1861), Chief Justice of the Massachusetts Supreme Court; portrait by William Morris Hunt. *(Courtesy Massachusetts Historical Society)*

Julia Bracken Wendt, *Insignia of the National Women's Trade Union League. (Courtesy Library of Congress)*

"Filling Cartridges at the United States Arsenal, Watertown, Massachusetts," *Harper's Weekly,* July 20, 1861. *(Courtesy Library of Congress)*

depression which lasted six years. Prolonged economic crisis led in 1877 to national strikes and violence, the first in the American labor movement. Secret societies were formed; industries were sabotaged. Responding to capitalists' demands for the protection of private property, the federal government intervened for the first time in labor disputes, dispatching troops to protect railroads and factories. To safeguard property and to infiltrate labor organizations, industrialists recruited private police. Of these, the Pinkerton Detective Agency was most effective.

In the Pennsylvania anthracite fields, immigrant miners, inspired by the legendary Irish heroine who thwarted English landlords' attempts to evict indigent farmers, formed the secret society known as the Molly Maguires. Although their goals were increased wages and redress of industrial abuses, the Mollies allegedly performed murderous reprisals against company officers. Hired by the coal companies, Pinkerton agent James McParlan infiltrated the Ancient Order of Hibernians, a supposed front for the terrorist organization. On the basis of McParlan's assertion that its members had confided in him a series of crimes committed between 1865 and 1875 and had conspired with him to commit further atrocities, ten men were tried, convicted, and executed.

Climaxing four years of depression, a national railroad strike against wage reductions and increased workloads began on July 16, 1877. The strike left in its wake over one hundred deaths and massive destruction of property. In Pittsburgh, local members of the National Guard, called up to protect the property of the Pennsylvania Railway Company, joined instead their striking neighbors. Infuriated by the firing of Philadelphia guardsmen, mobs set ablaze the roundhouse in which the troops were sequestered, forcing their retreat.

In 1886 violence led to American organized labor's rejection of foreign ideology. When a bomb exploded in Chicago's Haymarket Square on May 4, killing seven policemen and four workers, anarchist orators were promptly seized, convicted, and executed. For years after Albert R. Parsons's death, his widow, Lucy Eldine Gonzalez Parsons, fought to establish his innocence. Seven years later, Illinois Governor Altgeld declared the verdict unjustifiable

and commuted the life sentences of three surviving prisoners. The tragedy of Haymarket was twofold: lives were hastily taken and labor organizations were linked in the popular mind with terrorist activity, as the bombing had occurred during a national drive for the eight-hour workday. Fearing media exploitation of the coincidence, organized labor publicly dissociated itself from foreign radicalism, a position it has frequently maintained.

Despite damage to its public image, the progress of labor continued unchecked. In 1886 the American Federation of Labor was established, its president Samuel Gompers. That same year the Knights of Labor created its Women's Department, headed by Leonora Barry, the widowed mother of three, charged as general investigator to document "the abuses to which our sex is subjected by unscrupulous employers" and to "agitate the principles which our Order teaches, of equal pay and the abolition of child labor."[22] Also in 1886 the Working Women's Society was founded by Leonora O'Reilly, a rank-and-file organizer, assisted by Josephine Shaw Lowell, Mrs. Robert Abbé, Arria Huntingdon, and E. S. Perkins, a new generation of middle-class allies.[23] The growing strength of such labor organizations was matched by the formidable might of the robber barons, their new adversaries.

The power of the new industrialists and their antagonism toward trade unions were dramatized by the Homestead Strike of 1892, during which Carnegie Steel executive Henry Clay Frick determined to break the back of organized labor. Intent on using strikebreakers, Frick mustered 300 Pinkerton agents for their protection. The detectives, however, were overpowered by workers on July 6. On July 12 National Guardsmen entered Homestead, and the mills were reopened with scab labor. Misreading the strikers' militancy, Russian immigrants Emma Goldman and Alexander Berkman conspired to assassinate Frick. The attempt, ironically, was abortive, and turned the tide of public opinion against the unionists. Although seriously wounded, Frick recovered. Berkman was sentenced to twenty-five years in prison, and employees of Carnegie Steel were deprived of union representation for forty-five years. Despite her open avowal of complicity, Goldman was never tried.[24]

Frustrated by employers' brutal suppression of trade unions, the most important of labor's female allies, the wives and daughters of working America, often resorted to unorthodox methods when standing by their striking men. On September 16, 1897, for example, "Big Mary" Septek and her "Amazon army," armed with household appliances including rolling pins and pokers, drove scabs from the Hazelton, Pennsylvania, coal mines. Outraged by her audacity, the *Wilkes-Barre Record* commented, "Those who have made themselves so conspicuous in the past week . . . in the Hazelton region were the wives, mothers and sisters of the Hungarian, Polish and Italian strikers, and it is assumed that they had the sanction of their husbands, sons and brothers in their ill-advised and unwomanly demonstrations."[25] Such "ill-advised and unwomanly demonstrations" were to occur repeatedly until the rights of workers to organization and collective bargaining were assured by law.

Meanwhile, compassionate allies established settlement houses devoted to community service and workers' education. Among these were Chicago's Hull House, established by Jane Addams and Ellen Gates Starr in 1889; Boston's Denison House, founded by Katharine Coman in 1892; New York City's Henry Street Settlement, established by Lillian D. Wald in 1893; and Brooklyn's Greenpoint Settlement, founded by Mary White Ovington in 1896.

On November 14, 1903, during the American Federation of Labor's Boston convention, blue-collar and bourgeois women united to form the National Women's Trade Union League. Open to male and female members of all races "willing to assist those trade unions already existing, which have women members, and to aid in the formation of new unions of women wage earners," the league was supported by the personal fortunes of many of its members. Among its major functions were contribution to strike funds, service as labor's media liaison, and a training program for rank-and-file female organizers. During the 1909 "Uprising of 20,000" immigrant seamstresses in New York City, the league was particularly active, seventy-five of its members forming the "mink brigade," a picket line supporting Ladies Waist Makers Union No. 25 against the soon-to-be notorious Triangle Shirtwaist Company.[26] The conditions under which the National Women's Trade Union League supported a strike were specific: women must be involved; the league must be invited by the striking union; and two league representatives must sit on all executive board meetings of the striking union.[27] The conservative bent of the league was demonstrated by its withdrawal from the 1912 Lawrence, Massachusetts, textile strike in response to the presence of the International Workers of the World (IWW).

The measured methods of the National Women's Trade Union League stood in sharp contrast to the flamboyant tactics of the IWW. Founded in Chicago in 1905, the IWW was an international organization embracing all factory employees, in contrast to the exclusive American Federation of Labor, which admitted only skilled craftsmen. Among its founding members were the most colorful and controversial figures in labor history: feisty Mother Mary Harris Jones; one-eyed Bill Haywood; the martyred Joe Hill; Haymarket widow Lucy Eldine Gonzalez Parsons; and Elizabeth Gurley Flynn, later a prominent member of the Communist party. Insisting on the First Amendment rights of American citizens, the IWW participated in the "free speech" movement, delivering impromptu orations from soapboxes. The content of these lectures was always controversial. Because the IWW challenged the Protestant ethic, questioning the redemptive value of toil, the press suggested that its acronym stood for the declaration, "I Won't Work!"

The IWW also endorsed birth control and espoused pacifism. Among the historic strikes in which the organization participated were the 1912 Lawrence, Massachusetts, textile strike; the 1912 Little Falls, New York, textile strike; the 1913 Akron, Ohio, rubber strike; the 1913 Paterson, New Jersey, textile strike; the 1914 Wheatland, California, hops pickers' strike; and the 1917 Bisbee, Arizona, copper strike. Despite its dramatic propagandizing, the IWW was undermined by American entry into World War I, during which many members, because of their militant pacifism, were tried and convicted of conspiracy under the federal espionage act. The IWW had succeeded, however, in demonstrating the need for a national industrial union, a

The Working Women's Protective Union hears a complaint against a sewing machine dealer in 1874. *(Courtesy Library of Congress)*

Women aircraft-factory workers, World War II. *(Courtesy Archives of Labor History and Urban Affairs, Wayne State University)*

"The Female Slaves of New York—Sweaters and Their Victims," *Frank Leslie's Illustrated Newspaper,* Nov. 8, 1888. *(Courtesy Library of Congress)*

(Courtesy Library of Congress)

Women collecting money during IWW strike rally in Grace Park, Akron, Ohio, 1913. *(Courtesy Archives of Labor History and Urban Affairs, Wayne State University)*

Striking IWW hops pickers on Durst Ranch, Wheatland, California, 1914. *(Courtesy Archives of Labor History and Urban Affairs, Wayne State University)*

Fred B. Schell, *The Great Strike—Destruction of the Union Depot and Hotel at Pittsburgh. (Courtesy Library of Congress)*

Mother Mary Harris Jones at Ludlow, Colorado, 1914. *(Courtesy United Mine Workers of America)*

need later met by the CIO.

Lacking an effective national organization of industrial employees, however, labor was powerless to prevent the company violence which continued throughout the first third of the twentieth century. The unyielding arrogance of employers was best demonstrated by the declaration of George F. Baer, a coal company spokesman. Addressing a citizen who complained of the industrial abuse of employees, Baer assured his critic that "The rights and interests of the laboring man will be protected and cared for—not by the labor agitators—but by the Christian men to whom God in His infinite wisdom has given control of the property interests of this country. . . ."[28]

On Saturday, March 25, 1911, fire broke out at the Triangle Shirtwaist Company in New York. Located on the eighth floor of a ten-story building, the sweatshop's doors were locked to prevent the admission of union organizers and the egress of employees. Attempting to escape death, employees leapt from the windows. The tragedy claimed the lives of 143 female workers. Among those witnessing the holocaust were journalist Mary Heaton Vorse and future Secretary of Labor Frances Perkins, who recalled years later, "I felt I must sear it not only on my mind but on my heart as a never-to-be-forgotten reminder of why I had to spend my life fighting conditions that would permit such a tragedy."[29] Building codes and protective legislation inspired by the tragedy led gradually to the end of the sweatshop.

On April 20, 1914, wives and children of striking miners were killed when their Ludlow, Colorado, tent colony was set ablaze by National Guardsmen mustered to protect the properties and officers of the Colorado Fuel and Iron Company. Enraged by the murder of their loved ones, armed miners battled the militia, took possession of the mines, and set ablaze company property. In the conflict, over forty people were slain. On April 30 federal troops entered Ludlow and restored order.[30] Among the union organizers assisting the Ludlow strikers, eighty-three-year-old Mother Jones was the chief object of enmity of the National Guard commander, Adjutant General John C. Chase. Fearing her influence, he imprisoned her for nine weeks. Justifying her detention, the general argued, "She seems . . . to have in an exceptional degree the faculty of stirring up and inciting the more ignorant and criminally disposed to deeds of violence and crime. . . . [Her] . . . speeches are couched in course [sic] vulgar, and profane language, and address themselves to the lowest passions of mankind."[31]

A second United Mine Workers of America organizer, Fannie Sellins, was to feel the full force of the coal companies' hostility. While leading striking miners at the Allegheny Coal and Coke Company near Brackenridge, Pennsylvania, the widowed mother of four was shot to death by company guards.[32] Another widowed unionist, Ella May Wiggins, a textile worker, balladeer, and the mother of five, was slain by vigilantes en route to a strikers' meeting in Gastonia, North Carolina, on September 14, 1929.[33]

Illusions of national prosperity were shattered by the collapse of the stock market on October 29, 1929. By the end of 1932 one-third of the American work force was unemployed. Idled employees filed in breadlines and ate at soup kitchens. By 1933 the gross national product had declined from approximately $104 billion to $56 billion; national income from $87 to $40 billion; workers' compensation, from $51 to $29 billion. Despite this decline, the American Federation of Labor secured enactment of the Norris-La Guardia Act, signed by President Herbert Hoover on March 23, 1932. This guaranteed to the worker "full freedom of association, self-organization, and designation of representatives of his own choosing to negotiate the terms and conditions of his employment," "free from the interference, restraint, or coercion of employers," and heralded President Franklin D. Roosevelt's National Recovery Act.[34]

Inaugurated on March 4, 1933, in the depths of the Great Depression, Franklin D. Roosevelt consolidated many of labor's gains through the National Industrial Recovery Act (the Wagner Act), which affirmed the workers' "right to organize and bargain collectively through representatives of their own choosing."[35] For his secretary of labor, Roosevelt appointed Frances Perkins, the first female cabinet officer. First Lady Eleanor Roosevelt, also deeply interested in the problems of labor, was an active member of the Women's Trade Union League.

Heartened by presidential endorsement, labor launched massive organizing drives, during which John L. Lewis revitalized the United Mine Workers of America and established the Committee for Industrial Organization (CIO). Passage of the Wagner Act in 1935 solidified federal support of unionization and contributed to successful organizing campaigns in the steel and auto industries in 1937.

Fearful of company reprisals, however, families of members of the United Auto Workers of America organized themselves into emergency brigades. Armed with planks and placards, the wives of employees of Chevrolet Plant No. 9 in Flint, Michigan, stood guard outside, defending their striking husbands—engaged in a "sit-down" within—from company guards while deterring strikebreakers.[36] The anxiety of the Flint emergency brigade was not misplaced. Two months later, on Memorial Day, 1937, Chicago police attacked 300 pickets at the Republic Steel Company plant, killing ten unionists and seriously injuring many others, including Lupe Marshall, a linguist mother of three, and resident of Hull House.[37] The Memorial Day Massacre occasioned a public outcry, indicative of the widespread support for organized labor. Shortly thereafter, the steel industry capitulated to the demands of the strikers.

By 1944 women numbered 3,500,000 in a work force of 18,600,000. Their entry into the ranks of labor was spurred by the war effort and facilitated by a national network of day care centers supported by the federal government and private industry. In 1947, however, these day care centers vanished under a provision of the Taft-Hartley Act (Labor-Management Relations Act), which, passed over the veto of President Harry Truman, "prohibited payment into negotiated trust funds for such centers."[38] In 1959 the Landrum-Griffin Act (Labor-Management Reporting and Disclosure Act) further strengthened provisions of the Taft-Hartley Act.[39] Peacetime displacement had once again followed wartime opportunity.

The Equal Pay Act of 1963, the first statutory prohibition against sex discrimination, was passed by Congress in 1964. According to the act, employers were obliged to provide equal pay for "equal work on jobs the performance of which requires equal skill, efforts, responsibility, and which are performed under similar working conditions."[40] The Civil Rights Act, Title VII, was also enacted in 1964, establishing an Equal Employment Opportunity Commission.[41] The sex amendment to the bill, prohibiting discrimination because of gender, was ironically introduced as a delaying tactic by Congressman Howard Smith of Virginia, but was strongly supported by Representative Martha Griffiths of Michigan.

Passage of these landmark acts coincided with publication of Betty Friedan's *The Feminine Mystique,* an exposé of advertising techniques employed after World War II to return women workers to the home, there to become easy targets for radio and television commercials. Passage of these acts and publication of *The Feminine Mystique* opened a new chapter in the history of the labor and women's movements, in which working women were to reassert the right to toil guaranteed by the Founding Fathers and to demand fair compensation consistent with American ideals. By 1968 the number of women in the civilian labor force had grown to 37.1 percent.[42] Increasingly the sole support of families, women now entered new occupations in their search for a living wage. In 1973, for example, women, long active as organizers in the United Mine Workers of America, entered the mines for the first time as union members.[43]

During the late sixties, labor leaders and sympathizers cast a critical eye on the state of their unions. Finding the leadership of the United Mine Workers of America unresponsive to the needs of its membership, Joseph A. ("Jock") Yablonski challenged William Anthony ("Tony") Boyle for its presidency. Yablonski's campaign, recorded by photojournalist Jeanne M. Rasmussen, was addressed to the rank and file, and exposed misuse of pension funds and indifference to occupational disease. On January 6, 1970, the bodies of the martyred insurgent, his wife, Margaret Rita, and daughter, Charlotte, were discovered in their Clarksville, Pennsylvania, home. Four years later Boyle was convicted of masterminding the murder. The Yablonski family's sacrifice, however, outraged a new generation of unionists

The tragic aftermath of the Triangle Shirtwaist Company fire. *(Courtesy Library of Congress)*

At the urging of female unionists, including Rose Schneiderman, President Franklin D. Roosevelt reappointed Secretary of Labor Frances Perkins three times; here she watches him sign the Social Security Act, August 14, 1936. (Wide World Photos, Inc.) *(Courtesy Franklin D. Roosevelt Library)*

Women's Emergency Brigade, Flint, Michigan, Sit-down Strike, March 1937. *(Courtesy Archives of Labor History and Urban Affairs, Wayne State University)*

Organizer Mary Moultrie, UAW president Walter Reuther, and Rev. Ralph Abernathy join forces during the 1969 strike of hospital workers in Charleston, South Carolina. *(Courtesy UPI)*

Jack Delano, *C.I.O. Pickets Outside Textile Mill, Greensboro, Georgia. (Courtesy Library of Congress)*

Sisters Stephanie Wilson and Audrey Johnson, among the first women members of the United Mine Workers. *(Courtesy Jeanne M. Rasmussen)*

Louis Johnson of the National Union of Hospital and Health Care Employees attends meeting of the New York City Coalition of Labor Union Women. *(Courtesy David M. Wertheimer)*

The Coalition of Labor Union Women. *(Courtesy CLUW)*

anxious to restore the ideals of the pioneer unionists.

Women workers, many of whom were veterans of the civil rights struggle, responded enthusiastically to contemporary labor challenges. Among their achievements are the organization of groups previously thought to be beyond the reach of workers' associations, including southern, migrant, and domestic workers. In 1969, for example, Mary Moultrie of Charleston, South Carolina, led the successful campaign of black female hospital workers for union representation. The strike was strongly supported by a coalition of labor and civil rights groups, and by Coretta King, widow of the Rev. Dr. Martin Luther King, Jr., himself slain during a strike of sanitation workers in Memphis, Tennessee.

Since 1964 Dolores Huerta, the mother of ten, has organized migrant workers, in 1970 negotiating a contract with the Delano grape growers. In 1970 and 1973 she was elected vice president of the United Farm Workers.[45] Josephine Hulett, first female recipient of the Special Recognition Award of the Afro-American Labor Council, pioneered the organization of domestic workers in Youngstown, Warren, and Akron, Ohio, before joining the staff of the National Committee on Household Employment in 1970.[46] In 1973 Crystal Lee Jordan of the Textile Workers' Union of America participated in a successful campaign to organize the J. P. Stevens textile mill in Roanoke Rapids, North Carolina.[47]

Women politicians have recently shown strong appeal to working America. Congresswoman Bella Savitzky Abzug, a labor lawyer and strong supporter of trade unionism, was elected to the 92d Congress on November 3, 1970 and reelected to the 93d Congress on November 7, 1972.[48] Fiery Barbara Mikulski, the granddaughter of Polish immigrants, forged a coalition of blue-collar ethnic groups to win election to the Baltimore City Council in 1971. That same year she captured national attention as the voice of neglected working America, asserting that the American melting pot was boiling over. Challenging popular assumptions about her constituents, she debunked assimilation and praised cultural pluralism. In 1974 she waged a strong senatorial campaign against Charles Mathias, the popular Republican incumbent.[49]

The contemporary trade union woman's aware-

ness of her unique situation is reflected not only in the achievements of individuals, however, but in the establishment of new organizations devoted to her particular needs. In 1971, for example, Jean Maddox and Joyce Maupin founded the Union Women's Alliance to Gain Equality (Union W.A.G.E.). On January 19, 1974, the First New York Women's Trade Union Conference, sponsored by Cornell University, opened at the Martin Luther King Center.[50] The Coalition of Labor Union Women (CLUW), largest of the recent national organizations of female unionists, convened its founding convention in Chicago on March 22, 1974. During the convention Olga Madar, vice president of the United Auto Workers, was elected president, and Addie Wyatt, director of women's affairs for the Amalgamated Meat Cutters and Butcher Workmen of North America and former labor advisor to the Rev. Dr. Martin Luther King, Jr., national vice president. Expressing the resolve of CLUW's members, Myra Wolfgang of the Hotel and Restaurant Employees Union declared, "We didn't come here to swap recipes!"[51]

The exhibition and catalog, *Workers and Allies: Female Participation in the American Trade Union Movement,* would, of course, have been impossible without the generous contributions of time and resources made by the following individuals and organizations: Actors' Equity; the Amalgamated Clothing Workers of America; the AFL-CIO Library; the American Guild of Musical Artists; Bryn Mawr College; William Cahn; Anne Calderwood; Carnegie Library of Pittsburgh; the Chicago Historical Society; the Officers and Members of the Coalition of the Labor Union Women; Eleanor Coit; Clara Day; Mary Maples Dunn; the United Electrical, Radio and Machine Workers of America; Dorothy Ellsworth; William Emerson; Jennie Farley, the Feminist History Research Project; *Feminist Studies;* Alan Fern; Lois Fink; Janet Flint; Moe Foner; Sherna Gluck; Barbara Herndon; Historical Researchers, Inc.; Alice M. Hoffman; John N. Hoffman; District 1199 of the National Union of Hospital and Health Care Employees; Hotel and Restaurant Employees' and Bartenders' International Union; Nanette Jones; Joyce Kornbluh; Elissa Krauss; Henry P. Leifermann; the Library of Congress; Margery S. Long; the Massachusetts Historical Society; Edith P. Mayo; Paul McLaughlin; Amalgamated Meat Cutters and Butcher Workmen of North America; the Merrimack Valley Textile Museum; the United Mine Workers of America; *Ms.* magazine; the Museum of the City of New York; Museum of History and Technology, Smithsonian Institution; National Archives and Records Services; National Portrait Gallery, Smithsonian Institution; the New York Public Library; *The New Yorker;* Pauline Newman; 9 to 5 Organization for Women Office Workers; Tina Norelli; Ann M. Poraczky; Brotherhood of Railway, Airline and Steamship Clerks, Freight Handlers, Express and Station Employees; Jeanne M. Rasmussen; Retail Clerks' International Association; Bruce Roberts; Jolly Robinson; the Franklin D. Roosevelt Presidential Library; Arthur and Elizabeth Schlesinger Library on the History of Women in America, Radcliffe College; United Rubber, Cork, Linoleum and Plastic Workers of America; the Screen Actors' Guild; M. B. Schnapper; Elizabeth Shenton; Dorothy Swanson; United Steel Workers of America; Tamiment Library of New York University; International Brotherhood of Teamsters; Chauffers, Warehousemen and Helpers of America; Textile Workers' Union of America; Union Women's Alliance to Gain Equality; Wayne State University, Archives of Labor History and Urban Affairs; Jean Webber; Barbara Mayer Wertheimer; David M. Wertheimer; James L. Whitehead; and the Women's Bureau, U.S. Department of Labor. Deserving of special thanks is Hilary Erlbaum, who provided a checklist for our chronology and assisted in the preparation of the bibliography and biographies.

NOTES

1. *National Laborer,* October 29, 1836, in John B. Andrews and W. D. P. Bliss, *History of Women in Trade Unions,* vol. 10 of U. S. Bureau of Labor, *Report on Condition of Woman and Child Wage Earners in the United States* (Washington, D.C.: Government Printing Office, 1911), p. 30.
2. Edith Abbott, *Women in Industry* (New York: D. Appleton, 1909), p. 40.
3. *Ibid.,* p. 50; Alexander Hamilton, *Report on Manufacturers: Communication to the House of Representatives, December 5, 1791* (1792; reprint ed., Washington D. C.: U. S. Treasury Department, 1913), pp. 12-13.
4. *The Man* (New York), March 11, 1834, in Andrews and Bliss, *op. cit.,* p. 25.
5. A. G. Taylor, *Labor Problems and Labor Law* (New York: Prentice Hall, 1950), pp. 377-78.
6. Grace Hutchins, *Women Who Work* (New York: International Publishers, 1934), p. 214.
7. *Philadelphia National Gazette,* January 7, 1829, in Andrews and Bliss, *op. cit.,* p. 23.
8. *Boston Transcript,* February 18, 1834; *The Man* (New York), February 22, 1834; *New York Sun,* March 20, 1834; *New York Sun,* March 21, 1834, in Andrews and Bliss, *op. cit.,* p. 28.
9. Hutchins, *op. cit.,* pp. 210-279; Andrews and Bliss, *op. cit.,* pp. 11-49.
10. 45 Mass. (4 Met) 111, 38 AM. Dec. 346 (1842).
11. Elizabeth Faulkner Baker, *Technology and Women's Work* (New York and London: Columbia University Press, 1964), pp. 48-65.
12. William Cahn, *A Pictorial History of American Labor* (New York: Crown Publishers, 1972), pp. 53-54, 80; Andrews and Bliss, *op. cit.,* pp. 71-83. Other early labor organizations established by women include the United Tailoresses of New York (1825), the Society of Tailoresses and Seamstresses of Baltimore (1833), the Female Society of Lynn and Vicinity for the Protection and Promotion of Female Industry (1833), the Factory Girls' Association (1834), the Female Improvement Society for the City and County of Philadelphia (1835), the United Men and Women's Trading Society (1835).
13. Andrews and Bliss, *op. cit.,* pp. 82-83.
14. Helen Keller to Senator Robert M. La Follette, August 1924, in Philip Foner, ed., *Helen Keller: Her Socialist Years, Writings and Speeches* (New York: International Publishers, 1967), p. 113.
15. Israel Kugler, "The Trade Union Career of Susan B. Anthony," *Labor History* 2 (Winter 1961), pp. 90-100; Andrews and Bliss, *op. cit.,* p. 88.
16. Mary Harris Jones, *The Autobiography of Mother Jones* (1925; reprint ed., Chicago: Charles H. Kerr & Co., 1972), pp. 203-204. For a history of this often uneasy alliance see James J. Kenneally, "Women and Trade Unions, 1870-1920: The Quandry of the Reformer," *Labor History* 14 (Winter 1973), pp. 42-45; Nancy Schrom Dye, "Creating a Feminist Alliance: Sisterhood and Class Conflict in the New York Women's Trade Union League," *Feminist Studies* 2 (1975),

pp. 24-38; Patricia Cayo Sexton, "Workers (Female) Arise!," *Dissent* 21 (Summer 1974), pp. 380-96.

17. Abbott, *op. cit.*, pp. 138-139.

18. *Frank Leslie's Illustrated Newspaper,* March 17, 1860.

19. In Cahn, *op. cit.*, p. 90. See also Philip Foner, ed., *Abraham Lincoln: Selections From His Writings* (New York: International Publishers, 1944), pp. 84-88.

20. Baker, *op. cit.*

21. Andrews and Bliss, *op. cit.*, pp. 87-132.

22. *Ibid.*, pp. 116-23.

23. Alice Henry, *The Trade Union Woman* (New York and London: D. Appleton & Co., 1915).

24. Emma Goldman, *Living My Life* (New York: Alfred Knopf, 1931).

25. *Wilkes-Barre Record,* September 22, 1897, in Victor R. Greene, *The Slavic Community on Strike* (Notre Dame, Indiana: University of Notre Dame, 1968).

26. Henry, *op. cit.; Dye, op. cit.*

27. Henry, *op. cit.*

28. In Dale Fetherling, *Mother Jones, the Miners' Angel* (Carbondale and Edwardsville, Illinois: Southern Illinois University Press, 1974), p. 44.

29. Elisabeth P. Meyers, *Madam Secretary* (New York: J. Messner, 1972); Mary Heaton Vorse, *A Footnote to Folly* (Murray Hill, New York: Farrar & Rinehart, 1935), p. 39.

30. *Ibid.*, pp. 124-32.

31. See Justice Department File, National Archives Record Group 168733-A, Box 6036: Committee of Coal Mine Managers, *The Struggle in Colorado for Industrial Freedom,* August 17, 1914, p. 2; John Chase, *The Military Occupation of the Coal Strike Zone of Colorado by the Colorado National Guard* (Denver: Smith and Brooks, 1914). Jones, *op. cit.*, pp. 178-94.

32. *Pittsburgh Gazette Times,* August 27, 1919; *Pittsburgh Leader,* August 27, 1919; *Pittsburgh Post,* August 27, 1919; *Pittsburgh Press,* August 27, 1919; *Pittsburgh Sun,* August 27, 1919; Philip Murray to John L. Lewis, August 29, 1919, files of the United Mine Workers of America; George Korson, *Coal Dust on the Fiddle* (Philadelphia: University of Pennsylvania, 1943).

33. *Charlotte, North Carolina, Sunday Observer,* September 15, 1929.

34. Russell A. Smith, Leroy S. Merrifield, and Theodore J. St. Antoine, *Labor Relations Law: Cases and Materials* (Indianapolis and New York: Bobbs-Merrill, 1974), pp. 31-33, 291-98, 355-56, 666-71.

35. *Ibid.*, pp. 34-39, 44-49, 53-62, 489-530.

36. Mary Heaton Vorse, *Labor's New Millions* (New York: Modern Age, 1938).

37. *Ibid.*, pp. 118-27.

38. Lucretia M. Dewey, "Women in Labor Unions," *Monthly Labor Review* (February 1971), pp. 42-48; Smith, Merrifield, and St. Antoine, *op. cit.*, pp. 44-45.

39. *Ibid.*, pp. 47-49; 995-1003.

40. 77 Stat. 56, 29 U. S. C. § 206 (d).

41. 78 Stat. 253-66 as amended by Pub. L. No. 92-261 (1972), 86 Stat. 103, U. S. C. §§ 2000e-2000e-15.

42. Dewey, *op. cit.*, p. 42.

43. *United Mine Workers' Journal* (July 16-31, 1974), p. 12; *Pittsburgh Press,* June 23, 1974; *DuQuoin* (Illinois) *Evening Call,* June 25, 1974; *Daily Sentinel* (Middleport-Pomeroy, Ohio) June 26, 1974; *Washington Star News,* October 2, 1974.

44. Ronald Sarro, "Charleston's Civil Rights Battleground," *Washington Evening Star,* May 21, 1969; Jules Loh, "Charleston Alliance: Labor, Rights Groups," *Richmond Times-Dispatch,* August 24, 1969.

45. *Biographical Dictionary of American Labor Leaders* (Westport, Connecticut, and London: Greenwood Press, 1974), p. 167; *Playgirl* 3 (June 1975), p. 122.

46. "Josephine Hulett as Interviewed by Janet Dewart," *Ms.* (February 1973), pp. 45-48.

47. Henry P. Leifermann, "The Unions Are Coming," *New York Times Magazine,* August 5, 1973, pp. 10-11.

48. *Congressional Directory* (Washington, D.C.: Government Printing Office, 1974).

49. Barbara Ann Mikulski, "The Mikulski Papers: How We Lost the Election But Won the Campaign," *Ms.* 4 (July 1975), pp. 59-61.

50. *Ms. Magazine* 2 (June 1974), p. 19.

51. *Chicago Sun Times,* March 23, 1974; *Louisville* (Kentucky) *Courier-Journal,* March 24, 1974; *New York Times,* March 25, 1974; *Detroit Free Press,* March 25, 1974; *Philadelphia Inquirer,* March 25, 1974; *Chicago Defender,* March 25, 1974; *Chicago Tribune,* March 25, 1974; *Chicago Sun Times,* March 25, 1974; *Washington Star News,* March 25, 1974; *Toledo Blade,* March 25, 1974; *Milwaukee Journal,* March 26, 1974; *AFL-CIO News,* March 30, 1974; *Nation,* March 30, 1974; *Labor Challenge,* April 1, 1974; *IUE News,* April 1974; *Public Employee,* April 1974; *Guardian,* April 3, 1974; *Militant,* April 5, 1974; *Los Angeles Citizen,* April 5, 1974; *U. S. News,* April 8, 1974; *Machinist,* April 11, 1974; *Guild Reporter,* April 12, 1974; *Nation,* April 13, 1974; *Spokeswoman* 4 (April 5 1974); *National Observer,* April 20, 1974; *UAW Washington Reporter,* April 22, 1974; *Oregonian,* April 23, 1974; *Fifth Estate* 8 April 13-26, 1974); *Daily World,* April 27, 1974; *Railway/Airline Clerk,* May 1974; *UAW Solidarity,* May 1974; *Time,* May 6, 1974.

Power-loom weaving drew women workers from home to factory, about 1835. *(Courtesy Merrimack Valley Textile Museum)*

Immigrant women in a sweatshop. *(Courtesy National Archives and Records Service)*

Frenzeny and Tavernier, "The Strike in the Coal Mines—Meeting of 'Molly m'Guire' Men," *Harper's Weekly,* January 31, 1874. *(Courtesy Library of Congress)*

Lure of American Wages. *(Courtesy Museum of the City of New York)*

While employed by the National Child Labor Committee between 1908 and 1921, Lewis Hine photographed children working in manufacturing, mining, street trades, and agriculture. His photographs were instrumental in effecting legislation to restrict child labor. *(Courtesy National Committee on Employment of Youth)*

Edwin Rowe, *The Great Battle of Homestead: Defeat and Capture of the Pinkerton Invaders, July 6th, 1892. (Courtesy Library of Congress)*

Chronology

Female Participation in the American Trade Union Movement

1765 The first society of working women, the Daughters of Liberty, is organized as an auxiliary of the Sons of Liberty, a workingman's association.

1789 During a visit to the Boston Duck Sail Manufactory, President George Washington praises the spinners as "daughters of decayed families, and . . . girls of character."

1790 The first textile mill is established in Pawtucket, Rhode Island, equipped with machinery designed from memory by Samuel Slater for Ezekial Carpenter. It is staffed entirely by children under twelve years of age—seven boys and two girls.

1791 In his *Report on Manufactures,* communicated to the House of Representatives on December 5, Secretary of the Treasury Alexander Hamilton praises the industry of women workers, "rendered more useful . . . by manufacturing establishments than they would otherwise be."

1792 Mary Wollstonecraft publishes *Vindication of the Rights of Women.*

1793 Eli Whitney develops the cotton gin, reportedly from an idea of Catherine Littlefield Greene, his landlady.

1810 The first American cigar factory, its entire work force female, opens in Suffield, Connecticut.

1814 With the adoption of the power loom, weaving becomes a factory occupation, its first prominent female practitioner, Deborah Skinner.

1824 Women workers strike for the first time, in Pawtucket, Rhode Island. At a meeting "conducted . . . without noise, or scarcely a single speech," 102 female workers strike in support of brother weavers protesting the simultaneous reduction of wages and extension of the workday.

1825 Women workers strike alone for the first time when the United Tailoresses' Society of New York City demands a wage increase.

1828 Paterson, New Jersey, textile workers rally in support of the ten-hour workday.

Philadelphia and Manayunk, Pennsylvania, cotton spinners protest a wage cut of 25 percent.

Dover, New Hampshire, mill workers denounce company fines for tardiness and for talking on the job.

1829 Taunton, Massachusetts, textile workers protest a wage reduction.

1831 Led by Mrs. Phobe Scott, Mrs. Eliza Trulin, and Mrs. Lydabach, 1,600 members of the United Tailoresses' Society of New York City strike for a wage increase of 33⅓ percent.

1833 Led by Susan Stansbury, Hannah Moran, and Jacob Daley, the Society of Tailoresses and Seamstresses of Baltimore, Maryland, demands a wage increase.

The Female Society of Lynn, Massachusetts, and Vicinity leads shoebinders in a strike for increased wages.

1834 Recording industrial conditions, the British writer Harriet Martineau visits Massachusetts factories.

The Factory Girls' Association is formed by 2,500 textile workers in Lowell, Massachusetts. Signaled by the wave of a bonnet, they walk out to protest the dismissal of a sister employee and a wage reduction of 15 percent, asserting that "none of us will . . . [return] . . . unless they receive us all as one."

In Dover, New Hampshire, 800 women strike against wage reductions and for the right to organize; they form a union embracing sister workers in Great Falls and Newmarket.

Amesbury, Massachusetts, weavers decry a company proposal to tend two looms rather than one with no pay increase.

Manayunk, Pennsylvania, mill operatives denounce a wage reduction of 25 percent.

1835 In Philadelphia 500 women, including binders, corsetmakers, folders, mantuamakers, milliners, seamstresses, stockmakers, and tailoresses, establish the Female Improvement Society. The organization draws up a price scale and publishes lists of employers who violate it.

Workers in twenty Paterson, New Jersey, textile mills demand that the workday be shortened from thirteen and one-half hours to eleven hours.

New York City shoebinders strike for higher wages.

The United Men's and Women's Trading Society is established.

Journeymen Segar Makers of Philadelphia declare their support for sister workers, resolving that "we recommend them in a body to strike with us and thereby make it a mutual interest with both parties to sustain each other in their rights."

1836 In Lowell, Massachusetts, the Factory Girls' Association strikes, denouncing a 12½ percent increase in the cost of room and board at the company boardinghouses.

Dover, New Hampshire, textile workers strike to protest a wage reduction.

1837 Led by Lavinia Wright and Louisa Mitchell, 1,600 members of the Tailoresses' Society of New York City strike for a wage scale.

1840 *The Lowell Offering,* the journal of female textile workers in Lowell, Massachusetts, begins publication.

1842 Chief Justice Lemuel Shaw of the Massachusetts Supreme Court endorses the worker's right to organize in *Commonwealth v. Hunt,* declaring that "such agreement could not be pronounced a criminal conspiracy" and that unions "far from being criminal or unlawful . . . may be highly meritorious and public spirited." His landmark decision ends the American application of the English common law of criminal conspiracy to trade unions and provides a legal foundation for unionization.

1843 Women employed in the Pittsburgh cotton mills protest an extension of the workday without pay.

1844 Pioneer labor organizer Sarah G. Bagley founds the Lowell Female Reform Association; she also establishes the Lowell Industrial Reform Lyceum.

Boston seamstresses and journeymen tailors join forces to fight a wage reduction.

1845 Sarah Bagley's articles are rejected by *The Lowell Offering* editor Harriet Farley. Denouncing the journal as a company paper, Bagley on behalf of the Lowell Female Labor Reform Association acquires *The Voice of Industry,* in which she attacks company recruiting policies, health conditions in company boardinghouses, and the company store. Appearing before the Massachusetts legislature, she testifies in favor of extension of the ten-hour workday (adopted by the federal government in 1842) to private industry, presenting a petition signed by 1,000 sister workers.

The Lowell Female Labor Reform Association elects

Bagley president, Mary Eastman secretary, and Huldah J. Stone correspondent.

Female workers in five Allegheny, Pennsylvania, cotton mills strike for the ten-hour workday; they are supported by coworkers in Lowell, Massachusetts, and Manchester, New Hampshire.

The Female Industrial Association of New York City is formed; its president Elizabeth Gray, secretary Mary Graham, and chairman Annie S. Stevens. Among its members are bookfolders, bookstitchers, capmakers, crimpers, dressmakers, fringemakers, lacemakers, seamstresses, shirtmakers, strawmakers, and tailoresses.

1846 During the winter of 1845-1846, the Manchester, New Hampshire, Female Labor Reform Association is organized; Sarah Rumrill is elected president.

New York City seamstresses found the Shirt Sewers' Cooperative Union.

On February 21 Sarah Bagley becomes the first female telegraph operator, to the amusement of the *Boston Journal,* which speculates that "the long mooted question 'Can a woman keep a secret?' will now become more interesting than ever."

1847 Spurred by the efforts of the Female Labor Reform Association, the New Hampshire legislature enacts the ten-hour workday law.

Miss E. Kidder is elected president of the Manchester, New Hampshire, Female Labor Reform Association. .

The Dover, New Hampshire, Female Labor Reform Association is established by textile workers. Miss Burnham is its first president.

1848 The Pennsylvania legislature passes the ten-hour law; when it is violated by employers, female mill workers riot, attacking factory gates with axes.

Declaring that "all men and women are created equal," Elizabeth Cady Stanton, a champion of female suffrage ,and Lucretia Mott, a Quaker minister and militant abolitionist, open the first feminist convention in Seneca Falls, New York, Their *Declaration of Sentiments,* a paraphrase of the *Declaration of Independence,* castigating male tyranny, immediately unleashes a flood of ridicule.

1850 Lucretia Mott and Elizabeth Oakes Smith support a cooperative sewing shop established by a union of Philadelphia seamstresses.

1860 On January 10 the pillars supporting the central structure of the Pemberton Mills in Lawrence, Massachusetts, give way; eighty-eight working men, women, and children are killed.

On March 5 Abraham Lincoln declares his support for striking New England shoemakers and asserts his faith in unionization. "Thank God that we have a system of labor where there can be a strike. Whatever the pressure, there is a point where the working man may stop."

Breaking a decade of silence on the part of women workers—the aftermath of the financial crisis of 1848-1849 and the subsequent replacement of Anglo-Saxon employees by immigrants—800 female shoebinders in Lynn, Massachusetts, join 4,000 brother workers on March 7 to parade through a blinding snowstorm to demand higher wages. "American ladies will not be slaves," their banners proclaim. "Give us a fair compensation and we labour cheerfully."

1861 A massive influx of soldiers' wives and widows into the needle trades takes place.

1864 In New York City, 100 sewing-machine operators unite to collect dues and administer sick benefits; their president is M. Trimble, their secretary Ella Patterson.

1865 Philadelphia seamstresses petition President Abraham Lincoln for a living wage.

The Boston Women's Union of Pantaloon Makers is established.

Two hundred seamstresses found the Chicago Sewing Women's Protective Union.

Manufacturers, railroads, and steamship companies join forces to recruit European labor.

1866 Transcending the self-interest of male workers, the National Labor Union pledges "individual and undivided support to the sewing women, factory operatives, and daughters of toil."

The Working Women's Protective Union is established, empowered to collect back wages from recalcitrant employers.

1867 The Cigarmakers International Union amends its constitution to admit blacks and women.

1868 The eight-hour federal workday is declared.

Susan B. Anthony establishes *The Revolution,* a paper printed by females and dealing with issues of interest to women workers.

The New York Working Women's Association is founded by Susan B. Anthony, Elizabeth Cady Stanton, and Augusta Lewis Troup.

Augusta Lewis Troup becomes president of Women's Typographical Union No. 1.

Despite male opposition, Stanton and Anthony are seated as delegates at the convention of the National Labor Union.

Maggie McNamara is elected head of the Brooklyn Female Burnishers' Association.

1869 The membership of the National Labor Union votes against seating Susan B. Anthony as a convention delegate. Anthony is charged with underpaying her employees at *The Revolution,* encouraging female strikebreakers, and discharging Augusta Lewis Troup from *The Revolution* because of her union activities.

The first female national union, the Daughters of St. Crispin, is organized by women shoeworkers. They elect Carrie Wilson president and Abbie Jacques secretary. On July 28 the union holds its first convention in Lynn, Massachusetts.

The International Typographical Union admits female members.

The Knights of Labor is established, its membership open to blacks and females, its policy "To secure for both sexes equal pay for equal work."

The National Colored Labor Union is founded.

Kate Mullaney of the Troy, New York, Collar Laundry Workers calls a strike.

1870 Augusta Lewis Troup is elected corresponding secretary of the International Typographical Union.

At their second convention, the Daughters of St. Crispin

demand "for our labor the same rate of compensation for equal skill displayed, or the same hours of toil, as is paid other laborers in the same branches of business."

Victoria Woodhull and her sister, Tennessee Claflin, establish the first female brokerage, Woodhull, Claflin & Company, in New York City, and begin publication of *Woodhull & Claflin's Weekly,* a precursor of the "yellow journal," which features exposés of corporate fraud and political corruption, as well as articles on labor, divorce, free love, and abortion.

Victoria Woodhull declares her candidacy for president of the United States.

1871 *Woodhull & Claflin's Weekly* publishes an English translation of Karl Marx's *Communist Manifesto,* the first American press to so do.

Victoria Woodhull and Tennessee Claflin assume leadership of Section 12 of Marx's International Workingman's Party; they are later expelled.

1875 Named for the legendary Irish heroine whose reign of terror thwarted English landlords' attempts to evict indigent farmers, the Molly Maguires, a secret society of immigrant miners in eastern Pennsylvania, are penetrated by Pinkerton agent James McParlan. On the basis of McParlan's assertions, ten miners are tried, convicted, and executed.

In Fall River, Massachusetts, women textile workers vote to strike despite the acceptance of a wage cut by male employees. Later joined by their brother workers, the women win the strike.

The cigarmakers amend their constitution to prohibit local unions from discriminating against women workers.

1877 In New York City, several hundred women are recruited as strikebreakers during a work stoppage by unionized male cigarworkers. Employers hail the strike as "a blessing in disguise," because it has brought to their attention the value of female employees, "workers whose services may be depended on at low wages."

In Cincinnati, male unionists strike successfully to prohibit employers from hiring females. Commented the *Cincinnati Daily Inquirer,* "The men say the women are killing the industry. It would seem that they hope to retaliate by killing the women."

Climaxing four years of depression, a national railroad strike commences on July 16, leaving in its wake more than one hundred deaths and the massive destruction of property. In Pittsburgh, members of the Philadelphia National Guard fire upon strikers and their families.

1880 Frances Perkins, first female secretary of labor, is born on April 10.

1881 Mrs. Terence V. Powderly is admitted to the Knights of Labor.

The Federation of Organized Trades and Labor Unions of the United States and Canada, later to become the American Federation of Labor, is founded in Pittsburgh.

1883 Mary Stirling, a Philadelphia shoeworker, is the first female delegate to the convention of the Knights of Labor. Kate Dowling of Rochester, New York, is elected a delegate but does not attend.

1884 The first female local of the Knights of Labor, the Garfield Assembly, is organized.

Louisa M. Eaton, a Lynn, Massachusetts, shoeworker, and Mary Hannafin, a Philadelphia saleswoman, are delegates to the Knights of Labor convention.

1885 The Knights of Labor establish a committee to collect statistics on working women. Among its members are Mary Hannafin, Mary Stirling of Philadelphia, and Lizzie H. Shute of Haverhill, Massachusetts.

Charlotte Smith, president of the Women's National Labor League, attends the convention of the Federation of Organized Trades and Labor Unions of the United States and Canada.

1886 On May 4 a bomb explodes during a protest in Chicago's Haymarket Square; seven policemen and four workers are killed. Anarchist orators are promptly seized, convicted, and executed. For years after her husband Albert R. Parsons's execution, Lucy Eldine Gonzalez Parsons proclaimed his innocence.

The American Federation of Labor, headed by Samuel Gompers, holds its first convention in Columbus, Ohio.

Women delegates to the Knights of Labor convention number sixteen, among them Elizabeth Flynn Rodgers, master workman of District Assembly No. 24, who attends with her two-week-old child. The women's department of the Knights of Labor is organized, headed by Leonora Barry, a widow with three children and master workman of District Assembly No. 65, as general investigator. Her assignment is to examine "the abuses to which our sex is subjected by unscrupulous employers" and to "agitate the principles . . . of equal pay and the abolition of child labor."

The Working Women's Society is founded by Leonora O'Reilly of the Knights of Labor, assisted by Josephine Shaw Lowell, Mrs. Robert Abbé, Arria Huntingdon, and L. S. Perkins.

1887 Knights of Labor general investigator Leonora Barry is assisted in her documentation of the industrial exploitation of women and children by Mary O'Reilly of Providence, Rhode Island, vice president of the Knight's women's department and a former cotton mill worker.

1889 Jane Addams and Ellen Gates Starr open Hull House, the pioneer Chicago settlement.

1890 Alzina Parsons Stevens, founder of the Joan of Arc Assembly of the Knights of Labor, is elected master workman of District Assembly No. 72. At the convention of the Knights of Labor, however, she declines the post of general investigator vacated by Leonora Barry.

The first fully accredited female delegate, Mary Burke of the Retail Clerks of Findley, Ohio, attends the American Federation of Labor convention. The convention passes a resolution supporting women's suffrage and urging the appointment of female organizers.

Josephine Shaw Lowell helps to establish the Consumers League of the city of New York, dedicated to the patronage of those establishments which pay just wages and provide "reasonable hours, suitable seats, and decent sanitary conditions."

1891 At the American Federation of Labor convention, a women's committee headed by Eva McDonald Valesh and Ida Van Etten recommends the creation of the office of national organizer.

1892 Mary Kenney O'Sullivan of the Bindery Workers is appointed the American Federation of Labor's first female national organizer. Her activities include campaigns in Albany, Boston, New York City, and Troy, New York.

During a steelworkers' strike in Homestead, Pennsylvania, Russian immigrants Emma Goldman and Alexander Berkman misread the workers' militancy and conspire to assassinate Henry Clay Frick, the antiunion manager of the Carnegie Steel Company. The attempt, however, is abortive: Frick recovers and Berkman is sentenced to twenty-five years in prison. Despite her open avowal of participation, Goldman is never tried.

1893 An army of unemployed, led by businessman Jacob S. Coxey, marches on Washington. A company broadside is later to charge that Mother Mary Harris Jones, in 1893 a sixty-three-year-old United Mine Workers' organizer, as a madam made elaborate plans for their entertainment en route.

1896 The Union for Industrial Progress is founded by Mary Kimball Kehew and Mary Kenney O'Sullivan.

1898 The National Consumers' League is founded; John Graham Brooks is elected president, Florence Kelley executive secretary. Among its goals is protective legislation for women and children.

A resolution, vigorously opposed by the American Federation of Labor, is placed before Congress, barring all women from federal employment and "regulat[ing] them to the home."

Charlotte Perkins Gilman publishes *Women and Economics.*

1900 Emma Goldman begins publication of *Mother Earth.*

Hannah Mahoney Nolan organizes the Steam Laundry Workers' Union of San Francisco.

1902 "Petticoat butchers" Maggie Condon and Hannah O'Day found the Maud Gonne Club in Chicago.

Local 183 of the Amalgamated Meat Cutters and Butcher Workmen of New York City is organized; Mollie Day is elected president, Maud Sutter business agent.

1903 Mother Mary Harris Jones, veteran United Mine Workers' organizer, leads the March of the Mill Children, many of them victims of industrial accidents, from Philadelphia to President Theodore Roosevelt's home in Oyster Bay, New York.

On November 14, during the American Federation of Labor's Boston convention, blue-collar and bourgeois women unite to form the National Women's Trade Union League. The league is open to male and female members of all races "willing to assist those trade unions already existing, which have women members, and to aid in the formation of new unions of women wage earners." Among the officers elected are Mary Morton Kehew of Boston, president; Jane Addams of Chicago, vice president; Mary Kenney O'Sullivan of Boston, secretary; and Mary Donovan of the Boot and Shoe Workers, treasurer. Its board of directors includes Mary McDowell of Chicago; Lillian Wald of New York; Ellen Lindstrom of the United Garment Workers; Mary Trites of the Textile Workers; and Leonora O'Reilly of the Ladies Garment Workers' Union.

1904 Local branches of the National Women's Trade Union League are established in Chicago, New York City, and Boston.

Mary McLeod Bethune opens the Daytona Educational and Industrial School for Negro Girls.

1905 The founding convention of the Industrial Workers of the World (IWW) is held in Chicago. Those in attendance include the most colorful and controversial figures in labor history: one-eyed "Big Bill" Haywood; Joe Hill; feisty Mother Mary Harris Jones; Elizabeth Gurley Flynn; Haymarket widow Lucy Eldine Gonzalez Parsons; Eugene V. Debs; and Daniel DeLeon.

The laundry workers of Troy, New York, wage an unsuccessful strike.

1906 Mother Ella Reeve Bloor assists novelist Upton Sinclair, verifying for federal investigators charges made in *The Jungle,* an exposé of immigrant exploitation by Chicago meatpackers.

In Schenectady, New York, the International Workers of the World pioneer the sit-down strike: employees of General Electric fold their arms on the job for sixty-five hours.

1907 The National Women's Trade Union League begins publication of its journal, *Life and Labor.*

During the summer the National Women's Trade Union League sponsors simultaneous conventions of female unionists in Boston, Chicago, and New York City.

Margaret Dreier Robins of Chicago is elected president of the National Women's Trade Union League.

Josephine Clara Goldmark publishes *Labour Laws for Women in the United States.*

1908 The Supreme Court in *Muller v. Oregon,* 208 U. S. 412, upholds the constitutionality of maximum-hour laws for women workers, agreeing with Louis Brandeis that a female's "physical structure and a proper discharge of her maternal functions . . . justify legislation to protect her from the greed as well as the passion of men." Brandeis's brief is based on the research of Josephine Clara Goldmark, his sister-in-law.

1909 At a mass meeting of New York City garment workers held in Cooper Union on November 22, teenaged Clara Lemlich interrupts proceedings chaired by Samuel Gompers to declare, "What we are here for is to decide whether or not we shall strike. I offer a resolution that a general strike be declared—now!" Thus begins the "Uprising of 20,000" Jewish and Italian immigrant workers, the vast majority of whom are women. Seventy-five members of the New York Women's Trade Union League form the "mink brigade," a picket line supporting Ladies' Waistmakers' Union No. 25 against the Triangle Shirtwaist Company. Mary Dreier, president of the New York League, is arrested; because of her social standing, the arrest makes headlines.

Mary White Ovington helps to establish the National Association for the Advancement of Colored People.

1910 Margaret Dreier Robins, president of the National Women's Trade Union League, establishes a training program for female labor organizers. Among those to participate are Louisa Mittelstadt of the Kansas City Brewery Workers; Myrtle Whitehead of the Baltimore Brewery Workers; and Fannia Cohn of the International Ladies' Garment Workers' Union.

Organized labor mourns victims of the Triangle Shirtwaist Company fire. *(Courtesy Library of Congress)*

Elizabeth Gurley Flynn addresses Paterson, New Jersey, textile strikers, 1913. *(Courtesy Archives of Labor History and Urban Affairs, Wayne State University)*

Detroit women's emergency brigade and women's auxiliary, Chrysler sit-down strike, March 1937. *(Courtesy Archives of Labor History and Urban Affairs, Wayne State University)*

During a 1929 strike at the Loray Mills in Gastonia, North Carolina, female textile workers attempt to disarm a National Guardsman. *(Courtesy Archives of Labor History and Urban Affairs, Wayne State University)*

John Sloane, "Class War in Colorado," *The Masses,* June 1914. *(Courtesy Library of Congress)*

Russell Lee, *Officers of Workers Alliance, Muskogee, Oklahoma, July 1939. (Courtesy Library of Congress)*

Coretta King meets with employees of Johns Hopkins Hospital in Baltimore, Maryland, to urge union representation, August 27, 1969. *(Courtesy National Union of Hospital and Health Care Employees)*

Women aircraft factory workers, World War II. *(Courtesy Archives of Labor History and Urban Affairs, Wayne State University)*

The Founding Convention of the Coalition of Labor Union Women, 1974. *(Courtesy CLUW)*

"Jock" Yablonski campaigning, 1969. *(Courtesy Jeanne M. Rasmussen)*

Letha Richardson of District Council 37, American Federation of State, County and Municipal Employees, addresses participants at the New York Trade Union Women's Conference, 1974. *(Courtesy Jolly Robinson)*

In New York City 70,000 cloakmakers strike.

The Philadelphia needle trades' strike is strongly supported by the National Women's Trade Union League. Among the allies of labor are Margaret Dreier Robins, national president; Mary Dreier, president of the New York League; Agnes Nestor, rank-and-file Chicago League organizer; socialite Mrs. George Biddle; settlement resident Anna Davies; and Consumers' League representative, Anne Young.

During a strike by the makers of ready-made men's clothing, the Chicago United Garment Workers' District Council No. 6 appeals to the National Women's Trade Union League for speakers. In response, the league provides Margaret Bondfield and Mrs. Philip Snowden and contributes $70,000 in relief funds.

1911 On Saturday, March 25, fire breaks out at the Triangle Shirtwaist Company in New York City. The doors of the sweatshop, located on the eighth floor of a ten-story building, are locked to keep union organizers out and employees in. Attempting to escape, workers leap from the windows. The tragedy claims 143 lives. Among those witnessing the holocaust are labor journalist Mary Heaton Vorse and future secretary of labor Frances Perkins.

1912 In Lawrence, Massachusetts, 27,000 textile workers protest the reduction in wages accompanying the American Woolen Company's compliance with a state law shortening the work week. A female picket, Anne Lo Pizzo, is shot and killed. The National Women's Trade Union League withdraws from the strike because of the dominance of the International Workers of the World, among them Elizabeth Gurley Flynn.

Elisabeth Christman is elected president of the International Glove Workers' Union.

1913 In Paterson, New Jersey, 25,000 silk workers strike to protest an increase in the number of looms to be tended. Rose Pastor Stokes is active in the protest.

Members of the International Ladies' Garment Workers Union strike in New York City.

1914 On April 20 wives and children of striking miners are slain when their tent colony in Ludlow, Colorado, is set aflame by National Guardsmen mustered to protect the properties and officers of the Colorado Fuel and Iron Company, an interest of John D. Rockefeller, Jr. Among the union organizers assisting the Ludlow strikers is Mother Mary Harris Jones.

The Women's Trade Union League establishes a school for organizers in Chicago, which continues in operation until 1926.

1915 On November 19 labor balladeer and IWW organizer Joseph Hillstrom (Joe Hill) is executed in Salt Lake City, Utah. Among his pallbearers is Elizabeth Gurley Flynn.

Charlotte Perkins Gilman and Jane Addams found the Woman's Peace Party.

1917 Pacifists Kate Richards O'Hare Cuningham and Emma Goldman are convicted of obstructing the selective service law and are incarcerated in the federal prison in Jefferson City, Missouri.

1918 In June Secretary of Labor William B. Wilson, a former coal miner, establishes the Women in Industry divi-

sion of the U.S. Department of Labor. It is administered by Mary Van Kleeck and her assistant, Mary Anderson.

1919 On August 26 United Mine Workers' organizer Fannie Sellins, the widowed mother of four, is shot to death by coal company guards while leading strikers in Brackenridge, Pennsylvania.

Emma Goldman is deported to Russia on December 1.

The Women's International League for Peace and Freedom is founded.

Mother Mary Harris Jones participates in the steel strike in Pittsburgh.

1920 The women's suffrage amendment is ratified.

The Women in Industry division of the U.S. Department of Labor becomes the federal Women's Bureau.

Elizabeth Gurley Flynn helps to establish the American Civil Liberties Union.

1921 The Summer School for Women Workers in Industry is established at Bryn Mawr College by President M. Carey Thomas; Bryn Mawr Dean Hilda Smith is appointed director. Among the school's future instructors is Esther Peterson, assistant secretary of labor under President John F. Kennedy.

In North and South Carolina, 9,000 textile workers strike.

1922 Maud O'Farrell Swartz succeeds Margaret Dreier Robins as president of the National Women's Trade Union League.

1925 A resident school for workers is established at the University of Virginia.

1927 Sweetbriar College establishes its resident school for workers.

Barnard College initiates a nonresident seven-week course for New York City workers.

1929 On September 14 Ella May Wiggins, widowed mother of five and a labor balladeer, is slain by vigilantes while en route to a meeting of strikers in Gastonia, North Carolina.

1930 Ann Burlak, secretary of the National Textile Workers' Union, is arrested in Atlanta for calling a meeting of black and white workers.

1931 Clara Holden, National Textile Workers' Union organizer, is abducted and beaten by vigilantes in Greenville, South Carolina, on September 1.

Jane Addams receives the Nobel Prize for Peace.

1933 President Franklin Delano Roosevelt is inaugurated in March; as his secretary of labor, he appoints Frances Perkins.

Martha Roberts, wife of National Miners' Union organizer Robert F. Roberts, is arrested in Gallup, New Mexico, after leading wives of striking coal miners in a "Dawn Patrol."

Oberlin College establishes a School for Office Workers.

Section 7A of the National Industrial Recovery Act endorses the worker's right to unionization and collective bargaining.

The impromptu visits of First Lady Eleanor Roosevelt to coal mines inspire a cartoon by *New Yorker* artist Robert Day.

1935 The Social Security Act becomes law, guaranteeing help to eligible workers in times of unemployment, pensions for the elderly, and aid to dependents.

The Wagner Labor Relations Act guarantees to workers

the right to unionization and collective bargaining.

1936 During an organizing campaign among Akron, Ohio, rubber workers, John L. Lewis popularizes the sit-down strike, which renders unfeasible the use of strikebreakers.

In Flint, Michigan, United Auto Workers dieworkers make effective use of the sit-down in the General Motors plant, Fisher Body Shop. Flint strikers are strongly supported by the militant Women's Emergency Brigade.

1937 Ten workers are slain and eighty wounded during a demonstration at the Republic Steel plant in Chicago. Among those injured in the Memorial Day Massacre is Lupe Marshall, a social worker and the mother of three.

1938 The Fair Labor Standards Act establishes a minimum wage, minimum age, and maximum work week for employees engaged in interstate commerce.

1941 The Fair Employment Practice Committee is established by presidential mandate, its mission to investigate "discrimination in the employment of workers in defense industries or government because of race, creed, color or national origin."

1944 Women number 3,500,000 of 18,600,000 unionized workers. Their entry into the ranks of labor, like that of blacks, is spurred by the war effort.

1955 The American Federation of Labor, headed by George Meany, merges with the Congress of Industrial Organization, led by Walter Reuther.

1959 The Landrum-Griffin bill strengthens the provisions of the Taft-Hartley Act.

1961 The minimum wage specified under the Fair Labor Standards Act is increased to $1.25 an hour; minimum wage coverage is extended to 3,600,000 workers.

1963 The Equal Pay Act of 1963, 77 Stat. 56, 29 U. S. C. S. 206, the first statutory prohibition against sex discrimination, compels employers engaged in interstate commerce to provide equal pay "for equal work on jobs the performance of which requires equal skill, efforts, responsibility, and which are performed under similar working conditions."

1964 The Civil Rights Act, Title 7, 78 Stat. 253, 42 U. S. C. S. 2000e, is enacted, establishing an Equal Employment Opportunity Commission. The sex amendment to the bill, barring discrimination according to gender, is introduced ironically by Representative Howard Smith of Virginia, but strongly supported by Representative Martha Griffiths of Michigan.

1966 The minimum wage is raised to $1.40 an hour.

1968 The minimum wage is raised to $1.60 an hour.

The Equal Employment Opportunity Commission rules that protective "laws and regulations do not take into account the capacities, preferences, and abilities of individual females and that such laws tend to discriminate rather than to protect."

1969 Mary Moultrie organizes the successful strike of 550 black women hospital workers for union representation in Charleston, South Carolina. The strike is staunchly supported by Coretta King, wife of slain civil rights advocate the Reverend Dr. Martin Luther King, Jr.

Photojournalist Jeanne M. Rasmussen records the campaign of martyred United Mine Workers' candidate Joseph "Jock" Yablonski.

1970 Dolores Huerta is elected vice president of the United Farm Workers.

Labor lawyer Bella Savitzky Abzug is elected to the 92d Congress.

1971 Jean Maddox, a labor leader of Native American ancestry, and Joyce Maupin form the Union Women's Alliance to Gain Equality (Union W.A.G.E.).

Barbara Mikulski emerges as a spokeswoman for ethnic America during her successful campaign for the Baltimore, Maryland, city council.

1973 Women Office Workers is founded.

Barbara Wertheimer becomes director of Trade Union Women's Studies for Cornell University's New York State School of Industrial and Labor Relations.

In Roanoke Rapids, North Carolina, J. P. Stevens Company employee Crystal Lee Jordan participates in the organizing campaign of the Textile Workers' Union of America and is fired.

1974 On January 19 the New York Trade Union Women's Conference is held.

The founding convention of the Coalition of Labor Union Women (CLUW) opens in Chicago on March 22. Officers elected include president Olga Madar; vice president Addie Wyatt; secretary Linda Tarr-Whelan; and treasurer Gloria Johnson. Addressing an enthusiastic audience, Myra Wolfgang of the Hotel and Restaurant Employees' Union declares, "We didn't come here to swap recipes!"

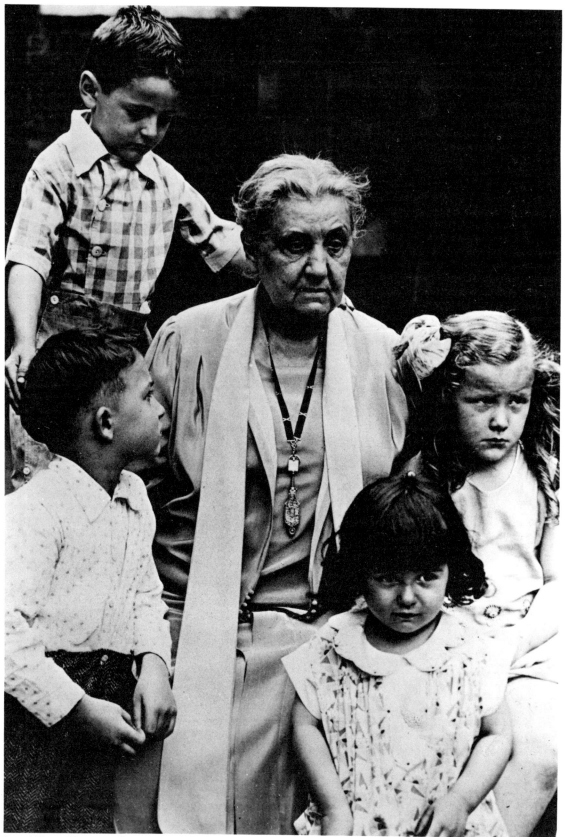

Jane Addams. (Courtesy Library of Congress)

Susan B. Anthony, by Frances Benjamin Johnston. *(Courtesy National Archives and Records Service)*

Lois Felder. (Courtesy Lois Felder)

Elizabeth Gurley Flynn and Joe Ettor. *(Courtesy Archives of Labor History and Urban Affairs, Wayne State University)*

Mary McLeod Bethune. (Courtesy Library of Congress)

Clara Day. (Courtesy Clara Day)

Fayee Bartz. (Courtesy URW)

BIOGRAPHIES

by Rosemary Gallick

The following biographies, intended to show the scope of female participation in the American labor movement, include those of past and present workers and allies who have contributed as members of the rank and file, organizers, union officials, educators, journalists, archivists, historians, and benefactresses. The bibliographic references at the end of the biographies are given in chronological order. Where they exist, works written by the subject, followed by works written by other authors, precede general references. The following abbreviations are used for frequently cited works:

BDALL

Biographical Dictionary of American Labor Leaders. Westport, Connecticut, and London: Greenwood Press, 1974.

NAW

Notable American Women 1607-1950. 3 vols. Cambridge, Massachusetts: Belknap Press of Harvard University, 1974.

Schlesinger Library Inventory
Arthur and Elizabeth Schlesinger Library on the History of Women in America; the manuscript inventories and the catalogs of manuscripts, books and pictures. Radcliffe College, Cambridge, Massachusetts. 3 vols. Boston: G. K. Hall, 1973.

Who's Who
  Who's Who in America.

Who Was Who
  Who Was Who in America.

Women in American Labor History
Soltow, Martha Jane; Forché, Carolyn; and Massre, Murray. *Women in American Labor History, 1825-1935; An Annotated Bibliography.* East Lansing: School of Labor and Industrial Relations and The Library, Michigan State University, 1972.

Edith Abbott, 1876-1957

Edith Abbott, like her sister Grace Abbott (q. v.) a pioneer sociologist, was born on September 26, 1876, in Grand Island, Nebraska, one of the four children of Othman Ali Abbott, a lawyer, and Elizabeth Griffin, a Quaker. She received a B.A. from the University of Nebraska in 1901 and a Ph.D. from the University of Chicago in 1905. After two years of study at the University of London, Abbott became an instructor at Wellesley College. From 1908 to 1920 she was a resident of Hull House, the Chicago settlement of Jane Addams (q. v.). She was a member of the faculty of the University of Chicago from 1913 to 1953, dean of the School of Social Service Administration from 1924 to 1942, and dean emeritus from 1942 to 1953. Her landmark study, *Women in Industry*, was published in 1910. Abbott was editor of the *Social Science Review,* an advisor to the International Labor Office of the League of Nations, and a member of the National Child Labor Commission, the Women's Trade Union League, the American Economic Association, and the American Association of Social Workers. She died July 28, 1957, and was buried in Grand Island Cemetery, Grand Island, Nebraska.

References: Edith Abbott: *The Wages of Unskilled Labor in the United States, 1850-1900* (Chicago: University of Chicago Press, 1905); "Wages of Unskilled Labor in the United States," *Journal of Political Economy* 13 (June 1905): 321-67; "Are Women Business Failures?" *Harper's Weekly* 49 (April 8, 1905): 496; *Employment of Women in Industries, Twelfth Census Statistics* (Chicago: Chicago Women's Trade Union League, 1906); "Industrial Employment of Women in the United States," *Journal of Political Economy* 14 (October 1906): 461-501; "Harriet Martineau and the Employment of Women in 1836," *Journal of Political Economy* 14 (December 1906): 614-26; "Employment of Women in Industries: Cigar-Making, Its History and Present Tendencies," *Journal of Political Economy* 15 (January 1907): 1-25; "Municipal Employment of Women in London," *Journal of Political Economy* 15 (November 1907): 513-30; "The History of Industrial Employment of Women in the United States: A Supplementary Note," *Journal of Political Economy* 15 (December 1907): 619-24; "Study of the Early History of Child Labor in America," *American Journal of Sociology* 14 (January 1908): 15-37; "English Working Women and the Franchise," *Atlantic Monthly* 102 (September 1908): 343-6; "Employment of Women in Cotton Mills," *Journal of Political Economy* 16 (November 1908): 620-1; *Women in Industry* (New York: Appleton & Co., 1910); *Chicago School of Civics and Philanthropy* (Chicago: Hollister Press, 1911); "English Poor-Law Reform," *Journal of Political Economy* 19 (January 1911): 47-59; "Women in Industry: the Chicago Stockyards," *Journal of Political Economy* 19 (October 1911): 632-54; "Women's Wages in Chicago," *Journal of Political Economy* 21 (February 1913): 143-58; *Chicago City Council Committee on Crime* (Chicago: Press of H. G. Adair, 1915); *The Real Jail Problem* (Chicago: Hale-Crossley Printing Company, 1915); *The Housing Problem in Chicago* (Chicago: University of Chicago Press, 1915); "Statistics in Chicago Suffrage," *New Republic* 3 (June 12, 1915): 151; *The One Hundred and One County Jails and Why They Ought to Be Abolished* (Chicago: Juvenile Protective Association of Chicago, 1916); *Truancy and Non-Attendance in the Chicago Schools* (Chicago: University of Chicago Press, 1917); "Experimental Period of Widow's Pension Legislation," *National Conference of Social Work Proceedings* (1917): 154-64; "Charles Booth," *Journal of Political Economy* 25 (February 1917):

195-200; "War and Women's Work in England," *Journal of Political Economy* 25 (July 1917): 641-78; *Democracy and Social Progress in England* (Chicago: University of Chicago Press, 1918); *The Administration of the Aid-to-Mothers Law in Illinois* (Washington, D.C.: Government Printing Office, 1921); "Police Brutality in Chicago," *Nation* 114 (March 8, 1922): 286-7; "Tragedy of the Excess Quota," *New Republic* 30 (March 8, 1922): 52-3; "English Census of 1921," *Journal of Political Economy* 30 (December 1922): 827-40; *Immigration* (Chicago: University of Chicago Press, 1924); "Immigration Legislation and the Problems of Assimilation," *National Conference of Social Work Proceedings* (1924): 82-91; "English Statistics of Pauperism during the War," *Journal of Political Economy* 33 (February 1925): 1-32; *Historical Aspects of the Immigration Problem* (Chicago: University of Chicago Press, 1926); "Training for the Policewoman's Job," *Woman Citizen* 10 (April 1926): 30; *Social Welfare and Professional Education* (Chicago: University of Chicago Press, 1931); "Poor People in Chicago," *New Republic* 72 (October 5, 1932): 209; "Fallacy of Local Relief," *New Republic* 72 (November 9, 1932): 348-50; "Crisis in Relief," *Nation* 137 (October 11, 1933): 400-2; "Don't Do It, Mr. Hopkins!" *Nation* 140 (January 9, 1935): 41-2; "Federal Relief Sold Down the River," *Nation* 142 (March 18, 1936): 346; *Some American Pioneers in Social Welfare* (Chicago: University of Chicago Press, 1937); "Grace Abbott, a Sister's Memories," *Social Service Review* 13 (September 1939); *Public Assistance* (Chicago: University of Chicago Press, 1940); *From Relief to Social Security* (Chicago: University of Chicago Press, 1941); "Grace Abbott and the Hull House, 1908-1921," *Social Service Review* 24 (September 1950); *The Tenements of Chicago, 1908-1935* (1936; reprint ed., New York: Arno Press, 1970); *The Delinquent Child and the Home* (1936; reprint ed., New York: Arno Press, 1970); *The Wage Earning Women and the State: A Reply to Miss Minnie Bronson* (Boston: Boston Equal Suffrage Association for Good Government, n. d.). Isaac M. Rubinow, "Women in Manufactures: a Criticism," *Journal of Political Economy* 15 (January 1907): 41-7. H. C. Baker, "Abbotts of Nebraska," *Survey Graphic* 25 (June 1936): 370-2. "Portrait of Edith Abbott," *Survey* 72 (June 1936): 168-72. "Portrait," *Survey* 73 (May 1937): 155. "Portrait," *Survey* 73 (June 1937): 190. "Portrait," *Independent Woman* 18 (November 1939): 357. *Current Biography* (1941), s. v. "Abbott, Edith," "Retirement as Dean of the School of Social Service Administration," *Survey* 78 (January 1942): 24. "Portrait," *Survey* 79 (May 1943): 130. O. A. Randall, "Edith Abbott Receives Survey Award," *Survey* 87 (June 1951): 278. Eleanor Roosevelt and Lorena Hickok, *Ladies of Courage* (New York: Putnam, 1954). Obituary, *New York Times*, July 30, 1957, p. 1. *Who Was Who* 3 (1951-60): 11. *Women in American Labor History*, Items No. 1, 2, 35, 36, 56, 57, 183, and 443. *Schlesinger Library Inventory*, vol. 3, s. v. "Abbott, Edith."

Grace Abbott, 1878-1939

Sociologist Grace Abbott, sister of author and educator Edith Abbott (q. v.), was born on November 17, 1878, in Grand Island, Nebraska. She received a B.A. from Grand Island College in 1898 and an M.A. in political science from the University of Chicago in 1909. From 1899 to 1907 she taught at Grand Island High School; from 1908 to 1915 she resided at Hull House, the Chicago settlement of Jane Addams (q. v.). Abbott participated in the garment workers' strikes of 1910-11, was director of the Immigrants Protective League of Chicago from 1908 to 1917, and taught at the Chicago School of Civics and Philanthropy from 1910 to 1917. In 1917 she was appointed director of the Child Labor Division of the federal Children's Bureau by President Wood-

row Wilson; she was named chief of the Children's Bureau in 1921, a position she retained until 1934, when she became professor of Public Welfare Administration in the School of Social Service of the University of Chicago. In 1933 Abbott was a delegate to the Nineteenth International Labor Conference; in 1937 she was a delegate to the Twenty-third International Labor Conference and chief of the United States delegation to the Pan American Child Welfare Congress in Mexico City. She died on June 19, 1939. Her papers are in the University of Chicago Library and in the National Archives.

References: Grace Abbott: "Chicago Employment Agency and the Immigrant Worker," *American Journal of Sociology* 14 (November 1908): 289-305; "Bulgarians of Chicago," *Charities and the Commons* 21 (January 9, 1909): 653-60; "Immigrant and Municipal Politics," *National Conference for Good City Government Proceedings* (1909): 148-56; "Study of the Greeks in Chicago," *American Journal of Sociology* 15 (November 1909): 379-93; "Education of Foreigners in American Citizenship," *National Conference for Good City Government Proceedings* (1910): 375-84; "Midwife in Chicago," *American Journal of Sociology* 20 (March 1915): 648-99; *The Immigrant and the Community* (New York: Century Co., 1917); "Enforcement of the United States Child Labor Law," *National Education Association Proceedings* (1918): 657-61; "After Suffrage—Citizenship," *Survey* 44 (September 1, 1920): 655-7; *Federal Aid for Protection of Maternity and Infancy* (Washington, D.C.: Government Printing Office, 1922); *Ten Years' Work for Children* (Washington, D.C.: Government Printing Office, 1923); "Child Labor Amendment," *North American Review* 220 (December 1924): 223-37; "History of Child Labor Laws," *Woman Citizen* 9 (December 27, 1924): 11; "Developing Standards of Rural Child Welfare," *National Conference of Social Work Proceedings* (1927): 26-37; "Case Work Responsibility of Juvenile Courts," *National Conference of Social Work Proceedings* (1929): 153-62; "Federal Government in Relation to Maternity and Infancy," *Annals of the American Academy of Political and Social Science* 151 (September 1930): 92-101; "Safeguarding the Child in America," *Current History* 33 (March 1931): 820-4; "Child," *American Journal of Sociology* 38 (May 1933): 880-8; "What about Mother's Pension Now?" *Survey* 70 (March 1934): 80-1; *From Relief to Social Security* (Chicago: University of Chicago Press, 1941). W. L. Chenery, "Grace Abbott of Nebraska," *New Republic* 35 (July 18, 1923): 203-4. "Boom for Miss Abbott as Secretary of Labor," *Woman's Journal* 15 (July 1930): 25. Alice Booth, "America's Twelve Greatest Women," *Good Housekeeping* 92 (May 1931): 50-1. "Champion of Women and Children," *World Tomorrow* 14 (September 1931): 294-7. "Resignation as Head of the Children's Bureau," *Nation* 139 (July 4, 1934): 3. H. C. Baker, "Abbotts of Nebraska," *Survey Graphic* 25 (June 1936): 370-2. Obituary, *New York Times*, June 20, 1939, p. 3. Edith Abbott. "Grace Abbott, A Sister's Memories," *Social Service Review* 13 (September 1939). Edith Abbott, "Grace Abbott and Hull House," *Social Service Review* 24 (December 1950). *Who Was Who*, 1 (1897-1942): 2-3. *Schlesinger Library Inventory*, vol. 1, s. v. "Abbott, Grace." *NAW*, vol. 1, pp. 2-4.

Bella Savitzky Abzug, 1920-

Congresswoman and attorney Bella Savitzky Abzug was born on July 24, 1920, in New York City, the daughter of Emanuel and Esther Savitsky. She attended public schools, received a B.A. from Hunter College in 1942 and an LL.B. from Columbia University Law School in 1945, and did graduate work at Jewish Theological Seminary. She married Maurice M. Abzug on June 4, 1944, and is the mother of two. From 1944 to 1970 she engaged in private practice, participating in labor law, women's rights, civil rights, and civil liberties cases. She was legislative director of Women Strike for Peace from 1961 to 1970. On November 3, 1970, she was elected to the Ninety-second Congress and on November 7, 1972, was reelected to the Ninety-third Congress, in which she serves on public works and government operations committees. Abzug is a member of the Urban League, the Women's Prison Association, the National Lawyers Guild, Hadassah, B'nai B'rith, the American Civil Liberties Union, and the Democratic Study Group.

References: *Congressional Directory* (Washington, D.C.: Government Printing Office, 1974). *Who's Who in American Women* (1975-1976): 3.

Jane Addams, 1860-1935

Settlement founder Jane Addams was born in Cedarville, Illinois, on September 6, 1860, the eighth of nine children of John Huy Addams, a state senator, and Sarah Weber. The Addams family was of Quaker ancestry, although Jane joined the Presbyterian Church in 1885. When she was two, her mother died; five years later her father married Anna H. Haldeman, a widow with two children. Jane graduated from Rockford Female Seminary in 1881; following her father's unexpected death the same year she entered the Woman's Medical College of Pennsylvania. Poor health, however, forced her withdrawal in May. During a tour of Europe with Ellen Gates Starr (q. v.) in 1887, she witnessed a strike by London matchgirls and visited Toynbee Hall, a settlement house in London's East End. Inspired, Addams returned to the United States. In 1889 Addams and Starr established Hull House, a Chicago settlement house serving working people and championing the cause of labor. Among its most notable residents were Edith Abbott (q. v.), Grace Abbott (q. v.), Sophonisba Breckinridge (q. v.), and Florence Kelley (q. v.). A staunch pacifist as well as a strong supporter of labor, Addams was elected chairman of the Women's Peace Party in 1915 and first president of the Women's International League for Peace and Freedom in 1919. In 1920 she helped to found the American Civil Liberties Union. She received the Nobel Peace Prize in 1931. On May 21, 1935, Addams died of cancer. Her papers are in the Swarthmore College Peace Collection and in the Ellen Gates Starr papers in the Sophia Smith Collection at Smith College.

References: Jane Addams: "Hull-House, Chicago: an Effort Toward Social Democracy," *Forum* 14 (October 1892): 226-41; *Philanthropy and Social Progress* (New York: Crowell & Co., 1893); "Art-Work Done by Hull-House," *Forum* 19 (July 1895): 614-17; "Trade Unions and Public Duty," *American Journal of Sociology* 4 (January 1899): 448-62; "College Women and Christianity," *Independent* 53 (August 8, 1901): 1852-5; "Housing Problem in Chicago," *Annals of the American Academy of Social and Political Science* 20 (July 1902): 99-107; "Humanizing Tendency of Industrial Education," *Chautauquan* 39 (May 1904): 266-72; "Present Crisis in Trade-Union Morals," *North American Review* 179 (August 1904): 178-93; "Problems of Municipal Administration," *American Journal of Sociology* 10 (January 1905): 425-44; "Recent Immigration," *Educational Review* 29 (March 1905): 245-63; "Child Labor Legislation—A Requisite for Industrial Efficiency," *Annals of the American Academy of Political and Social Science* 25 (May 1905): 542-50; "Fifteen Years at the Hull-House," *Ladies' Home Journal* 23 (March 1906): 13-4; *Newest Ideals of Peace* (New York: Macmillan Co., 1907); "Why Girls Go Wrong," *Ladies' Home Journal* 24 (September 1907): 13-4; *The Social Application of Religion* (Cincinnati: Jennings and Graham, 1908); "Chicago Settlements and Social Unrest," *Charities and the Commons* 20 (May 2, 1908): 155-66; "Failure of the Modern City to Provide Recreation for Young Girls," *Charities and the Commons* 21 (December 5, 1908): 365-8; *The Spirit of Youth and the City Streets* (New York: Macmillan Co., 1909); "When Youth Seeks a Mate," *Ladies' Home Journal* 26 (November 1909): 22; *Twenty Years at Hull-House* (New York: Macmillan Co., 1910); "Why Women Should Vote," *Ladies' Home Journal* 27 (January 1910): 21-2; "Autobiographical Notes," *American Magazine* 69 (April 1910): 722-34; *A New Conscience and an Ancient Evil* (New York: Macmillan Co., 1912); "Votes for Women and Other Votes," *Survey* 28 (June 1, 1912): 367-8; "Modern Lear: Strike at Pullman," *Survey* 29 (November 2, 1912): 131-7; "My Experience as a Progressive Delegate," *McClure's Magazine* 40 (November 1912): 12-4; *Women and the Larger Citizenship* (Chicago: Civics Society, 1913); "Has the Emancipation Act Been Nullified by National Indifference," *Survey* 29 (February 1, 1913): 565-6; "Minimum Wage Boards for Women," *Ladies' Home Journal* 30 (March 1913): 27; "If Men Were Seeking the Franchise," *Ladies' Home Journal* 30 (June 1913): 21; "Public Dance Halls of Chicago," *Ladies' Home Journal* 30 (July 1913): 19; "Sheltered Woman and the Magdalen," *Ladies' Home Journal* 30 (November 1913): 25; *A Plea for More Pay and More Education for Our Factory Girls and Boys* (Chicago: Chicago Association of Commerce, 1914); "Larger Aspects of the Women's Movement," *Annals of the American Academy of Political and Social Science* 56 (November 1914): 1-8; *The Overthrow of the War System* (Boston: Forum Publications, 1915); "As I See Women," *Ladies' Home Journal* 32 (August 1915): 11; "Women, War and Suffrage," *Survey* 35 (November 6, 1915): 148; *The Long Road of Women's Memory* (New York: Macmillan Co., 1916); "Reaction of the Simple Woman to Trade Union Propaganda," *Survey* 36 (July 1, 1916): 364-6; "War Times Challenging Women's Traditions," *Survey* 36 (August 5, 1916): 475-8; "World's Food Supply and Women's Obligation," *National Education Association Proceedings* (1918): 108-13; "Belated Industry," *Journal of Home Economics* 11 (August 1919): 355-64; "Feed the World and Save the League," *New Republic* 24 (November 24, 1920): 325-7; *Peace and Bread in Time of War* (New York: Macmillan Co., 1922); "Is Woman Suffrage Failing?" *Woman Citizen* 8 (April 19, 1924): 15-6; *The Second Twenty Years at Hull-House, September 1909 to 1929* (New York: Macmillan Co., 1930); "Aspects of the Woman's Movement," *Survey* 64 (August 1, 1930): 384-7; "Rise of Negro Education," *School Life* 18 (January 1933): 98; *Forty Years at Hull-House* (New York: Macmillan Co., 1935); "Julia Lathrop at Hull-House," *Survey Graphic* 24 (August 1935): 373-7; *Twenty Years at Hull House* (1910; reprint ed., New York: New American Library, 1961); *Women at the Hague* (1915; reprint ed., New York: Garland, 1972); *My Friend, Julia Lathrop* (1935; reprint ed., New York: Arno Press, 1974). "Women's Work for Chicago," *Municipal Affairs* 2 (September 1898): 502-8. Ella Wilkinson Peattie, "Women of the Hour," *Harper's Bazaar* 38 (October 1904): 1003-8. William Hard, "Chicago's Five Maiden Aunts," *American Magazine* 62 (September 1906): 481-9. "First Woman to Receive an Honorary Degree from Yale," *Craftsman* 18 (August 1910): 574-5. "Lady of the Melting Pot," *Current Literature* 49 (August 1910): 152-6. Amy Bradley, "Jane Addams," *American Magazine* 70 (August 1910): 562. "Twenty Years at Hull House, A Review," *Nation* 91 (December 29, 1910): 634-5. Taylor Graham, "Jane Addams' Twenty Years of Industrial Democracy," *Survey* 25 (December 3, 1910): 405-9. Elmer Cleveland Adams, *Heroines of Modern Progress* (New York: Sturgis & Walton Co., 1913). Floyd Dell, *Women as World Builders* (Chicago: Forbes, 1913). Helen Christine Bennett, *American Women in Civic Work* (New York: Dodd, Mead & Co., 1915). Paul U. Kellogg, "Miss Jane Addams," *Nation* 102 (February 24, 1916): 221. Mary Rosetta Parkman, "Heart of Hull-House," *St. Nicholas* 44 (January 8, 1917): 202-8. Ruth C. Mitchell, "Jane Addams," *Atlantic Monthly* 122 (November 1918): 634. Mildred Adams, "Jane Addams, Opener of Doors," *Woman Citizen* 9 (November 15, 1924): 12-3. R. M. Lovett, "Jane Addams at Hull-House," *New Republic* 62 (May 14, 1930): 349. "Hail to Hull-House," *Literary Digest* 105 (May 31, 1930): 21. "Jane Addams Receives Nobel Peace Prize," *Christian Century* 48 (December 23, 1931): 161. James Weber Linn, *Jane Addams, A Biography* (New York: Appleton-Century Co., 1935). Winifred Esther Wise, *Jane Addams of Hull-House* (New York: Harcourt, Brace, & Co., 1935). M. R. Rinehart, "Women of the Year," *Pictorial Review* 36 (January 1935): 7. "Nation Pays Tribute to Miss Addams," *Christian Century* 52 (May 29, 1935): 715. O. G. Villard, "Jane Addams and Her League," *Nation* 140 (May 29, 1935): 619. Paul Kellogg, "Jane Addams, 1860-1935," *Survey* 71 (June 1935): 175. "Jane Addams Shunned Life of Ease," *Literary Digest* 119 (June 1, 1935): 21. Obituary, *Newsweek* 5 (June 1, 1935): 23. "In Memoriam," *New Republic* 83 (June 5, 1935): 90-1. Obituary, *Commonweal* 22 (June 7, 1935): 158. Obituary, *Publishers' Weekly* 127 (June 15, 1935): 2291. Edward Shillito, "In Honor of Jane Addams," *Christian Century* 52 (June 19, 1935): 834. J. P. Gavit, "Spirit of Jane Addams," *Saturday Review of Literature* 13 (December 21, 1935): 6. Georgia Harkness, "Jane Addams in Retrospect," *Christian Century* 77 (January 13, 1960): 39-41. Roger Baldwin, "Jane Addams," *Nation* 190 (April 30, 1960): 375-6. "Jane Addams Centenary," *National Business Woman* 39 (September 1960): 4. Magaret Tims, *Jane Addams of Hull House, 1860-1935* (New York: Macmillan Co., 1961). Jean Wagoner, *Jane Addams* (Indianapolis: Bobbs-Merrill, 1962). Helen Stone Peterson, *Jane Addams, Pioneer of Hull House* (Champaign, Illinois: Garrard Publishing Co., 1965). Ronald Beam, *Cedarville's Jane Addams* (Freeport, Illinois: Wagner Co., 1966). Marshall W. Fishwick, *Jane Addams* (New Jersey: Silver Burdett Co., 1968). Elizabeth Comstock Mooney, *Jane Addams* (Chicago: Folett Publishing Co., 1968). Cornelia Meigs, *Jane Addams* (Boston: Little, Brown, 1970). Gail Keller, *Jane Addams* (New York: Crowell, 1971). Daniel Levine, *Jane Addams and the Liberal Tradition* (Madison: State Historical Society of Wisconsin, 1971). Jill Conway, "Women Reformers and American Culture, 1870-1930," *Journal of Social History*, Winter 1971-72. *Who Was Who* 1 (1897-1942): 9. *Women in American Labor History*, Item No. 118. *Schlesinger Library Inventory*, vol. 1, s. v. "Addams, Jane." *NAW*, vol. 1, pp. 16-22.

Louisa May Alcott, 1832-1888

Author and abolitionist Louisa May Alcott was born in Germantown, Pennsylvania, on November 29, 1832, and raised in Concord, Massachusetts, the second of the four daughters of Transcendentalist, educator, and social reformer Amos Bronson Alcott and Abigail May. Alcott descended on her mother's side from the noted diarist Samuel Sewall (1652-1730), a judge at the Salem, Massachusetts, witch trials. Despite her father's intimate association with Ralph Waldo Emerson and Henry David Thoreau, the Alcotts were often impecunious, and Louisa attempted to supplement the family income through work as a seamstress, domestic servant, teacher,

nurse, and writer. From 1861 to 1863 she was a nurse in Union Hospital, Washington, D.C.; a severe attack of typhoid fever, however, terminated her service. In January 1868 Alcott edited her first issue of *Merry's Museum*, a magazine for girls; *Little Women* appeared in two parts on September 30 and April 14, 1868, and was immediately critically acclaimed, as was her subsequent juvenile fiction. *Work*, an autobiographical novel exposing the exploitation of women workers and the evils of urban industrialization, appeared in 1873. The death of her mother in 1877 was the first in a series of personal tragedies, followed by the death of her sister May in 1879 and by her father's incapacitating stroke. Born on her father's birthday, she died on the day of his funeral, March 6, 1888, and was buried beside him at Sleepy Hollow Cemetery in Concord, Massachusetts. Her manuscripts are in the Concord Public Library, the Houghton Library at Harvard, the Louisa May Alcott Association at Orchard House in Concord, the New York Historical Society, and the New York Public Library.

References: Louise May Alcott: *Work: A Story of Experience* (Boston: Roberts Press, 1873). Frances E. Willard and Mary A. Livermore, *A Woman of the Century* (New York: Charles Wells Moulton, 1893). Lucile Gulliver, *Louisa May Alcott, A Bibliography* (New York: B. Franklin, 1973). Obituary, *New York Times*, March 7, 1888, p. 3. *Who Was Who*, Historical Volume (1607-1896): 85. *Schlesinger Library Inventory*, vol. 1, s. v. "Alcott, Louisa May." *NAW*, vol. 1, pp. 27-31.

Mary Anderson, 1872-1964

Mary Anderson, the first director of the Women's Bureau of the U.S. Department of Labor, was born in Lidkoping, Sweden, the daughter of farmers Magnus and Matilda Anderson, Lutherans. She immigrated to the United States in 1888. In 1894 she joined the International Boot and Shoe Workers Union in Chicago; from 1895 to 1910 she served as president of Stitchers Local 94. In 1903 she joined the newly established Chicago Women's Trade Union League (WTUL). For the WTUL she served as an organizer and investigator, participating in the Hart, Schaffner & Marx strike of 1910; the copper miners' strike in Calumet, Michigan, in 1913; and the spar miners' strike in Rosiclare, Illinois, in 1916. She served as assistant director of the Women in Industry Service of the Department of Labor from 1916 to 1919, when she became director. From 1920 to 1944 she headed the Women's Bureau of the U.S. Department of Labor. She retired in 1944 and devoted herself to writing. *Woman at Work*, an autobiography tracing the history of the Women's Bureau, was published in 1951. She died in Washington, D.C., on January 30, 1964.

References: Mary Anderson: "Working-Woman's Views," *Harper's Bazaar* 45 (May 1911): 246; "Organizing the Bureau of Engraving and Printing Girls," *Life and Labor* 7 (January 1918): 11-2; "Wages for Women Workers," *Annals of the American Academy of Political and Social Science* 81 (January 1919): 123-9; "Women's Wages," *American*

Federationist 32 (August 1925): 681-3; "Hours of Work," *American Federationist* 32 (September 1925): 769-72; "Should There Be Labor Laws for Women?" *Good Housekeeping* 81 (September 1925): 52-3; "Working Conditions," *American Federationist* 32 (October 1925): 946-9; "The Women Workers," *American Federationist* 32 (November 1925): 1073-6; "Women Workers in Textiles," *American Federationist* 36 (June 1929): 696-9; "What Use Is the Women's Bureau to the Woman Worker?" *American Federationist* 36 (August 1929): 939-42; *Women's Place in Industry in Ten Southern States* (Washington, D.C.: Government Printing Office, 1931); *Women at Work: the Autobiography of Mary Anderson as Told to Mary N. Winslow* (Minneapolis: University of Minnesota Press, 1951). *Who Was Who* 4 (1961-1968): 29. Obituary, *New York Times,* January 30, 1964, p. 3. *Women in American Labor History,* Items No. 4, 121, 184, 185, 186, 235, 236, 283, 341, and 382. *BDALL,* pp. 6-7.

Susan Brownell Anthony, 1820-1906

Feminist Susan Brownell Anthony was born in Adams, Massachusetts, on February 15, 1820, the second of eight children of Daniel Anthony, a Quaker cotton manufacturer, and Lucy Read. She was educated in public school in Battenville, New York, by her father, and at Friends' Seminary near Philadelphia, which was administered by Deborah Moulson. To assist her impecunious father, she taught at Eunice Kenyon's Friends' Seminary in New Rochelle, New York, from 1839, and at Canajoharie Academy near Rochester, New York, from 1846. In 1849 she returned home to manage the family farm; among those frequenting the Anthonys' home were Frederick Douglass, William Lloyd Garrison, and Wendell Phillips. In 1850 she met Elizabeth Cady Stanton (q. v.), who quickly converted her to the cause of women's suffrage. Denied permission because of her sex to speak at an Albany, New York, temperance meeting, she helped found the first state Women's Temperance Society in New York in 1852. In 1868 she established *The Revolution,* a paper printed by females and dealing with issues of interest to women workers. In 1868, together with Stanton, Anthony was admitted, despite male opposition, as a delegate to the convention of the National Labor Union. At its 1869 convention, however, the membership voted against seating Anthony, charging that she had underpaid her employees at *The Revolution,* encouraged female strikebreakers, and discharged printer Augusta Lewis from *The Revolution* because of union activity. During July Fourth festivities during the Centennial Exposition in Philadelphia, she presented a "Woman's Declaration of 1876," which demanded complete enfranchisement for females, a gesture which embodied Anthony's lifelong dedication to women's rights. In 1890 she settled in Rochester, New York, with her sister Mary; in 1900 she helped open the University of Rochester to women. Anthony died of heart disease on March 13, 1906, and was buried in Rochester's Mount Hope Cemetery. Her manuscripts are in the collections of the Susan B. Anthony Memorial in Rochester, New York; American Antiquarian Society in Worcester, Massachusetts; the Boston Public Library; the Henry Huntington Library, San Marino, California; the Library of Congress; the University of Rochester Library; the Schlesinger Library, Radcliffe College; the Seneca Falls, New York, Historical Society; the Sophia Smith Collection, Smith College; and the Vassar College Library.

References: Susan Brownell Anthony: "Status of Women, Past, Present, and Future," *Arena* 17 (May 1897): 901-8; *Out of the Kitchen* (New York: S. Daye, Inc., 1943); *The Ghost in My Life* (1933; reprint ed., New York: Chosen Books, 1971). "Woman's Half-Century of Evolution," *North American Review* 175 (December 1902): 800-10. "Sketch of Susan B. Anthony," *Outlook* 82 (March 24, 1906): 628-30. "Strenuous Life of a Woman Reformer," *Current Literature* 40 (May 1906): 492-4. Amanda T. Jones, "Susan Brownell Anthony," *Critic* 48 (May 1906): 392-3. Ida Minerva Tarbell, "Militant Advocate of Women's Rights," *American Magazine* 69 (February 1910): 471-5. Willis John Abbot, *Women of History* (Philadelphia: J. C. Winston Co., 1913). Fanny Garrison Villard, "Woman Suffrage Pioneer," *Nation* 110 (February 14, 1920): 197-9. Nanette Paul, *The Great Woman Statesman* (New York: Hogan-Paulus Corporation, 1925). "Susan B. Anthony on Trial," *Woman Citizen* 12 (September 1927): 3. L. E. Anthony, "Leaves from Family Scrapbooks," *Woman's Journal* 14 (December 1929): 23. Florence Horn Bryan, *Susan B. Anthony* (New York: J. Messner, 1947). Constance Buel Burnett, *Five for Freedom* (New York: Abelard Press, 1953). Katharine Anthony, *Susan B. Anthony: Her Personal History and Her Era* (Garden City, New York: Doubleday, 1954). Marjorie Longwell, *Susan B. Anthony* (New York: William Frederick Press, 1954). Alma Lutz, *Susan B. Anthony* (Boston: Beacon Press, 1959). Israel Kugler, "The Trade Union Career of Susan B. Anthony," *Labor History* 2 (Winter 1961): 90-100. Obituary, *New York Times,* March 13, 1906, p. 3. *Who Was Who* 1 (1897-1942): 28. *Schlesinger Library Inventory,* vol. 1, s. v. "Anthony, Susan B." *NAW,* vol. 1, pp. 51-7.

Rebecca Beck August, 1883-

Rank-and-file organizer Rebecca Beck August was born in Droya, Latvia, in 1883. In 1890 she immigrated to London with her father. After three years of schooling, the twelve-year-old August went to work in a tailor's shop; for fifty-three years she was to work in the needle trades, primarily as a buttonhole maker. In 1904 she came to Chicago, where she was to remain until 1910. While working at Hart, Schaffner & Marx, she protested a price cut and was immediately fired. As a union organizer she helped found the Hebrew Trades Council and a women's branch of The Workmen's Circle (Ladies' Branch Number 3). August was an associate of Jane Addams (q. v.) and a frequent visitor at Hull House. In 1910 she moved to Seattle, Washington, where she was active in the International Workers of the World and in the battle for the eight-hour workday. Following her marriage in 1912 and the birth of two sons, August continued to work. She was an active member of the Amalgamated Clothing Workers of America, from which she retired in 1948 and for which she helped establish a Retired Members Club. While a resident of the Jewish Home for the Aged in Los Angeles in 1973, August continued her organizational activities, agitating for the rights of senior citizens. The Feminist History Research Project, an archive of oral history, has taped three interviews with August.

Reference: "Rebecca Beck August—Biographical Sketch," mimeographed (Topanga, California: Feminist History Research Project, 1973).

Sarah G. Bagley, active 1836-1847

Sarah Bagley, the earliest female labor organizer known by name, was born in Meredith, New Hampshire. The date of her birth is unknown. From 1836 to 1842 she worked as a piece weaver at the Hamilton Manufacturing Company, a Lowell, Massachusetts, cotton mill, and later at the Middlesex Factory. Rebelling against working conditions, Bagley founded the Lowell Female Labor Reform Association in 1844; she later established the Lowell Industrial Reform Lyceum. Although Bagley was an early contributor to the *Lowell Offering,* a journal written by and for female textile workers, her later articles, highly critical of industrial abuse by employers, were rejected by editor Harriet Farley. Denouncing the *Lowell Offering* as a company paper, Bagley on behalf of the Lowell Female Labor Reform Association acquired the *Voice of Industry,* a paper previously published by the Working Men's Association, in which she exposed exploitative company recruiting policies. Appearing before the Massachusetts legislature in 1845, Bagley testified in favor of the ten-hour workday and presented a petition of endorsement signed by 1,000 sister workers. In 1845 Bagley was a delegate to the New England Working Men's Association; in 1846 she was a delegate to the American Union of Associationists' Boston convention. On February 13, 1846, Bagley's appointment as the first female telegraph operator was announced by the *Voice of Industry.* After 1847 she disappeared from public record.

Reference: Madeleine Stern, *We the Women* (New York: Burt Franklin Reprints, 1974). *BDALL,* pp. 11-12.

Elizabeth Balanoff, 1926-

Professor Elizabeth Balanoff was born in Salisbury, Missouri, on July 8, 1926. She attended the University of Missouri and received an M.A. from Roosevelt University in 1963 and a Ph.D. from the University of Chicago in 1974. In 1968 she joined the faculty of Roosevelt University. Since June 1968 she has been director of Roosevelt University's Oral History Project in Labor and Immigration History, a study funded in part by grants from the National Endowment for the Humanities.

References: Elizabeth Balanoff: "Negro Legislators in the North Carolina General Assembly, 1868-1872," *North Carolina Journal of History,* Winter 1972; "Close-Up on Civil Rights," *World Book Supplement* 1972; "A History of the Black Community of Gary, Indiana, 1906-1940" (Ph.D. diss., University of Chicago, 1974); "The Status of Women in American Labor Organizations From 1900" (paper delivered at the Pacific Coast Branch of the American Historical Association, Berkeley, California, August 22, 1975).

Angela Bambace, 1898-1975

Union organizer and official Angela Bambace was born in Brazil in 1898. After living for a short time in Italy, her family immigrated to the United States in 1904. At seventeen she went to work in a New York City garment factory; she joined the International Ladies Garment Workers Union (ILGWU) in 1919. She began her distinguished career as a labor organizer in 1936 in a Baltimore, Maryland, coat factory. Among the numerous strikes in which Bambace participated was that of garment workers in Elizabeth, New Jersey, in 1932. In 1956 she was elected vice president of the ILGWU, becoming the first woman to serve on the union's executive board. Bambace was cochairman of the American Trade Union Council for Histadrut and a member of the executive boards of the American Civil Liberties Union, the Italian-American Labor Council, and the Israel Histadrut Council of Greater Baltimore. In 1973 Bambace retired. She died in Baltimore on April 3, 1975.

Reference: Obituary, *Washington Post,* April 12, 1975, p. B-11.

Kate Barnard, 1875-1930

Organizer Kate Barnard, the first woman to win election to a statewide office, was born in Geneva, Nebraska, on May 23, 1875, the daughter of John P. Barnard, an Irish-American surveyer, and Rachel Schiell. Barnard's mother died when she was eighteen months old, and she was raised by her father in Oklahoma City, where she attended St. Joseph's parochial school. In 1892 the Barnards took up residence in an Oklahoma City slum, an experience which left an indelible impression. Barnard worked, in turn, as a teacher, stenographer, and clerk. While employed as a publicist by the Oklahoma Commission in 1904, Barnard visited the St. Louis World's Fair. Appalled by the uncontrolled industrial expansion, massive unemployment, and poor working conditions she witnessed in St. Louis, Barnard wrote a series of letters to the *Daily Oklahoman* which received great public attention. In 1905 she was appointed matron in charge of the Provident Association of Oklahoma City. As such, she emerged a champion of labor, battling for wage increases for municipal employees, posting bond for strikers, and organizing the jobless into the politically active Federal Labor Union. In 1906, as a representative of the American Federation of Labor, she attended the "Shawnee Convention," a farm-labor coalition seeking to create a common platform for the upcoming constitutional convention. Among the planks endorsed by the coalition and later adopted by the convention were compulsory education and abolition of child labor. The constitutional convention also created the office of Commissioner of Charities and Corrections, to which Barnard was elected in 1907 and 1910. While commissioner, Barnard championed pension benefits for widows, attacked the use of convict labor, and protested the blacklisting of unionists. Although sought as a lobbyist by organized labor, Barnard retired from public life in 1914. She became a semi-invalid, afflicted for the rest of her life by a respiratory illness and skin disease. She died on February 23, 1930, and was buried in Rosehill Cemetery in Oklahoma City. Her papers are in the Oklahoma State Archives in Oklahoma City.

References: Kate Barnard: "Working for the Friendless," *Independent* 63 (November 28, 1907): 1307-8; "Human Ideals in Government," *Survey* 23 (October 2, 1909): 16-20; "Through the Windows of Destiny," *Good Housekeeping* 55 (November 1912): 600-6; "Fighting the Lease with Pardons," *Survey* 29 (January 4, 1913): 457-8; "For the Orphans of Oklahoma," *Survey* 33 (November 7, 1914): 154-5. G. W. Hunt, "Appreciation of Miss Barnard," *Good Housekeeping* 55 (November 1912): 606-7. *NAW*, vol. 1, pp. 90-2.

Gertrude Barnum, 1866-1948

Social worker and labor reformer Gertrude Barnum was born in Chester, Illinois, on September 29, 1866, the second of the four children of Judge William Henry Barnum and Clara Hyde. She was educated at Evanston Township High School and at the University of Wisconsin. During the 1890s she worked with Jane Addams (q. v.) at Hull House and supervised the Henry Booth House from 1902 to 1903. In 1903 she helped found the National Women's Trade Union League (NWTUL). As a NWTUL representative she participated in strikes by female textile workers in Fall River, Massachusetts, and by corsetmakers in Troy, New York, in 1905. From 1911 to 1916 Barnum was special representative for the International Ladies Garment Workers Union. In 1914 President Woodrow Wilson appointed her consultant to the Walsh Commission on Industrial Relations; in 1917 she became associate director of Investigation Services of the U.S. Labor Department. She retired in 1919. At the time of her death Barnum was writing a history of labor from 1885 to 1930. She died in Los Angeles on June 17, 1948; her ashes are in Inglewood Cemetery.

References: Gertrude Barnum: "Fall River Mill Girl in Domestic Service," *Charities and the Commons* 13 (March 4, 1905): 550-1; "Industrial Experiment for Unemployed Women," *Charities and the Commons* 20 (August 1, 1908): 532-3; "How Industrial Peace Has Been Brought About in the Clothing Industry," *Independent* 73 (October 3, 1912): 777-81. "Pittsburgh Convention and Women Unionists," *Charities and the Commons* 15 (January 6, 1906): 441-2. Obituary, *New York Times*, June 19, 1948, p. 4. *Women in American Labor History*, Items No. 124 and 125.

Leonora Marie Kearney Barry, 1849-1930

Labor organizer, temperance leader, and Catholic activist Leonora Marie Kearney Barry was born on August 13, 1849, in Kearney, County Cork, Ireland, the only child of John Kearney and Honor Granger Brown. In 1852 the Kearneys immigrated to the United States, where they made their home in Pierpont, New York. Following her mother's death and father's remarriage, fifteen-year-old Leonora sought private instruction to supplement her public-school education. Receiving a teaching certificate at age sixteen, she taught for several years in a country school. On November 30, 1871, she married William E. Barry, an Irish immigrant and painter. Her husband died of a respiratory disease in 1881; her daughter, Marion Frances, born in 1873, died shortly thereafter. Now the the sole support of her sons, William Standish, born in 1875, and Charles Joseph, born in 1880, Leonora went to work as a millhand in Amsterdam, New York. Angered by the inadequate wages, long hours, and poor working conditions she experienced, she joined the Knights of Labor in 1884. As master workman of District Assembly 65, Barry attended the Albany Convention of the Knights of Labor in 1886. While a delegate to the General Assembly in Richmond, Virginia, that same year she was appointed general investigator of the department of women's work, empowered to investigate industrial conditions affecting women and child labor. In 1887, 1888, and 1889 she presented the results of her inquiry, the first systematic documentation of industrial abuse of women and children undertaken by a labor union. Barry's efforts led to the passage of the Pennsylvania factory inspection act in 1899; less successful were her attempts to establish cooperative industries. In 1890 she married Obadiah Read Lake, a St. Louis printer, and retired from union activities, devoting her time instead to suffrage and temperance agitation and to Catholic charities. Again widowed on July 18, 1923, Barry died of cancer of the mouth on July 15, 1930, and was buried in St. Mary's Cemetery in Minooka, Illinois. Barry's partial correspondence is in the Terence V. Powderly Papers at Catholic University of America.

References: John B. Andrews and W. D. P. Bliss, *History of Women in Trade Unions* (vol. 10 of *Report on Condition of Woman and Child Wage-Earners in the U.S.*, Senate Document No. 645, 61st Cong., 2d sess., 1911). *Who's Who*, (1914-1915). Obituary, *Joliet (Illinois) Herald-News*, July 16, 1930. *NAW*, vol. 1, pp. 101-2.

Oma Barton

Oma Barton, vice president of the Amalgamated Clothing Workers of America (ACWA), was honored in 1973 by organized labor of Georgia as the first "Woman of the Year." In 1941 Barton joined ACWA Local 365 in Atlanta. She was elected manager of the ACWA Georgia Joint Board in 1959, vice president in 1964, and assistant manager of the Southern Regional Joint Board in 1970. She is active in local and national politics and in community and state affairs. Barton serves on the advisory council of the Georgia Employment Security Agency and the American Trade Union Council for Histadrut.

Reference: "VP Barton named 'Woman of Year' in Ga. labor," *Advance*, June 1973, p. 4.

Fayee Bartz

Fayee Bartz, special representative for International Community Services of the United Rubber, Cork, Linoleum and Plastic Workers of America (URW), was born in Ontario, Wisconsin. After high school, she attended the University of Wisconsin. In 1942 she was employed by the Parker Pen Company in Janesville, Wisconsin; that same year she joined the Wisconsin Federal Labor Union. From 1943 to 1946 Bartz took a leave of absence from Parker Pen to serve in the Women's Army Corps, in which she attained the rank of sergeant. In 1946 she returned to Parker Pen and worked as an order clerk in the shipping depatment. Bartz joined Local 663 of the URW in 1962; in 1967 she was elected president of Local 663, a position she retained until 1973, when she was appointed special representative for International Community Services. Bartz's dedication to the trade union movement was shared by her late husband, a member of the United Auto Workers of America. Bartz is a frequent contributor to the URW journal, the *United Rubber Worker*.

Dorothy Jacobs Bellanca, 1894-1946

Organizer Dorothy Jacobs Bellanca was born on August 10, 1894, in Zemel, Russian Latvia, the fourth daughter of Harry Jacobs, a tailor, and Bernice Edith Levinson. In 1900 her family immigrated to the United States and settled in Baltimore, where she attended the public schools. At thirteen, she went to work as a buttonhole sewer in an overcoat factory. With other immigrant women workers she participated in 1909 in the founding of Local 170 of the United Garment Workers of America. While president of Local 170 in 1914, she led the membership into the maverick Amalgamated Clothing Workers of America (ACWA). She was elected secretary of the ACWA's Baltimore Joint Board in 1915, to the executive board in 1916, and was appointed the union's first full-time female organizer in 1917. From 1924 to 1926 she headed the ACWA's women's bureau. Among the numerous organizing drives in which Bellanca participated was the 1932-1934 ACWA campaign to organize garment workers in Connecticut, New Jersey, New York, and Pennsylvania. With Cornelia Bryce Pinchot (q. v.), the wife of Pennsylvania's governor, she led picket lines in Allentown, Pennsylvania. In 1938 Bellanca was appointed to the General Advisory Committee on Maternal and Child Welfare by Secretary of Labor Frances Perkins (q. v.). That same year she waged an unsuccessful campaign as congressional candidate from the 8th District of New York on the Republican and American Labor party tickets. She died on August 16, 1946, in New York City, survived by her husband August Bellanca, an Italian immigrant and ACWA organizer.

References: Obituary, *New York Times*, August 17, 1946. "Death of Dorothy Jacobs Bellanca," *Nation* 163 (August

Alva Erskine Smith Vanderbilt Belmont, 1853-1933

Feminist Alva Erskine Smith Vanderbilt Belmont was born in Mobile, Alabama, on January 17, 1853, the third of five children of merchant Murray Forbes Smith and Phoebe Ann Desha. She was educated in France, where her family had moved after the Civil War. Returning to the United States in the early 1870s, she took up residence in New York City. On April 20, 1875, she married the grandson of Cornelius Vanderbilt, William Kissam Vanderbilt, to whom she bore three children. As Vanderbilt's wife, she became the patroness of architect Richard Morris Hunt, who designed the renowned residence at Fifth Avenue and Fifty-second Street, New York City; Marble House, in Newport, Rhode Island; and Beacon Towers at Sands Point, Long Island. In 1895 she divorced her husband on grounds of adultery. She married Oliver Hazard Perry Belmont on January 11, 1896. Following Belmont's death in 1908, she became a champion of reform causes, including suffrage and the labor movement. She was a member of the National American Woman Suffrage Association and the Congressional Union, founder of the Political Equality League, and president of the National Woman's party. As a member of the Women's Trade Union League, she supported the garment workers' strikes of 1909 and 1916. In 1912 she provided backing for the financially troubled *Masses*. She died in Paris on January 26, 1933, and was buried in Woodlawn Cemetery in New York.

Reference: *NAW*, vol. 1, pp. 126-8.

Mary McLeod Bethune, 1876-1955

Educator Mary Jane McLeod Bethune was born on a farm in Mayesville, South Carolina, in 1876, the fifteenth of the seventeen children of Samuel McLeod and Patricia McIntosh, former slaves, and members of the Methodist Church. As a child, Bethune attended Mayesville Institute, a school for black children. From 1888 to 1893 she attended Scotia Seminary in Concord, North Carolina; her education there was made possible in part by Mary Crissman, a Denver, Colorado, Quaker dressmaker, who established with her life's savings a scholarship for a black student. Bethune was never to forget the generosity of this working woman. She supplemented the stipend by working in the school laundry and kitchen. From 1894 to 1895 she attended the Moody Bible College in Chicago, the first American black to so do. After graduation, however, she was denied appointment as a missionary to Africa by the Presbyterian Board of Missions. Instead, she taught at Haines Normal Institute in Augusta, Georgia, and at the Kindell Institute in Sumter, Georgia. In Sumter she met her husband, Albertus Bethune, to whom she bore a son, Albert McLeod Bethune. When Albert was nine months old, the Bethunes moved to Palatka, Florida, where she founded an elementary school for blacks. Four years later in Daytona Beach, Florida, alarmed by the exploitation of black workers and their families, she established the Daytona Educational and Industrial School for Negro Girls, which opened on October 3, 1904. In 1908 the school became the Daytona Educational Training School, and was opened to males. As the number of its students grew, it expanded to include a high school, a normal school in 1921, and merged with Cookman Institute in 1925. From its inception, Bethune-Cookman College was intended to serve the needs of the community. In 1911, for example, Bethune's high-school students investigated living conditions and health hazards in the nearby turpentine camps, where she established a chain of mission schools. That same year, distraught by the fact that blacks were denied regular admission to white hospitals, she founded McLeod Hospital. A close friend of Eleanor Roosevelt (q. v.), Bethune was appointed by President Franklin D. Roosevelt director of the Division of Negro Affairs in the National Youth Administration. In 1945 Bethune joined forces with black labor leader A. Philip Randolph, a graduate of Cookman Institute, to plan the March on Washington, a demonstration in support of equal job opportunity. Responding, Roosevelt issued Executive Order 8802, which abolished discrimination according to "race, creed, color, or national origin." Bethune was president of the National Association of Colored Women and founded the National Council of Negro Women and the Association for the Study of Negro Life and History. She died on May 18, 1955, and was buried near Bethune-Cookman College in Daytona Beach, Florida.

References: C. H. Tobias, "Some Outstanding Negro Christians," *Missionary Review of the World* 59 (June 1936): 298-9. E. A. Carter, "Modern Matriarch," *Survey Graphic* 25 (October 1936): 573-4. "Negro Angel: College Founder Sees Bright Future for Her Race," *Literary Digest* 123 (March 6, 1937): 8-9. "Pioneers in the Struggle Against Segregation," *Survey Graphic* 36 (January 1947): 91. "Matriarch," *Time* 48 (July 22, 1946): 55. Catherine Owens Peare, *Mary McLeod Bethune* (New York: Vanguard Press, 1951). Obituary, *New York Times*, May 19, 1955, p. 1. W. M. Brewer, "Mary McLeod Bethune," *Negro History Bulletin* 19 (November 1955); 48. R. L. Sloan, "Miracle Years of Mrs. Bethune," *Christian Century* 73 (February 1, 1956): 140-1. Emma Sterne, *Mary McLeod Bethune* (New York: Knopf, 1957). Rackham Holt, *Mary McLeod Bethune, A Biography* (Garden City, N.Y.: Doubleday, 1964). Ella Kaiser Carruth, *She Wanted To Read* (New York: Abingdon Press, 1966). Olive Burt, *Mary McLeod Bethune* (Indianapolis: Bobbs-Merrill, 1970). Ruby Lorraine Radford, *Mary McLeod Bethune* (New York: Putnam, 1973). *Who Was Who* 3 (1951-1960): 72. *Schlesinger Library Inventory*, vol. 1, s. v. "Bethune, Mary McLeod."

Ann Craton Blankenhorn

Industrial investigator Ann Craton Blankenhorn surveyed conditions in the garment trades in the 1920s and studied the influence of the church in industrial towns in the 1940s. From 1916 to 1918 she worked for the Bureau of Children's Guardians and from 1926 to 1931 was a caseworker for the American Red Cross. She was the wife of Heber Blankenhorn, co-director of the Bureau of Industrial Research. Her papers were presented to the Wayne State University Archives of Labor History and Urban Affairs in 1969.

Reference: "Women's Collections in the Archives of Labor History and Urban Affairs," *Wayne State University Archives of Labor History and Urban Affairs Newsletter* 2 (Summer 1972).

Mother Ella Reeve Bloor, 1862-1951

Labor organizer and veteran Communist Ella Reeve Bloor was born on July 8, 1862, the daughter of druggist Charles Reeve, a Presbyterian whom she once described as "a rich old Republican over on Staten Island," and Harriet Amanda Disbrow. Early visitors to the Reeve home included Walt Whitman and Henry Ward Beecher. Bloor was educated in the Bridgeton, New Jersey, public schools and at Ivy Hall Seminary, a private finishing school which she detested and quit in 1876. Her mother died in 1879, and care for four young siblings fell to her. In 1881 her father married a socialite; shortly thereafter, Bloor married her cousin, Lucien Ware, to whom within thirty-three months she bore three children. Tragedy struck the Wares with leveling force: two days after the birth of her daughter Grace, Bloor's infants, Pauline and Charlie, died. Their deaths were followed by the births of three more children. Overburdened by familial responsibility and frustrated aspirations, Bloor suffered a nervous breakdown. In 1895 she divorced Ware and moved to New York where she met Eugene Debs and joined Debs's workingman's association, "The Social Democracy of America." She married Louis Cohen, to whom she bore two children. She joined the Socialist Labor party in 1898, the Socialist party in 1900. Bloor conducted private investigations of child labor in the glass factories of Bridgeton, New Jersey; in the Catholic orphan asylum in Downington, Pennsylvania; and in mine companies in Johnstown, Pennsylvania. In 1906 she assisted novelist Upton Sinclair, verifying for federal investigators charges made in *The Jungle*, his exposé of immigrants' exploitation by Chicago meatpackers. Accompanied by Richard Bloor, a Welsh immigrant, she penetrated the stockyards, gathering evidence. Henceforth, she was known as "Mother Bloor." In 1909 she joined the Women's Suffrage Association, in which she became chairman of the Department of Working Women. With Elizabeth Gurley Flynn (q. v.), she founded the pacifist Workers Defense Union during World War I and agitated for the release of imprisoned antiwar activists, among them Kate Richards O'Hare (q. v., Kate Richards O'Hare Cunningham), Louise Olivereau, and Flora Foreman. In 1918 she was candidate for Lieutenant Governor of New York. Mother Bloor organized females during the Electrical Workers Union's strike in Schenectady,

New York, in 1911; organized for the United Cloth Hat and Cap Makers Union in New York City in 1917; hitchhiked across the United States on behalf of the Communist party in 1925; participated in the Passaic, New Jersey, textile workers' strike in 1926; raised funds for the defense of Italian immigrants Sacco and Vanzetti during a hitchhiking tour of the United States in 1927; was active in strikes by Pennsylvania and Colorado miners in 1927; and took part in the strike of North Carolina textile workers in 1931. On behalf of destitute farmers she organized the Farmer's Emergency Relief Conference, held in Washington, D.C., in 1932. In 1932 she married Andrew Omholt, a North Dakota farmer. From 1932 to 1948 she was chairman of the Communist party's Women's Commission. She died in Quakertown, Pennsylvania, on August 10, 1951.

References: Ella Reeve Bloor: *Women in the Soviet Union* (New York: Workers Library, 1938); *We Are Many: An Autobiography* (New York: International Publishers, 1940). "Trouble into Trouble," *Time* 26 (November 11, 1935): 13. Obituary, *New York Times*, August 11, 1951, p. 1. "Old Fashioned Radical," *Time* 58 (August 20, 1951): 15. Robert Patterson, "Funeral of Mother Bloor," *American Mercury* 73 (November 1951): 63-70. *Women in American Labor History*, Item No. 383. *Schlesinger Library Inventory*, vol. 1, s. v. "Bloor, Ella Reeve." *BDALL*, pp. 26-28.

Selma Munter Borchardt, 1895-1968

Selma Munter Borchardt, lawyer and educator, was born in Washington, D.C., on December 1, 1895, the daughter of Newman Borchardt and Sarah Munter. She received a B.S. from Syracuse University in 1919, a B.A. in 1922, an LL.B. from Washington College of Law in 1933, and an M.A. from Catholic University of America in 1937. She was a member of the Washington, D.C., and Supreme Court bars. In 1920 she became director of teacher training in Montgomery County, Maryland. She joined Local 8 of the American Federation of Teachers (AFT) in 1923, and served as vice president and legislative chairman of Local 8 through 1924. From 1924 to 1935 and from 1942 to 1962 she was AFT vice president and congressional legislative representative; from 1927 to 1946 she served as director of the World Federation of Education Associations. She was AFT representative to the Women's Joint Congressional Committee from 1927 to 1958 and secretary of the American Federation of Labor Committee on Education from 1929 to 1955. She was active in the Women's Trade Union League and taught at the Washington College of Law from 1934 to 1947. She died in Washington, D.C., on January 31, 1968. Her papers are in the Selma M. Borchardt Collection in the Wayne State University Archives of Labor History and Urban Affairs.

References: Selma Munter Borchardt: "Objection to S. 181 and Arguments for Passage of S. 717," *Congressional Digest* 25 (February 1946): 53; "Position of the American Federation of Labor and the American Federation of Teachers on Federal Subsidy for Higher Education," *Congressional Digest* 34 (August 1955): 212. Obituary, *New York Times*, Febru-

ary 1, 1968, p. 7. *Who Was Who* 5 (1969-1973): 75. *BDALL*, pp. 28-9.

Sophonisba Preston Breckinridge, 1866-1948

Sophonisba Preston Breckinridge, lawyer and sociologist, was born in Lexington, Kentucky, on April 1, 1866, the second of seven children of William Campbell Preston Breckinridge and Issa Desha. She graduated from Wellesley College in 1888 and, during her father's tenure as a congressman, taught mathematics in a Washington, D.C., high school. After her father was defeated in his bid for reelection in 1894, she returned to Lexington where, over paternal objections, she studied law. Breckinridge was the first woman to be admitted to the Kentucky bar. She received her Ph.D. from the University of Chicago in 1901, her J.D. in 1904. She joined the faculty of the University of Chicago that same year and taught there until 1942. She embarked on her life's work, the study of female workers, in 1906; in 1907 she met Margaret Dreier Robins (q. v.), joined the Women's Trade Union League, and became a resident of Hull House. In 1908 she became head of the research department of the Chicago School of Civics and Philanthropy, choosing as her assistant Edith Abbott (q. v.), with whom she studied the domestic consequences of urban industrialization and agitated for the federal regulation of child labor. In 1908 she became a cofounder of the Immigrants Protective League. She was elected vice president of the National Woman's Suffrage Association in 1911 and helped establish the *Social Service Review*, which she edited until her death in 1927. From 1934 to 1935 she served as president of the American Association of Schools of Social Work. She died in Chicago on July 30, 1948. Her papers are in the Library of Congress.

References: Sophonisba Preston Breckinridge: *Legal Tender* (Chicago: University of Chicago Press, 1903); "Two Decisions Relating to Organized Labor," *Journal of Political Economy* 13 (September 1905): 593-7; *Employment of Women in Industries* (Chicago: Chicago Women's Trade Union League, 1906); *Legislative Control of Women's Work* (Chicago: Chicago Women's Trade Union League, 1906); "Employment of Women in Industries: Twelfth Census Statistics," *Journal of Political Economy* 14 (January 1906): 14-40; "The Illinois Ten-Hour Law," *Journal of Political Economy* 18 (June 1910): 465-70; "Neglected Widowhood in the Juvenile Court," *American Journal of Sociology* 16 (July 1910): 53-87; *The Delinquent Child and the Home* (New York: Charities Publications, 1912); "Political Equality for Women and Women's Wages," *Annals of the American Academy of Political and Social Science* 56 (November 1914): 122-33; "Family in the Community, but Not Yet of the Community," *Conference of Charities and Corrections Proceedings* (1914): 69-75; *The Housing Problem in Chicago* (Chicago: University of Chicago, 1915); *The Modern Household* (Boston: Whitcomb & Barrows, 1919); *The Administration of Aid-To-Mothers in Illinois* (Washington, D.C.: Government Printing Office, 1921); "Home Responsibilities of Women Workers and Equal Wage," *Journal of Political Economy* 31 (August 1923): 521-43; *Family Welfare Work in a Metropolitan Community* (Chicago: University of Chicago Press, 1924); "How Women Came To Be Persons," *Woman's Journal* 14 (December 1929): 11; *Marriage and the Civil Rights of Women* (Chicago: University of Chicago Press, 1931); *The*

Family and the State (Chicago: University of Chicago Press, 1934); *Women in the Twentieth Century* (New York: Arno Press, 1972); *The Wage-Earning Woman and the State* (Boston: Boston Equal Suffrage Association for Good Government, n.d.). Obituary, *New York Times,* July 31, 1948, p. 1. *Who Was Who* 2 (1943-1950): 78. *Women in American Labor History,* Items No. 1, 6, 284, 340, and 443. *Schlesinger Library Inventory,* vol. 1, s. v. "Breckinridge, Sophonisba Preston."

Grace D. Brewer

Grace D. Brewer edited the woman's page and "Appeal Army" columns of the Socialist party paper *The Appeal to Reason.* She also headed the Appeal to Reason lecture bureau and the Non-Partisan League Speakers Bureau. Among her numerous correspondents were Eugene V. Debs and Katherine Debs. In the 1960s Brewer placed her papers in the Wayne State University Archives of Labor History and Urban Affairs.

Reference: "Women's Collections in the Archives of Labor History and Urban Affairs," *Wayne State University Archives of Labor History and Urban Affairs Newsletter* 2 (Summer 1972).

Elisabeth Christman

Union official Elisabeth Christman was born in Chicago, the daughter of Henry Christman and Barbara Guth. With Agnes Nestor (q. v.), she formed Operators Local 1 of the International Glove Workers Union (IGWU) and served as the local's shop steward and treasurer from 1905 to 1911 and president from 1912 to 1917. From 1916 to 1931 she was secretary-treasurer of the IGWU and from 1931 to 1937 vice president. A member of the Chicago executive board of the Women's Trade Union League (WTUL) from 1910 to 1929, she was elected to the WTUL national executive board in 1919 and became its secretary-treasurer in 1921. She edited *Life and Labor Bulletin,* the WTUL journal. On behalf of the WTUL, she petitioned the American Federation of Labor to charter separately women workers denied entrance to member unions, but met with failure. Christman was a member of President Herbert Hoover's Organization on Unemployment Relief and a representative to the Code Authority of the National Industrial Recovery Administration. In 1936 President Franklin D. Roosevelt appointed her to the Commission on Vocational Guidance. She joined the Advisory Committee of the Women's Bureau of the U.S. Department of Labor in 1940; in that capacity, she evaluated the performance of women in war industries from 1942 to 1943.

References: Elisabeth Christman: "Canvas Glove Workers Win Signal Victory," *Life and Labor* 6 (March 1916): 40; "Conventions – A Complement to Workers' Education," *American Federationist* 36 (August 1929): 921-5. E. E. Perkins, "Elisabeth Christman: Co-Worker," *Christian Science Monitor Monthly Magazine,* January 19, 1946, p. 6. *Women in American Labor History,* Items No. 298, 364, and 392. *BDALL,* pp. 58-9.

Tennessee Celeste Claflin, 1845-1923

Tennessee Celeste Claflin, publisher and stockbroker, was born on October 26, 1845, in Homer, Ohio, the ninth of ten children of Reuben Buckman Claflin, a one-eyed lawyer of dubious repute, and Roxanna Hummel. Tennessee's youth was spent touring the Midwest as part of her family's medicine show. On one occasion, she was arrested and charged with the death of a man to whom she had sold a patent medicine. On February 4, 1870, with her sister, the notorious Victoria Woodhull (q. v.), she established the New York City brokerage of Woodhull, Claflin & Company. The firm flourished, due in part to the tutelage provided by Cornelius Vanderbilt, who, Claflin was to assert, desired to marry her. With her sister she joined Marx's International Workingmen's Association in New York in 1871; that same year the sisters' journal, *Woodhull & Claflin's Weekly,* published Marx's *Communist Manifesto,* the first American publication to do so. In 1885 Claflin married Francis Cook, the well-to-do head of a London dry-goods firm. Cook became a baronet in 1886 and Claflin, Lady Cook. She died in luxury in London on January 18, 1923, and was buried in West Norwood Cemetery.

References: Tennessee Celeste Claflin: *Constitutional Equality a Right of Woman* (New York: Woodhull, Claflin, & Co., 1871); *The Human Body the Temple of God* (London, 1890). Madeleine Legge, *Two Noble Women, Nobly Planned* (New York: Walham Green, 1893). "Portrait," *Current Literature* 47 (December 1909): 603. G. W. Johnson, "Dynamic Victoria Woodhull," *American Heritage* 7 (June 1956): 44-7. Arlene Kisner, *Woodhull & Claflin's Weekly: the Lives and Writings of Notorious Victoria Woodhull and Her Sister Tennessee Celeste* (Washington, New Jersey: Times Change Press, 1972).

Fannia Mary Cohn, 1888-1962

Fannia Mary Cohn, International Ladies Garment Workers Union (ILGWU) author and educator, was born on April 5, 1888, in Kletz, Minsk, Russia, the daughter of Hyman Rozofsky and Anna Cohn. From 1901 to 1904 she was a member of the Social Revolutionary party. In 1904 she immigrated to the United States, where she worked in a New York City garment factory. Cohn joined the ILGWU in 1909 and quickly distinguished herself. From 1909 to 1914 she was a member of the executive board of Kimona, Wrappers and Housedress Workers Local 41; from 1911 to 1914 she was chairman of Local 41's executive board. In 1915 she organized striking garment workers at the Herzog Garment Company into Local 59, serving as its president. From 1915 to 1916 Cohn was general organizer for the Chicago ILGWU; in 1916 she was elected vice president, a position she retained until 1925. Cohn's organizational and administrative abilities were rivaled only by her excellence as an educator and editor. In 1921 she founded the Workers' Education Bureau of America, serving as executive secretary of the division until her retirement in

1961. That same year she helped to establish Brookwood Labor College. She served on its board of directors from 1926 to 1928 and as vice president from 1932 to 1937. Publication of *Workers' Education,* the quarterly journal of the Workers' Education Bureau of America, began in April 1923. Cohn established the Manumit School for Workers' Children in 1924, which she directed until 1933. She died in New York City on December 24, 1962. Her papers are in the manuscript division of the New York Public Library.

References: Fannia Cohn: "Strike Leaders in a Gymnasium," *Life and Labor* 11 (March 1921): 72-3; "Workers' Education," *Nation* 115 (November 29, 1922): 579-80; *Workers' Education* (New York: Workers' Education Bureau of America, 1923); "Women and the Labor Movement," *American Federationist* 32 (December 1925): 1186-8; "Winning Working Women," *Labor Age* 16 (April 1927): 18; "Working Women and the Written Word," *Labor Age* 16 (May 1927): 18; "Who Should Organize Working Women?" *Labor Age* 16 (June 1927): 18; "Can We Organize the Flapper?" *Labor Age* 16 (December 1927): 18; "Education Aids Working Women," *Labor Age* 17 (January 1928): 12; "Shaw Speaks to Women," *Labor Age* 17 (October 1928): 22; "Twelve Years Educational Activities — International Ladies' Garment Workers' Union," *American Federationist* 36 (January 1929): 105-11; "Uprising of Dressmakers," *American Federationist* 36 (November 1929): 1324-7; "Education and Social Activities," *American Federationist* 36 (December 1929): 1446-52; "The Uprising of Twenty Thousand," *American Federationist* 40 (October 1933): 1069-72; "Facing the Future," *American Federationist* 42 (November 1935): 1203-8; *Workers' Education in War and Peace* (New York: Workers' Education Bureau of America, 1943). *Who's Who in Labor* (New York: Dryden Press, 1946): 63. *Women in American Labor History,* Items No. 74, 128, 129, 130, 131, 132, 133, 134, 240, 299, 300, 365, 366, 367, and 368. *BDALL,* p. 63.

Eleanor Gwinnell Coit, 1894-

Eleanor Coit, former director of the American Labor Education Service, was born in Newark, New Jersey, on May 6, 1894, the daughter of Dr. Henry L. Coit, a pediatrician, and Emma Gwinnell. She attended public schools in Newark, Smith College, and Columbia University, where she received an M.A. in sociology. After graduation, she joined the Industrial Department of the Young Women's Christian Association and conducted classes in industrial history for unorganized women workers in the Oranges of New Jersey; Bayonne, New Jersey; and Buffalo, New York. She also served as field worker for the Children's Bureau of the U. S. Department of Labor. In 1929 Coit became educational secretary of the Affiliated Schools for Workers. She became director in 1934, when the organization's name was changed to the American Labor Education Service (ALES). Among Coit's pioneering work for the ALES was the establishment of resident schools for workers, labor education for white-collar workers, worker exchange programs with foreign countries, antidiscrimination education, and the study of farmer-labor relationships. Her papers are in the archives of the Wisconsin Historical Society.

References: Eleanor Coit: "Why Do Married Women Work?" *Survey* 64 (April 15, 1930): 79-80; "Workers' Education in the United States," *Monthly Labor Review* 49 (July 1939): 1-21; *Government Support of Workers' Education* (New York: American Labor Education Services, 1940). *Who's Who in Labor* (New York: Dryden Press, 1946): 63.

Katharine Coman, 1857-1915

Economist Katharine Coman was born in Newark, Ohio, on November 23, 1857, the fourth of seven children of Martha Seymour and Levi Parsons Coman, a lawyer and abolitionist. Coman was educated at Steubenville Female Seminary and at the University of Michigan, from which she received a Ph.D. in 1880. She then joined the faculty of Wellesley, where she became professor of political economy in 1883. Her appreciation of economics was not purely theoretical, however: in 1890 she established a club for working women in Boston and in 1892 helped to establish Denison House, a settlement in Boston's South End, which later became a center of organizational activity. As a member of the executive council of the Massachusetts Consumers' League from 1899 to 1905, she agitated for industrial reform. In 1910, as chairman of the Women's Trade Union League grievance committee, she participated in the successful strike of Chicago seamstresses. She retired from Wellesley in 1913 and toured Europe, studying social-security systems, the following year. She died in Wellesley, Massachusetts, on January 11, 1915, and was buried in Mount Auburn Cemetery in Cambridge, Massachusetts. Partial correspondence is in the Jane Addams Papers in the Swarthmore College Peace Collection.

References: Katharine Coman: *The History of Contract Labor in the Hawaiian Islands* (New York: Macmillan Co., 1903); *The Industrial History of the United States for High School and Colleges* (New York: Macmillan Co., 1905); "Government Factories: An Attempt to Control Competition in the Fur Trade," *American Economic Association Bulletin* 1 (April 1911): 366-88; *Economic Beginnings of the Far West* (New York: Macmillan Co., 1912). Obituary, *New York Times,* January 12, 1915, p. 4. O. S. Halsey, "Appreciation of Katharine Coman," *Survey* 33 (January 23, 1915): 450-1. *Who Was Who* 1 (1897-1942): 247. *Schlesinger Library Inventory,* vol. 1, s. v. "Coman, Katharine."

Sara Agnes Conboy, 1870-1928

Union official Sara Agnes Conboy was born in Boston on April 3, 1870. In 1915 she was elected secretary-treasurer of the United Textile Workers of America. In addition to her union activities, Conboy was a member of the executive board of the National Commissions on Prisons and Prison Labor, chairman of the advisory board on vocational training in the New York public schools, and American Federation of Labor representative to the British Trade Union Congress in Portsmouth, England, in 1920. She was appointed by President Warren Harding to the 1921 conference on unemployment in Washington, D.C., and was elected to the New York State Housing

Commission in 1923. She died in Brooklyn on January 8, 1928.

References: *Who Was Who* 1 (1897-1942): 249.

Alice Hanson Cook, 1903-

Professor Alice Hanson Cook, member of the executive board of Cornell University's Women's Studies Program, was born on November 28, 1903, the daughter of Flora Kays, a housewife, and August T. Hanson, a railroad auditor. She received a B.L. from the Northwestern University School of Speech in 1924 and attended the Goethe University in Frankfurt am Main in 1931. As a labor educator she taught at Commonwealth College, Bryn Mawr Summer School for Women in Industry, Southern Summer School for Workers, and Hudson Shore School. She was education director for the Textile Workers Organizing Committee and for the Industrial Union of Marine and Shipbuilding Workers, as well as consultant for the Brotherhood of Locomotive Enginemen and Firemen and for the Congress of Industrial Organizations' Community Services Committee. From 1950 to 1952 she was director of adult education for the Public Affairs Division of the High Commission in Germany; from 1952 to 1954, director of the project evaluating increased labor participation in community affairs in Syracuse, Utica, and Olean, New York; from 1950 to 1957, a member of the board of directors of the American Labor Education Service; from 1955 to 1972, professor of Trade Union History at Cornell ·University; from 1962 to 1963, Fulbright Visiting Scholar in Japan; and from 1969 to 1971, ombudsman, Cornell University. Professor Cook has written extensively on the role of women workers in the trade-union movement.

References: Alice Cook: *Labor's Role in Community Affairs*, 1955; *Labor Education Outside the Unions, Labor's Public Responsibility*, 1960; "Dual Government Unions," 1964; "Labor Relations in New York City," 1966; *Introduction to Japanese Trade Unionism*, 1966; "Organization Among Local Government Employees in the United States," 1966; "The ILO and Japanese Politics," 1968; "Women and Trade Unions," 1968; "The Status of Working Women," 1968; "Labor and Politics," 1969; "Labor Relations in the Public Service, A Unique Branch of Labor Relations Practice," 1969; "Political Action and Japanese Trade Unions," 1969; "Working Mothers, Problems and Programs in Nine Countries," 1972-74; "Mothers at Work Abroad," 1974; *The Working Mother*, 1975; "Equal Pay, Where Is It?" 1975; "Public Policy and Support Systems for Working Mothers," 1975.

Kate Richards O'Hare Cunningham, 1877-1948

Prison reformer and labor organizer Kate Richards O'Hare Cunningham was born on March 26, 1877, in Ottawa County, Kansas, the daughter of Andrew Richards, a disabled Union Army veteran, and Lucy Thompson. In 1894 she became a machinist's apprentice in her father's shop and joined the International Order of Machinists. At a training school for Socialist party workers in 1901 she met Francis Patrick O'Hare, whom she married in 1902. She was later elected to the national executive committee of the Socialist party, the only woman to be so honored until the establishment of the Socialist Party National Committee of Women in 1910. In 1912 the O'Hares became editors of the *National Rip-Saw*, a Socialist weekly published in St. Louis, Missouri. She ran for Congress from the 2d District of Kansas in 1910 and was a Socialist delegate to the Second International in London in 1913. After an antiwar speech in Bowman, North Dakota, on July 17, 1917, she was arrested, tried, and convicted of espionage and sentenced to five years in the Missouri State Penitentiary in Jefferson City. While imprisoned she met Emma Goldman (q. v.). Among those agitating for her release were Mother Ella Reeve Bloor (q. v.) and Elizabeth Gurley Flynn (q. v.). On May 29, 1920, she was pardoned by President Calvin Coolidge. Her three years' incarceration had inspired an interest in prison reform; in 1939 she was appointed assistant director of the California Department of Penology. In 1923 she became a founding trustee of Commonwealth College in Louisiana, an institution devoted to workers' education. She conducted a national survey of contract labor in prisons for the Garment Manufacturers Association and for the United Garment Workers in 1924. She divorced O'Hare in June 1928 and married attorney and mining engineer Charles C. Cunningham in November. In 1937 and 1938 she worked for Progressive Congressman Thomas R. Amlie of Wisconsin. She died in California on January 10, 1948.

References: Kate Richards O'Hare Cunningham: "Is Divorce a Step Forward or a Backward Step?" *Arena* 33 (April 1905): 413-4; *Common Sense and the Liquor Traffic* (St. Louis: National Rip-Saw Publishing Co., 1911); *Law and the White Slaver* (St. Louis: National Rip-Saw Publishing Co., 1911); *In Prison* (St. Louis: F. P. O'Hare, 1920). John Louis Engdahl, *Debs and O'Hare in Prison* (Chicago: National Socialist Party, 1919). *NAW*, vol. 1, pp. 417-20.

Diane Sutherland Curry, 1939-

Diane Sutherland Curry, director of publications and assistant editor for the Brotherhood of Railway, Airline and Steamship Clerks, Freight Handlers, Express and Station Employees Union (BRAC), was born on September 15, 1939, in Plainfield, New Jersey, the daughter of Alan Lawrence Sutherland, a banker, and Alice Hassler, a government worker. She was educated at St. Petersburg Junior College in Florida and at the University of Maryland. In 1966 she married James P. Curry, director of research for the Department of Development and Planning of the City of Chicago. From 1961 to 1967 she worked as administrative assistant to the executive secretary of the Railway Labor Executives Asociation. She joined the staff of BRAC in 1967 as assistant to the editor and in 1969 became director of publications. In 1974 Curry became a member of the steering committee of the Coalition of Labor Union Women (CLUW)

Olga Madar. (Courtesy CLUW)

Josephine Hulett. (Courtesy Chicago Tribune)

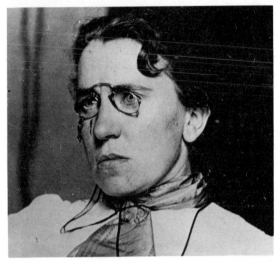

Emma Goldman. (Courtesy National Archives and Records Service)

Frances Benjamin Johnston. (Courtesy Library of Congress)

Mary McDaniel. (Courtesy IUE)

Crystal Lee Jordan. (Courtesy Bruce Roberts, Rapho-Guillumette Pictures)

and editor of *CLUW News*. Curry is a member of the International Labor Press Association, the Association of Railroad Editors, the Center for the Study of Democratic Institutions, the American Civil Liberties Union, and the National Organization for Women.

Rebecca Blaine Harding Davis, 1831-1910

Rebecca Blaine Harding Davis, the first American author to treat the theme of urban industrialization and worker exploitation with uncompromising realism, was born in Washington, Pennsylvania, on June 24, 1831, the first of five children of Richard Harding and Rachel Leet Wilson. In 1836 her family moved to Wheeling, West Virginia, the site of "Life in the Iron Mills," her first important publication. Appearing in the *Atlantic Monthly* in April 1861, the short story depicted the impoverished lives and thwarted yearnings of Wheeling mill workers and the desolation of the industrial environment. This was followed by "A Story of To-day," the narrative of a female clerk in an Indiana mill, serialized in the *Atlantic Monthly* from October 1861 to March 1862. She married an attorney, L. Clarke Davis, on March 4, 1863, and settled in Philadelphia; the couple had two sons. In 1869 she became contributing editor to the *New York Tribune*. She died in Mount Kisco, New York, on September 29, 1910; her ashes were interred in Leverington Cemetery, Philadelphia. After her death, her reputation declined. Publication of "Life in the Iron Mills" by Feminist Press in 1972 has contributed to a revival of interest in Davis.

References: Rebecca Harding Davis: *Silhouettes of American Life* (New York: Charles Scribner's Sons, 1892); *Stories of the South* (New York: Charles Scribner's Sons, 1894); "Curse in Education," *North American Review* 168 (May 1899): 609-14; *Bits of Gossip: An Autobiography* (Boston: Houghton, Mifflin & Co., 1904); "The Middle-Aged Woman," *Independent* 57 (September 1, 1904): 489-94; "Recovery of Family Life," *Independent* 59 (September 21, 1905): 673-5; *Life in the Iron Mills* (New York: Feminist Press, 1972). Helen Woodward Sheaffer, "Rebecca Harding Davis, Pioneer Realist" (Ph.D. diss., University of Pennsylvania, 1947). Margaret Wyman, "Women in the American Realistic Novel, 1860-1893" (Ph.D. diss., Radcliffe College, 1950). Gerald Langford, *The Richard Harding Davis Years: A Biography of a Mother and Son* (New York: Holt, Rinehart, & Winston, 1961). *Who Was Who* 1 (1897-1942): 303. *Schlesinger Library Inventory*, vol. 1, s. v. "Davis, Rebecca Harding." *NAW*, vol. 1, pp. 445-7.

Clara Day

Clara Day, midwestern vice president of the Coalition of Labor Union Women, was born in Northport, Alabama, the daughter of George Taylor and Belle Baylom. As assistant business representative of the International Brotherhood of Teamsters (IBT), Local 743, she organized employees at Montgomery Ward and Company. She is now director of Community Services for IBT. In 1963 she represented Local 743 at the March on Washington led by the Reverend Martin Luther King, Jr. Wife, mother, and grandmother, Day is also a West Side Board Member of the NAACP, a consultant to the Chicago Urban League, chairperson of the Employment Advisory Board of the Chicago Commission on Human Relations, and executive board member of the Greater Lawnsdale Conservation Commission. She is a member of the Illinois Commission on the Status of Women, the National Association of Human Rights Workers, and the Day Care Crisis Council of Chicago. Her numerous honors include the Woman of Distinction Award in labor, civic, and community work from the Chicago Citizens Scholarship Committee and a citation for civil rights work from the Jewish Labor Committee of Chicago.

Reference: *Who's Who in the Midwest (1974-1975)*: 160.

Catherine De Rorre, 1895-1960

The legendary Catherine De Rorre, known as "Sister Katie" and "the Good Samaritan of the Coal Fields," was born in 1895. For more than forty years she served the miners of Illinois, their wives, and children, in her famous soup kitchens, which she set up as an organizer for the Auxiliary of the Progressive Miners of America. She died on January 2, 1960, and was buried in the Holy Cross Lutheran Cemetery in Collinsville, Illinois. Her daughter, Catherine Mans, assembled a collection of clippings and memorabilia. Historian Barbara Herndon (q. v.) has also amassed material dealing with De Rorre and the Progressive Miners of America.

References: Gerry Allard, "Sister Katie Day," June 3, 1956. Agnes Burns Wieck to Katie De Rorre, June 1, 1956. Jack Battuello, "A Biography of Katie De Rorre," mimeographed, 1961. Obituary, *Collinsville (Illinois) Herald*, May 28, 1961.

Mary Williams Dewson, 1874-1962

Mary Williams Dewson, whose briefs in defense of minimum wage laws were presented before the Supreme Courts of the United States and California, was born on February 18, 1874, in Quincy, Massachusetts, the daughter of Edward Henry Dewson and Elizabeth Weld Williams. She received a B.A. from Wellesley College in 1897, did economic research for the Women's Educational and Industrial Union from 1897 to 1900, was superintendent of the Girls' Parole Department of Massachusetts from 1900 to 1912, operated a dairy farm in Massachusetts from 1912 to 1917, and was zoning chief for the Bureau of Refugees of the American Red Cross in France from 1917 to 1919. From 1919 to 1924 Dewson was research secretary of the National Consumers League and from 1925 to 1931 president of the New York Consumers League. In 1928, with Eleanor Roosevelt (q. v.), she developed state women's political caucuses. She became director of the Women's Division of the Democratic National Committee in 1933. Dewson was a member of the President's Committee on Economic Security, the Consumers' Advisory Board from 1933 to 1935, and the Social Security Board. She was director of the Franklin D. Roosevelt Memorial Foundation. Dewson died on October 25, 1962, in Castine, Maine.

References: Mary Williams Dewson: "Pay Rolls and Profits," *Survey* 29 (November 9, 1912): 174-5; *Next Steps in Social Security Legislation* (Chicago: University of Chicago Press, 1938). E. N. Blair, "Who's Who of Women in Washington," *Good Housekeeping* 102 (January 1936): 38. "Portrait of Mary Williams Dewson," *Newsweek* 10 (August 28, 1937): 14. Obituary, *New York Times,* October 25, 1962, p. 1. James T. Patterson, *Mary Dewson and the American Minimum Wage Movement* (New York: Tamiment Institute, 1964). *Who Was Who* 4 (1961-1968): 247. *Schlesinger Library Inventory,* vol. 1, s. v. "Dewson, Mary Williams."

Gladys Dickason, 1903-1971

Gladys Dickason, vice president of the Amalgamated Clothing Workers of America (ACWA) from 1946 to 1963, was born on January 29, 1903, in Galena, Oklahoma, the daughter of cotton farmers. She was educated at the University of Oklahoma and Columbia University. At Sweet Briar College and Hunter College she taught economics. In 1933 she joined the ACWA as an organizer. Dickason was ACWA director of research from 1935 to 1954. She became ACWA southern regional director in 1945 and assistant director of the Southern Organizing Committee of the Congress of Industrial Organizations in 1946. From 1937 to 1940 she was a member of the Advisory Committee of the United States Employment Service. In 1941 she directed a strike at the Cluett Peabody Company plants in Troy, New York, and Atlanta, Georgia; in 1946 she was elected ACWA vice president. Dickason was appointed by General Douglas MacArthur to instruct Japanese women workers in the principles of trade unionism in 1951; that same year she was honored by the National Council of Negro Women for her contributions to the woman worker. She was a member of the Industrial Committee of the Cotton Garment Code Authority of the National Recovery Administration; the New York City Board of Education committee to study vocational training; the federal Women's Bureau labor advisory committee; and the board of trustees of Antioch College. She retired in 1963 and died in New York City on August 31, 1971.

References: Gladys Dickason: "Women in Labor Unions," *Annals of the American Academy of Political and Social Science* 251 (May 1947): 70-8. "Ten Who Deliver," *Fortune* November 1946. "Gladys Dickason," mimeographed (Washington, D.C.: U.S. Information Service, 1953). Obituary, *New York Times,* September 1, 1971. Obituary, *Advance* September 17, 1971, p. 4. *Amalgamated Clothing Workers of America's General Executive Board Report and Proceedings of the 28th Biennial Convention,* May 29-June 2, 1972, pp. 428-9. *Women in American Labor History,* Item No. 78.

Mary Elisabeth Dreier, 1875-1963

Mary Elisabeth Dreier, the president of the New York Women's Trade Union League from 1906 to 1915, was born in Brooklyn, New York, on September 26, 1875, the daughter of Theodor Dreier and Dorothea Adelheid. From 1911 to 1915 she was a member of the New York State Factory Investigating Committee. In 1915 she was appointed to the Board of Education, an appointment she resigned to work for the suffrage movement. Dreier became chairman of the Industrial Section of the New York State Woman's Suffrage Party, chairman of the New York State Committee on Women in Industry for the National Defense Council, chairman of the Outlawry of War Committee of the National Women's Trade Union League in 1921, chairman of the New York State Conference for Ratification of the Federal Child Labor Amendment in 1937, and chairman of the War Labor Standards Committee in 1942. In 1950 she published a biography of her famous sister, Margaret Dreier Robins (q. v.). She died on August 17, 1963.

References: Mary Elisabeth Dreier: *Preliminary Report of the Factory Investigating Commission* (Albany, New York: Argus Co., 1912); "To Wash or Not to Wash: Aye, There's the Rub," *Life and Labor* 2 (March 1912): 68-72; *Second Report of the Factory Investigating Commission* (Albany: J. B. Lyon Co., 1913); *Fourth Report of the Factory Investigating Commission* (Albany, New York: J. B. Lyon Co., 1915); "The Neckwear Workers and Their Strike," *Life and Labor* 3 (December 1918): 356-58; *Margaret Dreier Robins, Her Life, Letters and Work* (New York: Island Press, 1950). *Who Was Who* 4 (1961-1968): 264. *Women in American Labor History,* Items No. 305, 306, and 385. *Schlesinger Library Inventory,* vol. 1, s. v. "Dreier, Mary Elisabeth."

Katherine Pollack Ellickson

Katherine Pollack Ellickson, former associate director of research and assistant director of the Social Security Department of the AFL-CIO, was active in the Women's Trade Union League from 1926 to 1928. She taught at the Bryn Mawr School for Women Workers from 1927 to 1929, the Brookwood Labor College from 1929 to 1932, and Southern Summer School in 1934. She was assistant to the director of the Congress of Industrial Organizations (CIO) from 1935 to 1937. After working for the National Labor Relations Board and for the Social Security Board, she rejoined the CIO as research director in 1942. In 1961 she was appointed to the President's Commission on the Status of Women. Ellickson presented her papers to the Wayne State Archives of Labor History and Urban Affairs in 1969.

Reference: "Women's Collections in the Archives of Labor History and Urban Affairs," *Wayne State University Archives of Labor History and Urban Affairs Newsletter* 2 (Summer 1972).

Christine Ellis

Rank-and-file organizer Christine Ellis, the daughter of Yugoslav immigrants, came to the United States in 1913. The family settled in Rathbun, Iowa, where her father worked as a miner. During the miners' strike of 1920-1921, she witnessed the Ku Klux Klan campaign against Slavic unionists. At age fifteen she left home, moving to Cleveland, where she worked at the American Can Company and at Continental Can Company. She organized Chicago's jobless in 1931 and organized in Arkansas, Iowa, Kansas, Missouri, Nebraska, Oklahoma, and Texas for the Communist party, with which she later became dissatisfied. Her outspoken opposition to the Korean War prompted an attempt by the U.S. Department of Justice to deport her under the McCarren Act. From 1952 to 1953 she was jailed without bail as a result of her pacifist beliefs. While imprisoned, she began her autobiography on the backs of Christmas and Easter cards. She has written a lengthy history of her participation in the American labor movement. In 1971 she addressed the Labor History Workshop in Gary, Indiana.

Reference: Christine Ellis, "People Who Cannot Be Bought," in *Rank and File*, ed. Alice Lynd and Staughton Lynd (Boston: Beacon Press, 1973), pp. 9-34.

Dorothy Ellsworth

Dorothy Ellsworth, legislative representative for the Brotherhood of Railway, Airline and Steamship Clerks (BRAC), is one of twenty-eight female registered lobbyists. In 1959 she became executive secretary to Congressman Walter Rogers of Texas. From 1960 to 1962 she was the executive assistant to the Senate Republican Policy Committee Staff Director; from 1963 to 1966 she was the executive secretary of the Seafarers International Union. She joined the staff of BRAC in 1966. Ellsworth is a member of the National Press Club and the Senate Press Club.

References: Dorothy Ellsworth: "We Have Met the Enemy and He Is Us," *Railway Clerk/Interchange* 72 (January 1973): 16-7. "Lady Lobbyist Rates 'Tops'," *Roll Call*, July 20, 1972, p. 5.

Dorothy Payne Whitney Straight Elmhirst, 1887-1968

Dorothy Payne Whitney Straight Elmhirst, suffragette, philanthropist, and educator, was born in 1887, the daughter of William C. Whitney, secretary of the navy under President Grover Cleveland. An active member of the Women's Trade Union League, Elmhirst campaigned for working women's residences, agitated for women's suffrage, and helped to establish the New School for Social Research. In 1911 she married banker Willard Straight, with whom she founded the *New Republic* in 1914; he died in 1918.

During World War I she headed the Women's Emergency Committee of the European Relief Council. In 1925 she married Leonard Elmhirst, an English agricultural student at Cornell University. At Darlington Hall, Elmhirst's estate in England, they established a progressive coeducational school. She died at Darlington Hall on December 15, 1968.

Reference: Obituary, *New York Times*, December 16, 1968, p. 1.

Elizabeth Glendower Evans, 1856-1937

Elizabeth Glendower Evans, suffragette and labor reformer, was born in New Rochelle, New York, on February 28, 1856, the fourth of five children of architect Edward Gardiner and Sophia Harrison Mifflin. She married Glendower Evans in 1882. Shortly after her husband's sudden death in 1886, she was appointed to the board of trustees of the Massachusetts reformatory system. With Florence Kelley (q. v.), Evans spearheaded a campaign in Massachusetts in 1911, which resulted in the first minimum wage act for women in the United States. As a member of the Women's Trade Union League, she participated in the 1910 weavers' strike in Roxbury, Massachusetts, and in the 1912 textile workers' strike in Lawrence, Massachusetts. From 1913 to 1935 she was a contributing editor to *La Follette's Weekly Magazine*, the reformist labor journal of Senator Robert and Belle La Follette (q. v.), and to the *Progressive*. For the National American Woman Suffrage Association she lobbied in Massachusetts and Washington, D. C., where she spoke with President Woodrow Wilson. National director of the American Civil Liberties Union, she was active in the defense of Sacco and Vanzetti. She died on December 12, 1937, and her ashes were scattered over her husband's grave in Boston's Forest Hills Cemetery. Her papers are in the Schlesinger Library of Radcliffe College.

References: Elizabeth Glendower Evans: "One Way to Settle Labor Troubles," *Survey* 22 (September 25, 1909): 844-6; "Step Forward in Democracy," *Outlook* 94 (February 12, 1910): 359-62; "Roxbury Carpet Factory Strike," *Survey* 24 (May 28, 1910): 337-8; *The Parable of Panama* (London: Independent Labor Party, 1914); "Case for Minimum Wage Boards," *Survey* 31 (January 10, 1914); "Social Aspects of the Public Regulation of Wages," *American Economy Review* 5 (March 1915): 270-7; "Sacco and Vanzetti Cases," *Nation* 112 (June 15, 1921): 842-3; "Woman's Party Is Wrong," *New Republic* 36 (September 26, 1923): 123; "Sacco and Vanzetti," *Survey* 56 (June 15, 1926): 364-5; "Mr. Justice Brandeis," *Survey* 67 (November 1, 1931): 138-41. Belle Case La Follette and Caroline L. Hunt, "Elizabeth Gardiner Evans — An Appreciation," *La Follette's Weekly Magazine* 4 (February 17, 1912): 10. "Leader in the Minimum Wage Movement," *Review of Reviews* 45 (April 1912): 442. Belle La Follette, "Fine Type of Woman Suffragist," *American Magazine* 78 (September 1914): 54-6. Obituary, *Survey* 74 (January 1938): 16. *Women in American Labor History*, Item No. 307. *Schlesinger Library Inventory*, vol. 1, s. v. "Evans, Elizabeth Glendower." *NAW*, vol. 1, pp. 588-9.

Harriet Farley, ca. 1813-1907

Textile worker and editor Harriet Farley was born in Claremont, New Hampshire, on February 18, ca. 1813, the daughter of the Reverend Stephen Farley and Lucy Saunders. By 1837 she was an operative in a Lowell, Massachusetts, textile mill. As such, she contributed articles on factory life to the *Lowell Offering,* a journal published by female textile workers in "the City of Spindles." In 1842 she became editor of the magazine. Farley's editorial policies were attacked by Sarah G. Bagley (q. v.), who charged that the *Lowell Offering* was a company paper. The *Lowell Offering* was supplanted by Bagley's militant *Voice of Industry* in 1845, although Farley revived the journal as the *New England Offering* from 1847 to 1850. Farley died in New York City on November 12, 1907.

References: Harriet Farley: *Happy Hours at Hazel Nook* (Boston: Wentworth, 1856). *Schlesinger Library Inventory,* vol. 1, s. v. "Farley, Harriet." *NAW,* vol. 1, pp. 596-7.

Lois Felder, 1933-

Lois Felder, codirector of the Community Relations Department of the Retail Clerks International Association (RCIA), was born on February 22, 1933, one of five children of the Reverend Anderson H. Felder, an African Methodist Episcopal Zion minister and his wife, Lena. After graduating from Duff's Iron City College in Pittsburgh, she studied industrial and labor relations at the University of California at Los Angeles. In 1968 she joined Local 770 of the RCIA. From 1972 to 1974 she was an organizer for the Southwestern Division of the RCIA. Felder is a member of the steering committee of the Coalition of Labor Union Women; she is an executive board member of the NAACP and former chairman of the NAACP's Labor and Industry Committee. In 1974 she served as a delegate to the Democratic Mid-Term Conference.

Reference: "Congratulations, Lois!" *Voice of 770,* December 1974, p. 8.

Elizabeth Gurley Flynn, 1890-1964

Elizabeth Gurley Flynn, a founding member of the International Workers of the World (IWW) and a veteran Communist, was born on August 7, 1890, in Concord, New Hampshire, the daughter of Thomas Flynn, an itinerant politician, and Annie Gurley. In 1905, with one-eyed "Big Bill" Haywood, labor martyr Joe Hill, Haymarket widow Lucy Parsons (q. v.), and United Mine Workers of America organizer "Mother" Mary Harris Jones (q. v.), she established the IWW. She quit high school in 1907 to participate more fully in the labor struggle. While on a speaking tour of the Mesabi Range, Flynn met Jack Jones, a member of the Western Federation of Miners, whom she married in January 1908. The couple's first child, John Vincent, died the evening of his birth. In April 1910 Flynn and Jones separated; their son Fred was born on May 19. They finally divorced in 1926. An outstanding orator, Flynn participated in the 1909 strike of New York waistmakers: the 1912 strikes of Lowell and Lawrence, Massachusetts, textile workers; the 1913 strike of Paterson, New Jersey, silk workers; the 1916 Mesabi Range miners' strike; and the 1926 Passaic, New Jersey, textile workers' strike. Flynn was active in the defense of Joe Hill, who dedicated his ballad "The Rebel Girl" to her. She was a pallbearer at Hill's funeral following his execution by a firing squad on November 15, 1915. Flynn helped to establish the Workers Defense Union in 1918 and the American Civil Liberties Union in 1920. From 1927 to 1930 she served as chairman of the International Labor Defense Committee. In 1926 she applied for membership in the Communist party, in which she quickly rose to prominence. She was suspended from the American Civil Liberties Union because of her Communist affiliation in 1940; that same year, her son Fred died. In 1952 she was tried and convicted under the Smith Act in New York City. From January 1955 to May 1957 she was imprisoned in the Federal Women's Reformatory in Alderson, West Virginia, where she received the sympathies of numerous supporters, among them Helen Keller (q. v.). She died in a Moscow hospital on September 4, 1964. After a monumental funeral in Red Square, her ashes were buried in Waldheim Cemetery in Chicago. Her papers are in the Institute for Marxist Studies in New York City. Other materials are in the Archives of Labor History and Urban Affairs, Wayne State University.

References: Elizabeth Gurley Flynn: "Weavers," *Survey* 35 (February 26, 1916): 648; *Debs, Haywood, Ruthenberg,* (New York: Workers Library Publishers, 1939); *I Didn't Raise My Boy to Be a Soldier—for Wall Street,* (New York: Workers Library Publishers, 1940); *Coal Miners and the War* (New York: Workers Library Publishers, 1942); *Women in the War* (New York: Workers Library Publishers, 1942); *Women Have a Date with Destiny* (New York: Workers Library Publishers, 1944); *Communists and the People* (New York: New Century Publishers, 1953); *I Speak My Own Piece: Autobiography of the Rebel Girl* (New York: Mainstream, 1955); *The Alderson Story* (New York: International Publishers, 1963). "Elizabeth Gurley Flynn: Labor Leader," *Outlook* 111 (December 15, 1915): 905. "Free Speech in Paterson; Case of Elizabeth Gurley Flynn," *Outlook* 111 (November 24, 1915): 692-3. Mary Heaton Vorse, "Elizabeth Gurley Flynn," *Nation* 122 (February 17, 1926): 175-6. R. N. Baldwin, "Early Years of a Radical," *Nation* 182 (May 12, 1956): 414. Obituary, *New York Times,* September 6, 1964, p. 4. "End of the Rebel Girl," *Time* 84 (September 18, 1964): 41. *Women in American Labor History,* Item No. 386. *Schlesinger Library Inventory,* vol. 1, s. v. "Flynn, Elizabeth Gurley." *BDALL,* pp. 108-9.

Mabel Edna Gillespie, 1877-1923

Mabel Gillespie was born in St. Paul, Minnesota, on March 4, 1877, the daughter of James Gillespie and Ida Scott. Orphaned at an early age, she was raised by an aunt in Concord, Massachusetts, where she graduated from Concord High School in June 1897. She attended Radcliffe College from 1898 to 1900. In 1900 she became a social worker in Boston where she resided at the Denison House settlement. She was appointed secretary of the Boston Association of Charities in 1903. She joined the newly established Women's Trade Union League (WTUL) in 1903 and participated in the Fall River, Massachusetts, strike for the eight-hour work day. From 1904 to 1909 she was executive secretary of the Buffalo branch of the New York Consumers' League and the Child Labor Commission; as such, she conducted investigations of New York canneries and of violations of child labor laws in Boston. In 1909 Gillespie became executive secretary of the Boston WTUL, a position she retained until her death. From 1911 to 1917 and from 1919 to 1922 she was on the executive board of the national WTUL. Headed by Gillespie, the Boston WTUL participated in the 1912 Lawrence, Massachusetts, textile workers' strike and organized newsstand, garment, hat, and jewelry workers, and stenographers. From 1912 to 1919 Gillespie was the employees' representative on the Massachusetts Minimum Wage Commission and in 1918 became the first woman elected to the executive committee of the Massachusetts American Federation of Labor (AFL). She was voted vice president of the Massachusetts AFL in 1918. Also active in workers' education, she helped establish Boston Trade Union College in 1919. She was a member of the joint administrative committee of Bryn Mawr Summer School for Women Workers in 1921. She died on September 24, 1923, and was buried in Mount Hope Cemetery in Dorchester.

References: *Who Was Who* 4 (1961-1968): 356. *NAW*, vol. 2, pp. 35-6.

Charlotte Perkins Stetson Gilman, 1860-1935

Feminist Charlotte Perkins Stetson Gilman was born in Hartford, Connecticut, on July 3, 1860, one of four children of Frederic Beecher Perkins, an itinerant librarian and editor, and Mary A. Fitch Westcott. Following his daughter's birth, Frederic Perkins left his wife, providing his family with little financial support thereafter, throwing them thereby on the charity of relatives. Charlotte attended the Rhode Island School of Design and in 1884 married Charles Walter Stetson, a Providence artist, to whom she bore a daughter, Katharine Beecher. Distraught by the confinement of married life, she suffered a nervous breakdown, the subject of her controversial short story, "The Yellow Wallpaper," which appeared in the *New England Magazine* in January 1892. In 1888 she left Stetson and moved with her daughter to Pasadena. She divorced Stetson in 1894; shortly afterward, he married her best friend, Grace Ellery Channing. Charlotte's decision to send her daughter to live with the couple occasioned heated public debate. A popular speaker, she supported herself through lecture tours, discoursing on suffrage and

the rights of labor. On June 11, 1890, she married her cousin, George Houghton Gilman, who died in 1934. With Sarah B. Cooper she planned the California Women's Conferences of 1894 and 1895. There she met Jane Addams (q. v.); at Addams's invitation she resided at Hull House in 1895. In 1896 she attended the International Socialist and Labor Congress in London, where she met George Bernard Shaw, who had a great influence on her thought. Her landmark study, *Women and Economics*, which posited the absolute necessity of financial autonomy for women and proposed a network of day-care centers, was published in 1898. From 1909 to 1916 she published, edited, and wrote for the *Forerunner*, her own monthly magazine. With Jane Addams she established the Woman's Peace party in 1915. Suffering from breast cancer and not wishing to burden her family, Gilman committed suicide on August 11, 1935.

References: Charlotte Perkins Gilman: *In This Our World* (Oakland: McCombs & Vaughan, 1893); *Women and Economics* (Boston: Small, Maynard & Co., 1898); *The Yellow Wall Paper* (Boston: Small, Maynard & Co., 1899); "Woman's Congress of 1899," *Arena* 22 (September 1899); *The Home, Its Work and Influence* (New York: McClure, Phillips & Co., 1903); *Human Work* (New York: McClure, Phillips & Co., 1904); "Duty of Surplus Women," *Independent* 58 (January 19, 1905): 126-30; *Women and Social Service* (Ohio: National American Woman Suffrage Association, 1907); "Child Labor in Schools," *Independent* 64 (May 21, 1908): 1135-9; "Why Are There No Women on the President's Commission?" *Good Housekeeping* 48 (January 1909): 1202; "What Are Women Anyway?" *Collier's National Weekly* 43 (June 5, 1909): 19; *The Man-Made World* (New York: Charlton Co., 1911); "To Labor," *Current Literature* 51 (October, 1911): 444-5; "Are Women Human Beings?" *Harper's Weekly* 56 (May 25, 1912): 11; "Is Feminism Really So Dreadful?" *Delineator* 85 (August 1914): 6; *His Religion and Hers* (New York: Century Co., 1923); "Woman's Achievements Since the Franchise," *Current History* 27 (October 1927): 7-14; *The Living of Charlotte Perkins Gilman, An Autobiography* (New York: Appleton-Century Co., 1935). Obituary, *Publishers' Weekly* 128 (August 24, 1935): 514. *Who Was Who* 1 (1897-1942): 458. *Schlesinger Library Inventory*, vol. 1, s. v. "Gilman, Charlotte Perkins." *NAW*, vol. 2, pp. 39-42.

Elinor Marshall Glenn, 1915-

Actress, teacher, and labor organizer Elinor Marshall Glenn was born on March 11, 1915, one of the four children of Abraham Marshall, a building tradesman, union painter, and builder, and Annabelle Marshall, a suffragette. She graduated from New York University in 1934 and attended Southwestern Law School in Los Angeles. A teacher of remedial reading in New York City for the Federal Works Progress Administration, she organized for the American Federation of Teachers. During World War II she worked for the National Refugee Service in New York City. In Los Angeles, she served on the negotiating committee for the State, County and Municipal Workers, Congress of Industrial Organizations (CIO). From 1946 to 1953 Glenn organized Los Angeles County hospital workers for the United Public Workers. As general manager of Local 434 of the Service Employees International Union (SEIU), she has continued to organize municipal workers. Glenn participated in the historic 1966 strike of the Los Angeles hospital workers, which led to the first collective bargaining law for public workers. Glenn also negotiated the first child-care provision in a union contract with Los Angeles County, and, in 1970, on behalf of hospital workers, negotiated the first contract for public workers in Los Angeles County. She was the first woman elected to the International Executive Board of the SEIU. Glenn is a member of the California Democratic Central Committee, the Los Angeles City Attorney Employee Relations Committee, and the Federation of Women in the Work Force Committee. In 1974 she became West Coast vice president of the Coalition of Labor Union Women. She is married to Haskell Glenn, a former union organizer; the couple have one son.

Emma Goldman, 1869-1940

Anarchist Emma Goldman was born in Kovno, Lithuania, on June 27, 1869, the daughter of Abraham Goldman and Taube Blenowitch. In 1885 she immigrated to the United States with her sister, Helena. In 1889 in New York City she met Alexander Berkman, a fellow immigrant who was to become her lover and lifelong friend. During the Homestead, Pennsylvania, steel strike of 1892 Goldman conspired with Berkman to assassinate Henry Frick, supplying the gun to be used. Following the abortive attempt on Frick's life Berkman was sentenced to twenty-five years in prison. Although she proclaimed her part in the plot, Goldman was never indicted. She was, however, convicted in 1893 of inciting to riot at a Union Square demonstration in support of Debs's railway strike. She was released from Blackwell's Island Prison in 1894. In 1900 she founded the journal *Mother Earth*. On September 6, 1901, President William McKinley was slain in Buffalo, New York. Leon Czolgosz, the assassin, stated that he had been influenced by the writings of Emma Goldman. She was arrested and later released due to lack of evidence linking her with McKinley's assassination. A staunch pacifist, she was convicted in 1917 of obstructing the selective service law, fined $10,000, and sentenced to two years in the federal prison in Jefferson City, Missouri, where she met Kate Richards O'Hare Cunningham (q. v.). On December 1, 1919, Goldman and Berkman were deported to Russia. Disillusioned with the Soviet system, Goldman was readmitted to the United States in 1934. In 1936 Berkman died, and Goldman participated in the anti-Franco movement during the Spanish Civil War. After suffering a stroke, she died on May 14, 1940, and was buried in the Waldheim Cemetery in Chicago. Her papers are in the Labadie Collection, University of Michigan, New York Public Library, and the International Institute for Social History in Amsterdam. Information about Goldman is in the Justice Department, State Department, and Post Office Department files of the National Archives.

References: Emma Goldman: *Patriotism: A Menace to Liberty* (New York: Mother Earth, 1908); *The White Slave Traffic* (New York: Mother Earth, 1909); *Anarchism and Other Essays* (New York: Mother Earth, 1910); *The Crushing of the Russian Revolution* (London: Freedom Press, 1922); *My Disillusionment in Russia* (New York: Doubleday, Page & Co., 1923); *Living My Life* (New York: Alfred Knopf Co., 1931). Norman Hapgood, "Emma Goldman's Anarchism," *Bookman* 32 (February 1911): 639-40. "Berkman and Goldman," *Outlook* 123 (December 24, 1919): 529-30. Margaret Goldsmith, *Seven Women Against the World* (London: Methuen & Co., 1935). Ethel Edith Mannin, *Red Rose* (London: Jarrolds, 1941). Richard Drinnon, *Rebel in Paradise, A Biography of Emma Goldman* (Chicago: University of Chicago Press, 1961). Alix Kates Shulman, ed., *Red Emma Speaks* (New York: Random House, 1972). Obituary, *New York Times*, May 14, 1940, p. 1. Obituary, *Newsweek* 15 (May 20, 1940): 8. Obituary, *New Republic* 102 (June 3, 1940): 747. *Who Was Who* 4 (1961-1968): 364. *Women in American Labor History*, Item No. 388. *Schlesinger Library Inventory*, vol. 1, s. v. "Goldman, Emma." *NAW*, vol. 2, pp. 57-9.

Josephine Clara Goldmark, 1877-1950

Josephine Clara Goldmark, researcher of the briefs of Louis Brandeis and Felix Frankfurter, was born in Brooklyn, New York, on October 13, 1877, the last of ten children of Dr. Joseph Goldmark, a physician, and Regina Wehle. Her father died in 1881. Among her famous brothers-in-law were Felix Adler, founder of the Society for Ethical Culture, who married her sister Helen in 1880, and Louis D. Brandeis, who married her sister Alice in 1891. She served as Brandeis's researcher, providing data upon which his famous *Muller v. Oregon* (1908) brief was based. She graduated from Bryn Mawr in 1898 and attended Barnard College for a year. She joined the National Consumers' League, serving as a volunteer assistant to Florence Kelley (q. v.). In 1903 Goldmark became the league's publications secretary and chaired the committee on legal defense of labor laws. In 1907 her *Child Labor Legislation Handbook* was published; *Fatigue and Efficiency* appeared in 1912. As a member of the Factory Investigating Committee from 1912 to 1914, she studied the Triangle Shirtwaist Company fire of 1911. She died on December 15, 1950, in White Plains, New York. Her papers are in the National Consumers' League records of the Library of Congress.

References: Josephine Clara Goldmark: "Children Who Work at Night," *Charities and the Commons* 10 (June 6, 1903): 569-73; *Labour Laws for Women in the United States* (London: Women's Industrial Council, 1907); *Child Labor Legislation* (New York: National Consumers' League, 1908); *The Economic Position of Women* (New York: Academy of Political Science, 1910); *Fatigue and Efficiency* (New York: Charities, 1912); *Handbook of Laws Regulating Women's Hours of Labor* (New York: National Consumers' League, 1912); "Labor Laws for Women," *Survey* 29 (January 25, 1913): 552-5; "New York Nightwork Law for Women Upheld," *Survey* 53 (August 1, 1914): 450; *The Eight Hours Day for Wage Earning Women* (New York: National Consumers' League, 1916); *Comparison of an Eight Hour Plant and a Ten Plant* (Washington, D.C.: Government Printing

Office, 1920); "Women Workers' Wages," *Woman Citizen* 10 (December 1925): 25; *Impatient Crusader: Florence Kelley's Life Story* (Urbana: University of Illinois Press, 1953). Obituary, *New York Times,* December 16, 1950, p. 3. Obituary, *Wilson Library Bulletin* 26 (February 1951): 412. *Women in American Labor History,* Items No. 43, 288, 343, 344, and 389. *Schlesinger Library Inventory,* vol. 1, s. v. "Goldmark, Josephine Clara." *NAW,* vol. 2, pp. 60-1.

Joan M. Goodin, 1934-

Labor leader Joan Goodin, assistant director of the Internal Affairs Department of the Brotherhood of Railway, Airline and Steamship Clerks (BRAC), was born on April 2, 1934, in St. Petersburg, Florida. She was educated at George Washington University. In 1960 she joined the staff of BRAC. Goodin is a member of the board of directors of the United States Committee of Cooperation, Inter-American Commission of Women. She is chairperson of the Union Committee for Salaried and Professional Women of the Council of AFL-CIO Unions for Professional Employees; a member of the National Coordinating Committee of the Coalition of Labor Union Women; a member of the advisory board of the U.S. Center for International Women's Year; and a member of the Washington Union Women Leaders of the Women's Bureau, U. S. Department of Labor.

Martha W. Griffiths

Martha W. Griffiths congresswoman and lawyer, was born in Pierce City, Missouri, the daughter of Charles Elbridge and Nelle Sullinger Wright. In 1934 she received a B.A. from the University of Missouri and in 1940 a J.D. from the University of Michigan. She was admitted to the Michigan bar in 1941, and to practice before the Supreme Court in 1955. She was a contract negotiator for the Detroit Ordnance District from 1942 to 1946. She served in the Michigan State Legislature from 1949 to 1952 and in 1953 became the first woman judge and recorder of the Detroit Recorder's Court. In 1962 she was a delegate to the Interparliamentary Union Council Meeting held in Rome. Griffiths represented the Seventeenth District of Michigan in the U.S. Congress from 1955 to 1975. During her tenure, she sponsored the historic Equal Rights Amendment and guided its passage through the House of the Ninety-first Congress; argued in favor of barring discrimination according to sex in the 1964 Civil Rights Act; and persuaded the Ways and Means Committee to extend Social Security coverage to the children of a deceased mother, despite her absence from the work force for more than one and a half years. She is the wife of attorney Hicks G. Griffiths.

References: "Women on Both Sides of Equal Rights Amendment Argument," *Washington Post,* February 8, 1975, p. A7. *Who's Who in American Women (1974-75):* 348.

Margaret Angela Haley, 1862-1939

Margarget Angela Haley, business agent for the Chicago Federation of Teachers (CFT), was born in Joliet, Illinois, in 1862, the second of eight children of Michael Haley and Elizabeth Tiernan. She attended school in Channahon, Illinois, and at St. Angela's Convent in Morris, Illinois. She taught in Dresden Heights, Town of Lake, and Chicago, Illinois. Dissatisfied with wages and working conditions in the Chicago Public Schools, she joined the fledgling CFT. In 1900 Haley, then CFT vice president, and Catherine Goggin, CFT president, spearheaded a court fight for salary increases. In 1901 Haley became business agent of the CFT, a position she retained until her death. Under her leadership the CFT joined the Chicago Federation of Labor in 1902. As national vice president of the Women's Trade Union League, Haley agitated for protective legislation and female suffrage. In 1916 she became an organizer for the American Federation of Teachers. With Agnes Nestor (q. v.), she served on the executive committee of the Labor party in 1919. She died in Chicago on January 5, 1939, and was buried in Mount Olivet Cemetery in Joliet, Illinois. Her papers are in the Chicago Historical Society.

References: Margaret Angela Haley: "Work in the Teachers' Association of Chicago," *Current Literature* 36 (June 1904): 612-3; "A Factory System," *New Republic* 40 (November 12, 1924): 18-9. David Swing Ricker, "Unionizing School Teachers," *World To-Day* 8 (April 1905): 394-402. William Hard, "Chicago's Five Maiden Aunts," *American Magazine* 62 (September 1906): 481-9. "Portrait," *World To–Day* 13 (August 1907): 796. "Portrait," *Delineator* 73 (January 1909): 100. Obituary, *New York Times,* January 8, 1939, p. 2. *NAW,* vol. 2, pp. 115-7.

Alice Kessler Harris, 1941-

Professor Alice Kessler Harris, director of women's studies at Sarah Lawrence College, was born in Leicester, England, in 1941 and immigrated to the United States in 1955. She received a B.A. from Goucher College in 1961. From 1961 to 1962 she taught in the Baltimore City public schools. In 1963 she received an M.A. in history from Rutgers, in 1968 her Ph.D. She joined the faculty of Hofstra University in 1968. From 1974 to 1975 she was a visiting professor at Sarah Lawrence College. She has received grants from the Danforth Foundation Auxiliary, the National Institute of Mental Health, the Louis M. Rabinowitz Foundation, and the American Philosophical Society. At present she is completing a study of the changing role of the American working woman from 1820 to 1970.

References: Alice Kessler Harris: "The Lower Class As a Factor in Reform: New York, the Jews, and the 1890's" (Ph.D. diss., Rutgers University, 1968); "Ethnicity and Class Consciousness" (paper delivered at the Socialist Scholars' Conference, September 1969); "The Usefulness of

Violence," *Proceedings of the John Jay College Faculty Seminars* 2 (1969-1970): 1-19; "The Uses of Violence for Minority Groups" (paper delivered at Columbia University Seminar in American Civilization, March 1970); "New Perspectives on Women's History" (panel, Organization of American Historians, April 1971); "Education and Social Change" (paper delivered at the Mid-Atlantic American Studies Association, Temple University, February 1973); "Women, Work and the Social Order" (paper delivered at the Conference on Labor Marker Segmentation, Harvard University, March 1973); "The Connally Connection," with Blanche Cook in *Sacramento Bee*, July 15, 1973; "Women in Advanced Capitalism," *Social Policy*, July/August, 1973, pp. 16-22; "Industrial Discontent," in *The Study of American History*, vol. 2, ed. Ernest Kohlnitz (Dushkin Publishing Co., 1974); "Between the Real and the Ideal: Conflict in the Lives of Working Women" (paper delivered at the Organization of American Historians, April 1974); "Organizing the Unorganizable: Jewish Women and Their Unions" (paper delivered at the Conference on Class and Ethnicity in Women's History, S.U.N.Y. at Binghamton, New York, September 1974); "Where Are All the Women Unionist?" (paper delivered at the Berkshire Conference on the History of Women, October 1974); "A Voice From a Different Past: Anzia Yezierska and the Experience of a Jewish Immigrant Woman" (paper delivered at Lake Forest College, Chicago, January 1975); Introduction to *Bread Givers*, by Anzia Yezierska (George Braziller, forthcoming); Introduction to *Envelopes of Sound: Six Practitioners Discuss the Theory and Method of Oral History*, by Ronald J. Grele, ed. (Precedent Press, forthcoming); "European Immigrants," with Virginia Yane-McLaughlin in *Minority Report*, ed. Thomas Sowell (Urban Institute, forthcoming); "Stratifying by Sex: Notes on the History of Working Women," in *Labor Market Segmentation*, eds. David Gordon et. al. (Lexington Books, forthcoming); "Three Jewish Women and Their Union," *Labor History*, in press; "Women, Work and the Social Order," in *Liberating Women's History: Theoretical and Critical Essays*, ed. Bernice Carroll (University of Illinois Press, forthcoming).

Ellen Hayes, 1851-1929

Ellen Hayes, Socialist and educator, was born on September 23, 1851, in Granville, Ohio, the daughter of Charles C. Hayes and Ruth Wolcott. She received a B.A. from Oberlin College in 1878. In 1880 she became an instructor at Wellesley, where she taught astronomy and applied mathematics. A political activist and labor ally, Hayes was the Socialist candidate for secretary of state in Massachusetts in 1912. She also edited *Relay* and was a fellow of the American Association for the Advancement of Science.

Reference: *Who Was Who* 1 (1897-1942): 539.

Ellen Martin Henrotin, 1847-1922

Ellen Martin Henrotin, the affluent ally of Chicago women workers, was born in Portland, Maine, on July 29, 1847, the second of six children of Edward Byam Martin and Sara Ellen Norris. She was educated in London, Paris, and Dresden. On September 2, 1869, she married Charles Henrotin and settled in Chicago; the couple had three sons. In the 1880s she joined the politically active Chicago Women's Club. At her behest the club conducted a conference in 1904 on "Women in Industry." From 1904 to

1907 she served as president of the National Women's Trade Union League. She conducted workshops on women workers at the General Federation of Women's Clubs' 1906 convention and the National American Woman Suffrage Association Convention in 1907. During the 1910 strike of Chicago garment workers, she led a citizens' committee which investigated the strikers' grievances. She died on June 29, 1922, and was buried in Rose Hill Cemetery in Chicago. Her papers are in the Schlesinger Library, Radcliffe College.

References: Ellen Martin Henrotin: *The Social Status of European and American Women* (Chicago: C. H. Kerr & Co., 1887); "Organizing for Women," *American Federationist* 12 (November 1905): 824; "Trade Unions Among English Women," *Charities and the Commons* 17 (March 2, 1907): 1023-5. "Portrait of Ellen M. Henrotin," *Harper's Weekly* 52 (July 4, 1906): 16. *Who Was Who* 1 (1897-1942): 551. *Women in American Labor History*, Item No. 145. *NAW*, vol. 2, pp. 881-3.

Alice Henry, 1857-1943

Alice Henry was born on March 21, 1857, in Richmond, Australia, the first of three children of Charles Ferguson Henry, an accountant, and Margaret Walker, a seamstress. In 1884 she became a feature writer for the *Melbourne Argus*, contributing articles on women's suffrage and the rights of labor. She immigrated to the United States in January 1906. At Hull House in Chicago she met Margaret Dreier Robins (q. v.) and entered the employ of the National Women's Trade Union League (WTUL). In 1908 she edited the WTUL section of the Chicago *Union Labor Advocate;* from 1911 to 1915 she edited *Life and Labor,* the WTUL monthly. In 1910 Henry was invited by the United Brewery Workers Union to investigate the conditions affecting women workers. Her history of female trade unionism, *The Trade Union Woman*, was published in 1915. From 1918 to 1920 Henry was a WTUL organizer and lecturer. From 1920 to 1922 she led the Education Department of WTUL. Among her duties was the training of labor leaders. In 1921 she lectured at the newly established Bryn Mawr Summer School for Women in Industry; in 1924 she attended the International Workers' Education Conference at Ruskin College, Oxford. She died on February 14, 1943.

References: Alice Henry: "Country Without Strikes," *Westminister Review* 159 (January 1903): 24-8; "Industrial Democracy," *Outlook* 84 (November 3, 1906): 566-70; "Mary MacArthur and the Women's Trade Union Movement," *Charities and the Commons* 18 (April 6, 1907): 46-7; "Forward Step in the Labor Movement," *Charities and the Commons* 18 (August 31, 1907): 623-5; "The Campaign in Illinois for the Ten Hour Law," *American Federationist* 17 (August 1910): 669-72; "The Way Out," *Life and Labor* 2 (April 1912): 120-1; "The Hart, Schaffner and Marx Agreement," *Life and Labor* 2 (June 1912): 170-2; "Chicago Conference of Women Trade Unionists," *Life and Labor* 4 (November 1914): 324-9; *The Trade Union Woman* (New York: Appleton & Co., 1915); "Service Is Their Watchword," *Life and Labor* 11 (July 1907): 205-7; *Women and the Labor Movement* (New York: George H. Doran Co., 1923). Nettie Palmer, ed., *Memoirs of Alice Henry* (New

York: Melbourne, 1944). *Women in American Labor History,* Items No. 13, 87, 146, 196, 289, 313, 391, 392, and 413. *Schlesinger Library Inventory,* vol. 1, s. v. "Henry, Alice." *BDALL,* p. 154. *NAW,* vol. 2, pp. 183-4.

Barbara Herndon, 1930-

Barbara Herndon, executive director of Historical Researchers, Inc., was born April 10, 1930. She attended Carleton College in Northfield, Minnesota, from 1948 to 1952. In 1952 she received a B.A. from the University of Illinois, and in 1972 an M.A. in history from Sangamon State University. From 1972 to 1974 she was coordinator of the Oral History Project at Sangamon State University. She served as oral historian for the Illinois Bicentennial Commission in 1974. That same year, she established Historical Researchers, Inc., dedicated to the establishment of an archive of trade-union oral history. Herndon has lectured at the Illinois Labor History Society; the Southwest Labor History Society in Stockton, California; and the Oral History Association. She is a member of the Sangamon County Historical Society; the Illinois State Historical Society; the National Historical Society; Labor History Society; and the Oral History Association.

References: Barbara Herndon: "An Eyewitness Account of the Dome Building Fire at the Illinois State Fairgrounds," *Historico,* April, 1973; "Another Side of the Account of the Dome Building Fire," *Historico,* May 1973. Taped oral history interviews: 28 narrators, 143 hours.

Elinore Morehouse Herrick, 1895-1964

Elinore Morehouse Herrick was born in New York City on June 15, 1895, daughter of the Reverend D. W. Morehouse, a Unitarian minister, and Adelaide Bird, the first registrar of Pratt Institute in Brooklyn, New York. After attending Barnard College and the Columbia School of Journalism, she received a B.A. from Antioch College in 1929. In 1933 she was chosen by Grover Whalen director of the National Recovery Administration (NRA) in New York City, to train a team of factory inspectors; that same year, she chaired the NRA Mediation Board of New York City. From 1933 to 1935, at the behest of President Franklin D. Roosevelt, she served as executive vice chairman of the National Labor Board, Region II. In 1942 she was a member of the New York State committee to draft laws concerning women in war plants. During World War II she was the director of personnel and labor relations for Todd Shipyards Corporation. In 1945 she became a member of the editorial staff and director of personnel for the *New York Herald Tribune.* She was a member of the Governor's Advisory Committee of the New York Constitutional Convention; a trustee of Freedom House; a member of the League of Women Voters; director of the Hudson Guild Settlement; and vice president of the Consumers' League of New York. She died on October 11, 1964.

References: Elinore Morehouse Herrick: "Behind the Scenes in Canneries," *Woman's Journal* 15 (June 1930): 28; "Why People Strike," *Forum* 92 (December 1934): 336-42; "Need for Federal Labor Laws," *Nation* 141 (July 10, 1935): 49-50; "How Can We Raise Women's Status?" *Independent Woman* 17 (September 1938): 280; *Labor, Defense, and Democracy* (New York: Workers Defense League, 1941); "With Women at Work, the Factory Changes," *New York Times Magazine,* January 24, 1943, p. 4. "They Stand Out From the Crowd," *Literary Digest* 117 (January 20, 1934): 9. D. D. Bromley, "Mrs. Herrick of the Labor Board," *Harper's Magazine* 183 (October 1941): 501-11. Obituary, *New York Times,* October 12, 1964, p. 3. *Who Was Who* 4 (1961-1968): 432.

Mary J. Herrick

Mary J. Herrick, vice president and codirector of research of the American Federation of Teachers, was president of the Women High School Teachers in Chicago from 1933 to 1936. In 1970 Herrick placed her papers in the Wayne State University Archives of Labor History and Urban Affairs. Additional material is in the collections of the Chicago Historical Society.

Reference: "Women's Collections in the Archives of Labor History and Urban Affairs," *Wayne State University Archives of Labor History and Urban Affairs Newsletter* 2 (Summer 1972).

Bessie Hillman, 1889-1970

Bessie Abramowitz Hillman, vice president of the Amalgamated Clothing Workers of America (ACWA), was born in a village near Grodno, Russia, on May 15, 1889, and immigrated to the United States in 1905. She worked in a Chicago sweatshop from 1905 to 1910. She led the 1910 Hart, Schaffner & Marx strike in Chicago, and served as ACWA representative at Hart, Schaffner & Marx from 1911 to 1916. From 1915 to 1916 she served on the ACWA executive board. In 1926 she married Sidney Hillman, the first president of the ACWA. She organized shirt workers from 1932 to 1937 and was the educational director of the Amalgamated Laundry Workers' Joint Board in New York City from 1937 to 1944. She directed the ACWA members' war activities in New York City from 1942 to 1945 and served on the Child Welfare Committee of New York, which operated day-care centers for the children of war workers. She became the vice president of the ACWA in 1946. She was a member of the National Consumers' League, the National Civil Liberties Clearing House, the Henry Street Settlement, and served on the executive board of the Needle Trades Fashion Institute. She was a member of the protective labor legislation committee of the President's Commission on the Status of Women from 1961 to 1963. She died in New York on December 23, 1970.

References: Bessie Hillman: "Gifted Women in the Trade Unions," in *American Women: The Changing Image,* ed. Beverly Benner Cassara (Boston: Beacon Press, 1962). "Former General Executive Board Members at Boston Convention," *Advance*, May 21, 1920, p. 5. Obituary, *New York Times*, December 24, 1970. Obituary, *Advance*, January 15, 1971, p. 3. "Tribute to Bessie Hillman," *Advance*, February 5, 1971, p. 2. Frank Rosenbloom, "In Memory of Bessie Hillman," mimeographed (Chicago: Amalgamated Clothing Workers of America, April 18, 1971), pp. 1-3. *Amalgamated Clothing Workers of America General Executive Report and Proceedings of the 28th Biennial Convention,* May 29-June 2, 1972.

Elizabeth Hoeppel

In 1934 organizer and opera singer Elizabeth Hoeppel founded and became first president of the Grand Opera Artists Association. She helped to establish the American Guild of Musical Artists in 1936 and served as a member of the Executive Board. She now resides in Queens.

References: Quaintance Eaton, "Guild Formed To Aid Performing Artists," *Musical America,* May 25, 1936. Olin Downes, "Guild of Artists," *New York Times,* October 4, 1936.

Alice Hoffman, 1929-

Professor Alice Hoffman, president of the Oral History Association, was born in New York City on June 17, 1929, the daughter of Nelson H. Cruikshank, the director of the AFL-CIO's Department of Social Insurance, and Florence Crane, a household manager. She received a B.A. from Earlham College in 1951 and an M.A. from Pennsylvania State University in 1965. Hoffman is a member of Local 3 of the Philadelphia Federation of Teachers and a member of the Industrial Relations Research Association. She teaches in the Department of Labor Studies at Pennsylvania State University, where she is coordinator of the university's Oral History Project. She is married to Professor Howard S. Hoffman; the couple have three children.

References: Alice Hoffman: "Introducing Graduate Students to Oral History," *Oral History Association Newsletter,* April 1968: "The Art of Interviewing and Techniques of Training Interviewers," in *Third National Colloquium on Oral History,* ed. Peter Olch, 1969; "Basic Problems in Oral History," in *Fourth National Colloquium on Oral History,* ed. Gould Colman, 1970, pp. 98-103; "Oral History in Great Britain," *Journal of Library History,* July 1971, pp. 275-7; "Oral History in the United States," *Journal of Library History,* July 1971, pp. 277-85; *Preserving Your Local Union History Through the Tape–Recorder Interview* (Pittsburgh: United Steelworkers of America, 1972); "Bicentennial Recalls Labor's Participation in the Revolution," *Pennsylvania AFL-CIO News,* February 1972; "Pennsylvania Launches Labor Movement with the Creation of a City Central Body," *Pennsylvania AFL-CIO News,* May 1972; "The Homestead Steel Strike," *Pennsylvania AFL-CIO News,* July 1972; "William Sylvis, 1828-1869," *Pennsylvania AFL-CIO News,* November 1972; "The First Labor Newspaper," *Pennsylvania AFL-CIO News,* January 1973; "The Knights–Noble and Holy Order," *Pennsylvania AFL-CIO News,* March 1973; "One Hundred Years Ago," *Pennsylvania AFL-CIO News,* June 1973; "Validity and Reliability in Oral History," *Today's Speech,* Winter 1974.

Rebecca Holland, 1895-

Rank-and-file labor organizer Rebecca Holland was born in Latvia in 1895 and immigrated to the United States in 1909. She attended public school in Chicago for two years, then became a garment worker, organizing her shop for the International Ladies' Garment Workers Union (ILGWU). In 1915 she moved to Wisconsin, where she kept house for a Socialist family and attended high school. She studied at the University of Wisconsin. In 1919 she returned to Chicago where she became secretary and, later, president of ILGWU Local 100, the only woman delegate on the joint board, and a delegate to the Chicago Federation of Labor. In 1921 she moved to New York; in 1922 she participated in a general strike there. From 1923 to 1925 she attended the Brookwood Labor College. She married an ILGWU member in 1927 and moved to Los Angeles, where she continued to participate in union activities, including the 1940 strikes. The Feminist History Research Project has taped four interviews with Holland.

Reference: "Rebecca Holland (Goldberg)—Biographical Sketch," mimeographed (Topanga, California: Feminist History Research Project, 1974).

Dolores Huerta

Dolores Huerta, vice president of the United Farm Workers (UFW), was born in New Mexico. In 1955 she organized agricultural workers while working for the Community Service Organization (CSO); that same year she met Cesar Chavez. In 1962 she quit the CSO and moved to Delano, California, where she assisted Chavez in organizing for the Farm Workers' Association. In 1964 she organized migrants in Stockton and Modesto, California, and became a member of the United Farm Workers' Organizing Committee (UFWOC). As such, she negotiated a contract with the Delano grape growers in 1970. That same year she took part in the lettuce boycott against Bud Antle Company and Dow Chemical. She was elected vice president of the UFW in 1970 and 1973. Twice married, Huerta is the mother of ten.

References: *BDALL,* p. 167; "People," *Playgirl* 3 (June 1975): 122.

Josephine Hulett, 1927-

Josephine Hulett, a pioneer organizer of domestic workers and a field officer of the National Committee on Household Employment (NCHE), was born in 1927 in Portland, Arkansas. She graduated from the Philadelphia School of Practical Nursing in 1957 and attended the Temple Business School in Washington, D. C., from 1971 to 1973. Before moving to

Washington, D. C., in 1970 she had organized household workers in Youngstown, Warren, and Akron, Ohio. Hulett joined the staff of NCHE in 1969. From 1969 to 1970 Hulett served as president of the Youngstown Household Technicians. In 1972 she established the Ohio Coalition of Household Employees and served on the Afro-American Labor Council. She became the first female recipient of the Special Recognition Award of the Afro-American Labor Council in 1971; was presented the key to the city of Dayton, Ohio, in 1973, and the key to the city of New Orleans in 1974. Hulett is a member of the NAACP, the Urban League, the National Organization for Women's Black Caucus, and the Women in Poverty Task Force.

References: "Josephine Hulett as Interviewed by Janet Dewart," *Ms.*, February 1973, pp. 45-8. Joan Kent, "Household Workers Demand," *New Orleans States–Item*, October 14, 1974. Ellen Graham, "To Household Help, Difficult Times Are a Normal Way of Life," *Wall Street Journal*, February 13, 1975.

Grace Hutchins

The papers of author Grace Hutchins, whose landmark study, *Women Who Work*, was published in 1934, are in the collection of the University of Oregon.

References: Grace Hutchins: *Jesus Christ and the World Today* (New York: George H. Doran Co., 1922); "Seeing Red in Canton," *Survey* 57 (March 15, 1927): 775-6; *Labor and Silk* (New York: International Publishers, 1929); *Women Who Work* (New York: International Publishers, 1934). *Schlesinger Library Inventory*, vol. 1, s. v. "Hutchins, Grace." *Women in American Labor History*, Item No. 151.

Aunt Molly Jackson (Mary Stames), 1880-1960

Balladeer and folk historian Mary Stames, known as "Aunt Molly Jackson," was born in Clay County, Kentucky, in 1880. Her first husband, Bill Jackson, was a Kentucky miner. In 1931 she was discovered by authors Theodore Dreiser and John Dos Passos during their investigation of oppression of striking miners in the Harlan County, Kentucky, coalfields. At the behest of Sherwood Anderson and Lewis Mumford, she toured the United States on behalf of miners' relief. She died in Sacramento, California, in 1960.

Reference: Obituary, *New York Times*, September 3, 1960, p. 4.

Maxine Jenkins, 1936-

Maxine Jenkins was born on September 22, 1936, in Aberdeen, Mississippi, the daughter of sharecroppers Cleo Jenkins and Raymond Best. In 1964 she organized her own local of the American Federation of State, County and Municipal Employees (AFSCME).

After organizing clerks, maids, and janitors at the University of California at Berkeley, she was hired by the AFSCME International as a Bay Area organizer. In 1972 she joined the Service Employees International Union (SEIU) as an organizer. As such, she organized the clerks and blue-collar workers of Bay Area Rapid Transit and the San Francisco city and county clerical personnel. Jenkins is the subject of a forthcoming article by Denise D'Anne, to be published in *Ms.* magazine.

References: Maxine Jenkins: "Labor-Feminists Win Victory at the Polls," *Union W.A.G.E.*, November-December 1974, p. 1. Denise D'Anne, "Rank and File Victory!" *Union W.A.G.E.*, May-June 1975, p. 1. "New Union Forms!" *Union W.A.G.E.*, July-August 1975, p. 1.

Gloria Tapscott Johnson

Gloria Tapscott Johnson, director of education and women's activities for the International Union of Electrical, Radio and Machine Workers (IUE), received a B.A. and an M.A. from Howard University. From 1950 to 1952 she worked as a wage analyst for the Wage Stabilization Board; from 1952 to 1953 as an economist for the U. S. Department of Labor; and from 1951 to 1954 as an instructor at Howard University. Johnson was appointed to the Kennedy Commission on the Status of Women, and served on a committee of the Maryland Commission on the Status of Women. Johnson is the IUE representative on the AFL-CIO Bicentennial Planning Committee and National Health Insurance Committee and an instructor at the AFL-CIO Labor Studies Center. She is also a member of the Washington, D. C., Women Union Leaders; the Equal Rights Ratification Council; the Task Force for the Equal Rights Amendment; the Clearing House on Women's Issues; the Coalition of Labor Union Women; and the advisory committee on the Study of Women in Trade Unions at Cornell University. She is married to David F. Johnson; the couple have two children.

Frances Benjamin Johnston, 1864-1952

Photojournalist Frances Benjamin Johnston was born in Grafton, West Virginia, on January 15, 1864, the daughter of Anderson Donophon Johnston and Frances Antoinette Benjamin. She attended Notre Dame Convent in Govanston, Maryland, and studied at the Academie Julien in Paris and at the Art Students' League in Washington, D. C. (later the Corcoran Art School). She was a photographer for the Smithsonian Institution. Among her notable portraits are those of Susan B. Anthony (q. v.), Mark Twain, and George Washington Carver. Not only did Johnston photograph the rich and famous, she also studied women workers as well as anonymous black and native Americans. Her lens captured significant moments in American history; for example, she photographed Admiral Dewey after the 1889 Battle of

Manila Bay. In 1947 Johnston donated her prints, negatives, and correspondence to the Library of Congress. She was a member of the Women's National Press Club and an honorary member of the American Institute of Architects. She died on March 16, 1952, and was buried in Rock Creek Cemetery, Washington, D. C.

References: Obituary, *Time* 59 (June 2, 1952): 79. "Capital Education: Photographs from 1899," *American Heritage* 23 (June 1972): 26-35. Pete Daniel and Raymond Smock, *A Talent for Detail: The Photographs of Miss Frances Benjamin Johnston* (New York: Harmony Books, 1974). *Who Was Who* 3 (1951-1960): 454.

Brownie Lee Jones, 1897-

Educator Brownie Lee Jones was born on September 7, 1897, near Neosho, Missouri, the daughter of Richard Fred Jones and May McElhany. She received her B.A. from the Oklahoma College for Women at Chicksha in 1920, and studied at the University of Denver, Columbia University, the University of Washington, and the University of California at Berkeley. From 1922 to 1938 she was secretary of the Industrial Department of the YMCA, working in Denver; Flint, Michigan; Richmond; and San Francisco. Jones was director of the Southern School for Workers in Richmond from 1944 to 1951. In 1952 she joined the American Labor Education Service, from which she retired in 1961. She is a member of Local 189 of the American Federation of Teachers; the NAACP; the United Nations Association; and the United States-China Peoples' Friendship Association, as a member of which she toured the People's Republic in 1974.

Mother Mary Harris Jones, 1830-1930

On May Day 1930, reported an observer, "hundreds of men and women struggled through the ruts and mudholes of the Old Powder Factory Road in Prince George's County, Maryland, to celebrate the hundredth birthday anniversary of Mother Jones." Although bedfast during what was to be the last year of her long life, the veteran labor leader continued to "talk vigorously—and profanely—to visitors." "I was born in revolution," Mother Jones once declared. She was born on May 1, 1830, the daughter of "Irish agitator" Richard Harris. In 1835 Harris immigrated to America, where his family joined him in 1838. Harris's employment as a laborer with railway construction crews took the family to Toronto, where Mary Harris attended common and normal schools, studying elementary education and dressmaking. After teaching in a convent school in Morrae, Michigan, however, Mary Harris realized that she "preferred sewing to bossing little children," and moved to Chicago, where she became "forewoman in a dress making establishment." In 1861 she accepted a teaching position in Memphis, Tennessee, and married George Jones, "a staunch member of the Iron Moulders' Union" and organizer for the Knights of Labor in the southern and southwestern coalfields. In his extensive travels for the Knights of Labor, Jones was accompanied by Mary Harris and their four children. In 1867, however, yellow fever struck their Memphis home, in a single week fatally afflicting the four children and father. "One by one, my four little children sickened and died. I washed their little bodies and got them ready for burial. My husband caught the fever and died. I sat alone through the nights of grief. No one came to me. No one could. Other homes were as stricken as mine. All day long, all night long, I heard the grating of the wheels of the death cart." From this experience Mary Harris Jones was to emerge with a fearlessness of death and absolute commitment to the struggles of the working man. "Mary Jones had lost her family, but 'Mother Jones' adopted in their stead the workers of America." Among the many struggles in which Mother Jones participated were the 1892 Homestead strike against Carnegie Steel, the 1894 railmen's strike, and (as a United Mine Workers of America organizer) numerous coal strikes in Pennsylvania, West Virginia, and Colorado. As Clarence Darrow pointed out, the most effective weapon in Mother Jones's war against monied interests was her sense of drama; for example, the "march of the mill children" on July 7, 1903. Setting out from Independence Park in Philadelphia, the grim procession of children—many of them victims of industrial accidents — passed through Trenton, Princeton, Stony Brook, Hoboken, Jersey City, and down New York's Fourth Avenue and Twentieth Street, resting at Coney Island before proceeding to Oyster Bay, the home of President Theodore Roosevelt, who refused to see the pathetic army. During the crusade, Mother Jones decried repeatedly the ironic disparity between the promise of the American Dream and its actual fulfillment for the workingman. Such effective "pageants of poverty, processions of the ill-used," outraged the foes of labor, and campaigns of defamation were mounted against the aging labor matriarch. On June 8, 1914, for example, Representative George J. Kindel of Colorado, protesting that his state's labor troubles were caused by outside agitators, read into the *Congressional Record* two issues of "Polly Pry," the type of broadsheet circulated by the coal companies to discredit Mother Jones's cause. Quoting a secret file purportedly assembled by the Pinkerton Detective agency, a "Polly Pry" of January 2, 1904, depicted the aged dame as a "vulgar, heartless, vicious creature, with a fiery temper and a cold-blooded brutality rare even in the slums," as well as a familiar fixture "not alone in the 'red light' district of Denver, but in Omaha, Kansas City, Chicago, and far-off San Francisco." In addition to being the target of whisper campaigns, Mother Jones was also chided for her efforts on behalf of organized labor by various public figures. "Do you think the things you do are ladylike?" inquired a United States senator. Responded Mother Jones, "It's the last thing on earth I want to be." Elsewhere, Mother Jones ridiculed the conception of "ladyship," declaring it a debilitating class invention. "No matter what your fight," exhorted Mother Jones, "don't be ladylike! God Almighty made women and the Rockefeller gang of thieves made the ladies."

References: "Portrait," *Everybody's Magazine* 28 (May 1913): 619. "Prisons in the Foreground: the Indomitable Spirit of Mother Jones," *Current Opinion* 55 (July 1913): 19-20. "Props of Labor Propaganda," *Collier's National Weekly* 58 (November 4, 1916): 17. George Creel, "Prisoners of Public Opinion," *Harper's Weekly* 59 (November 7, 1914): 437. "Portrait," *Independent* 81 (February 8, 1915): 196. "Mother Jones and Mr. Rockefeller," *Outlook* 109 (February 10, 1915): 302. "Mother Jones: An Impression," *New Republic* 2 (February 20, 1915): 73-4. Peter C. Michelson, "Mother Jones," *Delineator* 86 (May 1915): 8. G. P. West, "Mother Jones Among the Twelve," *Nation* 115 (July 19, 1922): 70-1. "Portrait," *World's Work* 47 (March 1924): 524. Mary Field Parton, ed., *Autobiography of Mother Jones* (Chicago: C. H. Kerr & Co., 1925). "Mother Jones," *Survey* 64 (May 15, 1930): 180-1. Obituary, *Nation* 131 (December 10, 1930): 637. R. E. Smith, "March of the Mill Children," *Social Service Review* 41 (September 1967): 298-303. Irving Werstein, *Labor's Defiant Lady* (New York: Crowell, 1969). E. M. Steel, "Mother Jones in the Fairmont Field, 1902," *Journal of American History* 57 (September 1970): 290-307. Dale Fethering, *Mother Jones, the Miners' Angel* (Carbondale: Southern Illinois University Press, 1974). *Who Was Who* 4 (1951-1960): 505. *Women in American Labor History*, Item No. 398. *Schlesinger Library Inventory*, vol. 1, s. v. "Jones, Mary Harris." *BDALL*, pp. 179-80. *NAW*, vol. 2, pp. 286-8.

Crystal Lee Jordan, 1940-

Textile worker Crystal Lee Jordan, an organizer for the Textile Workers Union of America (TWUA), was born in Roanoke Rapids, North Carolina, in 1940. Her father was a loom mechanic and her mother a mill weaver. Both of her brothers and her sister also work in textile mills. At the age of seventeen, Jordan, a junior in high school, began working the four to midnight shift in a Burlington, North Carolina, cotton mill. She married for the first time at age nineteen; the couple's son was born in October 1960; Jordan was widowed four months later. In 1962 Jordan gave birth to her second son. In 1963 she married Larry "Cookie" Jordan, Jr.; their daughter was born in 1965. From 1969 to 1972 Jordan worked as a waitress and as a seamstress in a garment factory. During a TWUA organizing campaign in Roanoke Rapids, Jordan, a J. P. Stevens employee, joined the union on April 29, 1973. On May 30 she was dismissed from her job. Undeterred, she continued to agitate on behalf of the union, uniting black and white employees in a common cause. In 1974 Jordan was the subject of the *Ms.* magazine—KERA-TV documentary, *Woman Alive!*

References: Henry P. Leifermann, "The Unions Are Coming," *New York Times Magazine*, August 5, 1973, pp. 10-11. Judy Bachrach, "Woman: Alive And Well," *Washington Post*, June 19, 1974. Patricia Simmons, " 'Women Alive!' Gives a Pause to the Cause," *Washington Star-News*, June 19, 1974. Henry P. Leifermann, *Crystal Lee: A Woman of Inheritance* (New York: Macmillan, forthcoming).

Mary Morton Kimball Kehew, 1859-1918

Mary Morton Kimball was born in Boston on September 8, 1859, the fourth of eight children of Susan Tillinghast Morton and Moses Day Kimball, a Unitarian and a banker. She married an oil merchant, William Brown Kehew, on January 18, 1880. In 1886 she joined the Women's Educational and Industrial Union of Boston; in January 1892 she became its president. With Chicago rank-and-file organizer Mary Kenney O'Sullivan (q. v.), she founded the Union for Industrial Progress, which embraced bookbinders, laundry workers, tobacco workers, and garment workers. In 1903 she was elected first president of the fledgling National Women's Trade Union League. She died on February 13, 1918, in Boston and was buried in Mount Auburn Cemetery in Cambridge.

Reference: *NAW*, vol. 2, pp. 313-4.

Helen Adams Keller, 1880-1968

Although better known for her personal triumph over the handicaps of blindness and deafness, Helen Adams Keller was a lifelong labor ally. One of the first causes she championed after graduating from Radcliffe College was an effort to bring attention to the blindness inflicted on workers by industrial accidents resulting from poor working conditions. She was born on June 27, 1880, in Tuscumbia, Alabama, the daughter of Arthur H. Keller, a captain in the Confederate Army and later publisher of the *North Alabamian*. At the age of seventeen months, her sight and hearing were destroyed by an undiagnosed disease. When she was seven years old, her family hired Anne Sullivan, a noted teacher of the blind. With Sullivan's help, she entered Radcliffe in 1900; her tuition was paid from funds raised by Mark Twain. Keller later came under attack because of her sympathetic attitude toward socialism and her involvement in politics. Responding to such attacks in 1924, Keller stated in a letter endorsing presidential candidate Senator Robert M. La Follette: "So long as I confine my activities to social service and the blind, they [newspapers] compliment me extravagantly, calling me 'archpriestess of the sightless,' 'wonder woman,' and 'a modern miracle' . . . but to advocate that all human beings should have leisure and comfort, the decencies and refinements of life, is a Utopian dream, and one who seriously contemplates its realization must indeed be deaf, dumb and blind."

References: Helen Keller: *The Story of My Life* (New York: Doubleday, Page & Co., 1903); *The World I Live In* (New York: Century Co., 1908); *Midstream: My Later Life* (Garden City: Doubleday, Doran & Co., 1929); "Put Your Husband in the Kitchen," *Atlantic Monthly* 150 (August 1932): 140-7; *The Open Door* (Garden City: Doubleday, 1937). "Helen Keller's Development into a Social Philosopher," *Current Opinion* 55 (November 1913): 345-6. "Miss Keller on the War," *Outlook* 111 (December 29, 1915):

1012. John Williams Tibble, *Helen Keller* (New York: Putnam, 1958). Catherine Owens Peare, *The Helen Keller Story* (New York: Crowell, 1959). Richard Harrity, *Three Lives of Helen Keller* (Garden City: Doubleday, 1962). Norman Wymer, *The Young Helen Keller* (New York: Roy Publishers, 1965). Eileen Bigland, *Helen Keller* (New York: S. G. Phillips, 1967). Philip S. Foner, ed., *Helen Keller, Her Socialist Writings* (New York: International Publishers, 1967). Obituary, *New York Times*, June 2, 1968, p. 2. Obituary, *Time* 91 (June 7, 1968): 30. Obituary, *Newsweek* 71 (June 10, 1968): 33. Obituary, *Publishers' Weekly* 193 (June 17, 1968): 48. Katharine Wilkie, *Helen Keller* (Indianapolis: Bobbs-Merrill, 1969). Margery Weiner, *Helen Keller* (London: Heron, 1970). *Who Was Who* 5 (1969-1973): 386. *Schlesinger Library Inventory*, vol. 1, s. v. "Keller, Helen."

Florence Kelley, 1859-1932

Florence Kelley was born in Philadelphia on September 12, 1859, the third of eight children of Congressman William Darrah Kelley and Caroline Bartram Bonsall, a Quaker. Florence's five sisters died in infancy. She was educated at Miss Longstreth's school and the Friends' Central School in Philadelphia. She graduated from Cornell University in 1882. Denied admission to the University of Pennsylvania graduate school, she instituted evening classes for women workers at Philadelphia's New Century Club. Touring Europe in 1883 she met M. Carey Thomas (q. v.), who encouraged her to study in Zurich. She married Lazare Wischnewetzky, a Russian medical student, on June 1, 1884; the couple had three children, and separated in 1891. From 1891 to 1899 Kelley was a resident of Hull House in Chicago; in 1892 she became the first female factory inspector in Illinois, a position she retained until 1897. She received a law degree from Northwestern University Law School in 1894. In 1899 she moved to New York to become the general secretary of the National Consumers' League, a position she retained until her death. With Lillian Wald (q. v.), she established the New York Child Labor Committee in 1902. In 1904 she founded the National Child Labor Committee. She was secretary of the Board of Control of Labor Standards for Army Clothing in 1917; a founding member of the Women's International League for Peace and Freedom in 1919; and vice president of the National Woman Suffrage Association. She died on February 18, 1932, and was buried in Brookline, Massachusetts.

References: Florence Kelley: "Hull House," *New England Magazine* 18 (July 1889): 550-60; "United States Supreme Court and the Eight Hours' Law," *American Journal of Sociology* 4 (July 1898): 21-34; "Aims of the Consumers' League," *Review of Reviews* 20 (December 1899): 773; "Child Labor Legislation," *Annals of the American Academy of Political and Social Science* 20 (July 1902): 155-64; "Fall of the Great Industrial States," *Charities and the Commons* 9 (December 6, 1902): 567-9; *Some Ethical Gains Through Legislation* (New York: Macmillan, 1905); "Industrial Democracy: Women in the Trade Unions," *Outlook* 84 (December 15, 1906): 926-31; "Legal End of the Working Woman's Day," *Charities and the Commons* 17 (December 29, 1906): 553-4; "Unskilled Mothers," *Century* 73 (February 1907): 640-2; "Socialism and Charity," *Charities and the Commons* 18 (July 6, 1907): 394-8; "Congestion and Sweated Labor," *Charities and the Commons* 20 (April 4, 1908): 48-50; "Factory Inspection in Pittsburgh," *Charities and the Commons* 21 (March 6, 1909): 1105-16; "Invasion of Family Life by Industry," *Annals of the American Academy of Political and Social Science* 34 (July 1909): 90-6; "Withdrawal of Industry an Empty Threat," *Survey* 22 (August 21, 1909): 697-8; "Home and the New Woman," *Outlook* 93 (October 16, 1909): 363; *The Economic Position of Women* (New York: Academy of Political Science, 1910); "Forestalling Shirt-Waist Strikes," *Survey* 23 (January 29, 1910): 577-8; "Limiting Women's Working Hours," *Survey* 25 (January 21, 1911): 651-2; "Minimum Wage Boards," *American Journal of Sociology* 17 (November 1911): 303-14; *A Privileged Industry* (New York: National Consumers' League, 1912); *Minimum Wage Boards* (New York: National Consumers' League, 1912); *Modern Industry in Relation to the Family, Health, Education, Morality* (New York: Longmans, Green & Co., 1914); *Women in Industry* (New York: National Consumers' League, 1916); *Wage-Earning Women in War Time* (New York: National Consumers' League, 1919); "Laborers in Heat and in Heavy Industries," *Annals of the American Academy of Political and Social Science* 109 (September 1923): 175-8; "Leisure by Statute for Women," *Woman Citizen* 8 (May 17, 1924):16-7; "Skeleton in Industry's Closet," *Survey* 59 (January 15, 1928): 523-5; "Labor Legislation for Women and Its Effects on Earnings and Conditions of Labor," *Annals of the American Academy of Political and Social Science* 143 (May 1929): 286-300; "Thirty Years of the Consumers' League," *Survey* 63 (November 15, 1929): 210-2; "Ending of Women's Nightwork in Cotton," *Survey* 67 (Ocober 15, 1931): 84-5; "Woman's Work," *Collier's* 99 (May 8, 1937): 82. Paul Kellogg, "Secretary of the National Consumers' League," *American Magazine* 70 (July 1910): 322-4. Mildred Adams, "Pioneer in Social Justice," *Woman Citizen* 9 (November 29, 1924): 9. Obituary, *New York Times*, February 18, 1932, p. 2. "Florence Kelley, Pioneer," *Nation* 134 (March 2, 1932): 677. J.C. Lathrop, "Florence Kelley 1859-1932," *Survey* 67 (March 15, 1932): 677. Paul Kellogg, "Living Spirit of Florence Kelley," *Survey* 76 (January 1940): 6-8. Josephine Clara Goldmark, *Impatient Crusader: Florence Kelley's Life Story* (Urbana: University of Illinois Press, 1953). Dorothy Rose Blumberg, *Florence Kelley* (New York: A. M. Kelley, 1966). Louis Athey, "Florence Kelley and the Quest for Negro Equality," *Journal of Negro History*, (October 1971). *Who Was Who* 1 (1897-1942): 661. *Women in American Labor History*, Items No. 347 and 414. *Schlesinger Library Inventory*, vol. 1, s. v. "Kelley, Florence." *NAW*, vol. 2, pp. 316-19.

Ola Kennedy

Ola Kennedy, member of the steering committee of the Coalition of Labor Union Women (CLUW), was born in Madison, Arkansas. At the age of seven she moved to Gary, Indiana, her present home. She graduated from Roosevelt High School and attended Indiana University. As a clerk at the Hammond Valve Corporation, she successfully brought suit to promote women to supervisory positions and to eliminate many discriminatory practices against women and blacks. She is treasurer of Local 1273 of the United Steelworkers of America and a founding member of CLUW. Kennedy is a member of the executive committee of the Coalition of Black Trade Unionists; the Gary Commission on the Status of Women; and of the Steelworkers for Sadlowski. She was elected to "Who's Who Among Black Americans" and was honored as the outstanding black woman in organized labor by the National Black Labor Leaders.

Mary Dublin Keyserling

Mary Dublin Keyserling, director of the Columbia Commission on the Status of Women and former director of the Women's Bureau of the U. S. Department of Labor, received a B.A. from Barnard College and studied at the London School of Economics and Columbia University. From 1933 to 1938 she taught economics and statistics at Sarah Lawrence College; from 1938 to 1941 she was general secretary of the National Consumers' League. Keyserling was director of the International Economic Analysis Division of the U. S. Department of Commerce from 1946 to 1953 and associate director of the Conference on Economic Progress from 1953 to 1964. In 1964 she became director of the federal Women's Bureau. She is the wife of Leon H. Keyserling, chairman of the Council of Economic Advisors during President Harry Truman's administration.

Susan Myra Kingsbury, 1870-1949

Susan Myra Kingsbury, a pioneer researcher in the field of maternal employment and child labor, was born in San Pablo, California, on October 18, 1870, one of two children of Willard B. Kingsbury and Helen DeLamater. When she was six years old, her father died; her mother supported the family as dean of women at the College of the Pacific, where Susan received her B.A. in 1890. She received an M. A. from Stanford University in 1899 and a Ph.D. from Columbia in 1905. From 1892 to 1900 she taught history at Lowell High School in San Francisco; from 1904 to 1905 she was an instructor of history at Vassar College. Kingsbury investigated child labor for the Massachusetts Commission on Industrial and Technical Education in 1906. The following year she became head of the research department of the Women's Educational and Industrial Union of Boston. She was a professor of economics at Simmons College in Boston from 1906 to 1915 and director of Social Economy and Social Research at Bryn Mawr College from 1915 to 1936. In 1921 she helped M. Carey Thomas (q. v.) establish the Bryn Mawr Summer School for Working Women. She died on November 28, 1949.

References: Susan Myra Kingsbury: *The Economic Position of Women* (New York: Academy of Political Science, 1910); *Licensed Workers in Industrial Home Work* (Boston: Wright & Potter, 1915). *Who Was Who* 2 (1943-1950): 300. *NAW*, vol. 2, pp. 335-6.

Odessa Komer, 1925-

Odessa Komer, vice president of the United Auto Workers of America (UAW) since 1974, was born on June 29, 1925. She joined the UAW in 1944 during the union's organizing drive at Ex-Cell-O in Detroit. In 1953 she went to work as an assembler at Ford, becoming a member of Local 228. Since that time she has been elected to many positions in the 7,000 member local. These include the executive board (1956-58), the district committee (1958-65), delegate to the Ford Council and Sub-Council 5 (1961-67), the bargaining committee (1962-66), recording secretary (1966-67), delegate to the 1964 and 1966 UAW constitutional conventions, education chairperson, the bylaws committee, and the credit union. In each instance Komer was the first woman so elected. In 1974 she was elected vice president of the UAW, a post she presently holds. She is the wife of Leo Komer; the couple have two children and two grandchildren.

Reference: "Biographical Sketch of UAW Vice President Odessa Komer," mimeographed (Detroit: United Auto Workers, 1974).

Elizabeth Duncan Koontz

Elizabeth Duncan Koontz, director of the Women's Bureau of the U. S. Department of Labor from 1969 to 1973, received a B.A. from Livingstone College in 1938 and an M.A. in Elementary Education from Atlanta University in 1941. In 1969 she was appointed delegate to the United Nations, and in 1972 Koontz became deputy assistant secretary of labor and special counselor to the secretary for women's programs. Koontz is a past president of the National Education Association and consultant to the Committee on the Status of Women of the National Council of Administrative Women in Education.

Joyce L. Kornbluh

Professor Joyce L. Kornbluh, since 1972 a research associate at the Institute of Labor and Industrial Relations, the University of Michigan/Wayne State University, has been involved in workers' education since 1947. She received a B.A. from the University of Pennsylvania in 1948 and an M.A. from the University of California at Los Angeles in 1950. From 1947 to 1948 she wrote materials for workers' education classes conducted by the Philadelphia Labor Education Association and for the Labor Extension Program of the Board of Education and, from 1949 to 1953, for the UCLA Institute of Industrial and Labor Relations and various unions in the Los Angeles area. She has worked as assistant education director for the Amalgamated Clothing Workers of America (1953-1959), as a labor consultant of the Fund for the Republic (1956), and as an editor of the newspaper of Detroit Local 876, Retail Clerks International Union (1959-1961). From 1969 to 1972 she was the editor at the University of Michigan Center for Research on Utilization of Scientific Knowledge, Institute for Social Research. In 1974 she established the summer school for women workers at the University of Michigan. She is a member of the American Federation of Teachers, the American Civil Liberties Union, the National Organization for Women, and the Workers Defense League. Her papers are in the Wayne State University Archives of Labor History and Urban Affairs.

References: Joyce L. Kornbluh: *Rebel Voices: An IWW Anthology* (Ann Arbor: University of Michigan Press, 1964); *Poverty in America* (Ann Arbor: University of Michigan Press, 1965); *Negroes and Jobs* (Ann Arbor: University of Michigan Press, 1968).

Belle Case La Follette, 1859-1931

Editor Belle Case La Follette was born in Summit, Juneau County, Wisconsin, on April 21, 1859, one of six children of Anson T. Case and Mary Nesbitt. In 1875 she met Robert M. La Follette, the future senator and labor champion, whom she married on December 31, 1881. She received her B.A. from the University of Wisconsin in 1879 and became the university's first female law school graduate in 1885. An outspoken suffragette, she edited the labor and consumer affairs department of *La Follette's Magazine,* a weekly journal founded in 1909 in Madison, Wisconsin. Among its contributors was Elizabeth Glendower Evans (q. v.). Following Senator La Follette's death on June 18, 1925, she declined to run for public office despite an outpouring of popular support. Instead, she devoted herself to her husband's biography, working in Madison, the home of her son Philip and in Washington, D.C., the home of her son Robert. On August 18, 1931, she died unexpectedly in Washington, D.C. Senator La Follette's biography was completed by his daughter Fola in 1953. Belle Case La Follette's papers are in the Library of Congress and in the Wisconsin Historical Society.

References: Belle Case La Follette: *Robert M. La Follette, June 14, 1855-June 18, 1925,* 2 vols. (New York: Macmillan, 1953). Obituary, *New York Times,* August 19, 1931. *NAW,* vol. 2, pp. 356-8.

Yetta Land, 1887-

Yetta Land, civil rights lawyer, was born in 1887 in Warren, Ohio, the daughter of immigrant parents. At the age of fourteen she began working in a cigar factory. In 1903 she organized and became the secretary of the World Cigarmakers, the first cigarmakers union in Cleveland. She was active in the cigar industry until her marriage in 1909. In 1918 she began night school, completing high school, two years of college, and law school. In 1926 she began her law practice. She specialized in labor cases, representing various unions before the National Labor Relations Board. In 1931 she overturned the criminal syndicalism laws of Ohio; another legal triumph was the acquittal of Smith Act defendants in Cleveland in 1931. The Feminist History Research Project has recorded two interviews with Yetta Land.

Reference: "Yetta Land — Biographical Sketch," mimeographed (Topanga, California: Feminist History Research Project, 1973).

Lucy Larcom, 1824-1893

Textile worker, writer, and educator Lucy Larcom was born on May 5, 1824, in Beverly, Massachusetts. Of Puritan ancestry, Lucy was the ninth of ten children of Benjamin Larcom, a ship's captain and merchant, and Lois Barrett. Alone among their eight daughters, Lucy elected to remain single. In 1835 Lois Larcom, newly widowed, moved her family to Lowell, Massachusetts, where she had obtained a position as the supervisor of a textile company boardinghouse. Her daughters soon entered the mills, where Lucy worked for ten years. Lucy's early writings were published in *The Lowell Offering,* the journal of the female textile workers, in the 1840s. She chronicled her experiences as a millworker in *An Idyl of Work* (1875), "Among the Lowell Mill-Girls: A Reminiscence," *Atlantic Monthly* (November 1881), and *A New England Girlhood* (1889), which describes her life to 1852. From 1849 to 1852 she attended Monticello Seminary in Godfrey, Illinois, where she was strongly influenced by president Philena Forbes. From 1854 to 1862 she taught rhetoric at Wheaton Seminary in Norton, Massachusetts. She edited *Atlantic Monthly* publishers Ticknor & Fields' children's magazine, *Our Young Folks,* from 1865 to 1873. In 1871 she assisted John Greenleaf Whittier in the preparation of *Songs of Three Centuries.* She died on April 17, 1893, and was buried in Beverly, Massachusetts. Her papers are in the Massachusetts Historical Society and the Essex Institute in Salem, Massachusetts.

References: Lucy Larcom: *Breathings of the Better Life* (Boston: Ticknor & Fields, 1867); *An Idyl of Work* (Boston: J. R. Osgood & Co., 1875); *A New England Girlhood* (New York: Houghton, Mifflin & Co., 1889); *As It Is In Heaven* (New York: Houghton, Mifflin & Co., 1891); "American Woman's Life," *Outlook* 51 (February 16, 1895): 270. Obituary, *New York Times,* April 19, 1893, p. 2. Obituary, *Critic* 22 (April 22, 1893): 258. Obituary, *Dial* 14 (May 1, 1893): 267-8. Eleanor Maria Sickels, *In Calico and Crinoline, True Stories of American Women* (New York: Viking Press, 1935). Daniel Dulaney Addison, *Lucy Larcom* (Freeport: Books for Libraries Press, 1971). *Who Was Who,* Historical Volume (1607-1896): 373. *Women in American Labor History,* Item No. 199. *Schlesinger Library Inventory,* vol. 1, s. v. "Larcom, Lucy." *NAW,* vol. 2, pp. 368-9.

Julia Clifford Lathrop, 1858-1932

Julia Clifford Lathrop, first head of the federal Children's Bureau, was born in Rockford, Illinois, on June 29, 1858, the eldest of five children of William Lathrop, an attorney and congressman, and Sarah Adeline Potter, a suffragette. She attended Rockford Seminary and graduated from Vassar College in 1880. Shocked by the Haymarket Riot and the reprisals of 1886, she took up residence at Hull House, the Chicago settlement of Jane Addams (q. v.) and

Pauline Newman. (Courtesy Pauline Newman, ILGWU)

Agnes Nestor. (Courtesy Library of Congress)

Lucy Parsons. (Courtesy William Cahn)

Lucretia Mott, about 1850. *(Courtesy Library of Congress)*

Yvonne Porter. (Courtesy USWA)

Barbara Mikulski. (Courtesy Barbara Mikulski)

Ellen Gates Starr (q. v.), where she remained from 1890 to 1910. As a county agent during the depression of 1893, she investigated relief applicants; that same year she was appointed by Governor John P. Altgeld to the Illinois Board of Charities. In 1908 she helped to establish the Illinois Immigrants' Protective League; in 1912 she was appointed by President William H. Taft director of the newly established federal Children's Bureau, a post to which she was reappointed by President Woodrow Wilson. From 1916 to 1918 the bureau undertook enforcement of the child labor law, later declared unconstitutional. In 1921 she resigned from the Children's Bureau and was succeeded by Grace Abbott (q. v.). From 1925 to 1931 she served on the Child Welfare Committee of the League of Nations. She died in Rockford, Illinois, on April 15, 1932.

References: Jane Addams, "Julia Lathrop at Hull-House," *Survey Graphic* 24 (August 1935): 373-4. Jane Addams, *My Friend, Julia Lathrop* (1934; reprint ed., New York: Arno Press, 1974). *NAW,* vol. 2, pp. 370-2.

Mary Lease, 1853-1933

Populist lecturer Mary Elizabeth Lease was born in Ridgway, Elk County, Pennsylvania, on September 11, 1853, the sixth of eight children of Joseph P. Clyens and Mary Elizabeth Murray. She was educated in parochial schools in Ceres Township, McKean County, Pennsylvania, and graduated from St. Elizabeth's Academy in Allegany, New York, in 1868. In 1870 she accepted a teaching position at a Catholic girls' school in Osagi Mission, Kansas. On January 20, 1873, she married pharmacist Charles L. Lease; the couple had four children. An accomplished orator, she toured the United States on behalf of the Irish National League in 1885. A champion of farmers, she addressed the Union Labor party's 1885 Kansas convention. In 1888 she edited the *Union Labor Press.* She founded the *Colorado Workman* in 1889 and was elected master workman of the Kansas assembly of the Knights of Labor in 1891. From 1890 to 1894 she lectured for the Farmers' Alliance and the People's Party. In 1895 she published *The Problem of Civilization Solved,* which posited the need for a Socialist messiah. In 1902 she divorced her husband and moved to Brooklyn where she later served as president of the National Society for Birth Control. She died on October 29, 1933, and was buried in Cedar Grove Cemetery, Long Island, New York. A Lease archive is in the State Historical Society, Topeka, Kansas.

References: Dorothy Rose Blumberg, "Mary Lease: Popular Campaigner" (paper delivered at the Second Berkshire Conference, Radcliffe College, October 26, 1974). *Who Was Who* 1 (1897-1942): 713. *NAW,* vol. 2, pp. 380-2.

Alice K. Leopold

Alice Koller Leopold, former director of the federal Women's Bureau, was born in Scranton, Pennsylvania, the daughter of E. Leonard Koller and Leonora Edwards. She graduated from Goucher College in 1927, and married Joseph Leopold in 1931. She was elected to the Connecticut General Assembly in 1949 and authored and sponsored the equal pay bill, which became law in Connecticut in October 1949. In 1953 she was appointed director of the Women's Bureau by President Dwight D. Eisenhower. She founded the Industrial Relations Club of Fairfield County and has served as state chairman of the Connecticut League of Women Voters. She is a member of the Board of Trustees of Goucher College and of the Business and Professional Women's Club.

Gerda Lerner, 1920-

Gerda Lerner, director of Women's Studies and professor of history at Sarah Lawrence College, received her M.A. in 1965 and her Ph.D. in 1966 from Columbia University. In 1968 she was awarded an American Association of University Women Research Fellowship; in 1970, a research fellowship from the Social Science Research Council. In 1973 Lerner undertook the direction of Women's Studies at Sarah Lawrence College, a program financed by a grant from the Rockefeller Foundation. In 1974 she received the Robert H. Lord Award for Excellence in Historical Studies from Emmanuel College in Boston.

References: Gerda Lerner: *The Grimke Sisters from South Carolina: Rebels Against Slavery* (Boston: Houghton, Mifflin Co., 1967); *The Woman in American History* (Reading, Massachusetts: Addison-Wesley, 1971); *Black Women in White America: A Documentary History* (New York: Pantheon Books, 1972); *Women in the Making of the Nation* (Indianapolis: Bobbs-Merrill, forthcoming).

Lena Morrow Lewis, 1862-1950

Lena Morrow Lewis, editor of *Labor World* from 1925 to 1930, was born in 1862. She was active in Alaska from 1912 to 1917 and in the California Socialist party from 1925 to 1930. Among her many correspondents were Eugene V. Debs, Norman Thomas, Warren K. Billings, and Iva Ettor. Her papers are in Collection 15, the Tamiment Library, New York University.

Josephine Shaw Lowell, 1843-1905

Josephine Shaw Lowell was born in West Roxbury, Massachusetts, on December 16, 1843, one of five children of abolitionists Francis George Shaw and Sarah Blake Sturgis. She was educated in Paris, Rome, Miss Gibbon's School in New York, and Boston. On October 31, 1863, she married Col. Charles Russell Lowell. She was widowed on October 20, 1864, and gave birth to her daughter shortly thereafter. In 1890 she helped to establish the New

York Consumers' League, which she headed until 1896. In 1892 she rose to the defense of Homestead, Pennsylvania, striking steel workers. With Lillian Wald (q. v.), she established a work relief committee in New York during the 1893-1894 depression. She died on October 12, 1905, and was buried in Auburn Cemetery in Cambridge, Massachusetts.

References: Josephine Shaw Lowell: *Public Relief and Private Charity* (New York: G. P. Putnam's Sons, 1884); *Industrial Arbitration and Conciliation* (New York: G. P. Putnam's Sons, 1893); "Methods of Relief for the Unemployed," *Forum* 16 (February 1894): 655-62; "Industrial Arbitration and Conciliation," *Dial* 16 (May 16, 1894): 307; *The Work House, New York City* (New York: State Board of Social Welfare, 1888). Obituary, *New York Times*, October 13, 1905, p. 6. Joseph Dana Miller, "City's Saint," *Outlook* 81 (December 23, 1905): 974. Richard Watson Tilder. "Woman of Sorrows," *Critic* 48 (January 1906): 74-5. "Peace Movement and Mrs. Lowell," *Charities and the Commons*, 15 (February 17, 1906): 701-2. "The Work of Josephine Shaw Lowell," *Chautauquan* 49 (January 1908): 264-7. W. R. Stewart, "Philanthropic Work of Josephine Shaw Lowell," *Survey* 27 (December 9, 1911): 1342-4. *Who Was Who* 1 (1897-1942): 750. *Schlesinger Library Inventory*, vol. 1, s. v. "Lowell, Josephine Shaw." *NAW*, vol. 2, pp. 437-9.

Olga M. Madar, 1915-

Olga Madar, president of the Coalition of Labor Union Women (CLUW), was born on May 17, 1915, in Sykesville, Pennsylvania, a coal-mining town. At the age of fifteen she came to Detroit with her parents. In 1933 she was hired by Chrysler Corporation in Detroit, where she worked summers while attending Eastern Michigan University. After receiving her B.S. in 1938, she worked as a therapist at the Ypsilanti, Michigan, State Hospital and as a teacher in Flat Rock, Michigan. She joined the recreation department of the International United Automobile, Aerospace, and Agricultural Implement Workers of America (UAW) in 1944 and became director of the department in 1947. She was a Detroit parks and recreation commissioner from 1958 to 1966. She was elected to the UAW's Executive Board in 1966, the first woman to achieve that distinction, and was reelected in 1968. Madar became director of the Technical, Office and Professional Workers Servicing Department in 1966 and was selected by Walter Reuther to head the newly established Department of Consumer Affairs of the UAW. Madar was elected vice president of the International Union in 1970 and reelected in 1972. In 1974 she was elected first president of CLUW. She is a member of the advisory committee on women of the U.S. Department of Labor and a member of the National Women's Political Caucus. Her papers are in the Archives of Labor History and Urban Affairs, Wayne State University.

Reference: "Biographical Sketch of UAW Vice President Olga M. Madar," mimeographed (Detroit: United Automobile, Aerospace and Agricultural Implement Workers of America, 1974).

Jean Maddox, 1915-

Jean Maddox, founder of the Union Women's Alliance to Gain Equality (Union W.A.G.E.), was born on August 30, 1915, in Pocatello, Idaho. She was raised in the Idaho mountains and educated at home until the fifth grade by her father, John E. Irby, a forest ranger of Native American ancestry, and her mother, Murtle Tindell, a schoolteacher. In 1932 her father was murdered during a range war near Soda Springs, Idaho. She graduated from high school in Ventura, California. Unable to find office work, she worked as a waitress until she married. She remained at home, raising her twin daughters, until 1941 when she went to work as a Teamster, driving a milk truck to relieve a man for active war duty. Later, she worked in a soap factory as an inside oganizer for the West Coast Congress of Industrial Organizations, became a steward, participated in grievance negotiations, and was active in the union's steward council. In 1952 she went to work in an office and joined Local 29 of the Office and Professional Employees Union. She served as shop steward, as founding president of the union's steward council, and on the executive board. On March 8, 1971, she became the founding president of Union W.A.G.E., a union of women workers dedicated to achieving equal rights, equal pay, and equal opportunities for working women. In 1975 Maddox was named California Woman of the Year by the California Commission on the Status of Women.

References: Jean Maddox: "Learning The Rules — And Building A Caucus," *Union W.A.G.E.*, July-August, 1975, pp. 6-7; "How To Organize A Union: You Can Do It If You Try!" *Union W.A.G.E.*, July-August, 1975, pp. 6-7.

Elizabeth Maloney, active 1911-1921

Elizabeth Maloney of Chicago was elected first female vice president of the Hotel and Restaurant Employees International Alliance in July 1911 and served on the union's executive board from 1911 to 1921.

Reference: *Mixer and Server* 20 (July 15, 1911): 1.

Gloria Marigny

Gloria Marigny, secretary-treasurer of Local 399 of the Hospital and Service Employees Union, was born in New Orleans. For eight years she worked as a nurse's aide at the Charity Hospital there. In 1958 she moved to Los Angeles, where she joined Local 399 at the Lincoln Care Retreat. She was an employee picket captain at Lincoln in 1960, and following the strike became an organizer. She was appointed assistant to the director of the Hospital Division in 1968, and is on the Executive Board of the union's International.

Helen Marot, 1865-1940

Helen Marot was born on June 9, 1865, in Philadelphia, the fourth of five children of Quakers Henry Marot, a publisher, and Hannah Griscom. She was educated at the Friends' schools in Philadelphia. While working in the Wilmington, Delaware, public library in 1897, she established a library of labor literature in Philadelphia; in 1899 she published *A Handbook of Labor Literature*. At the behest of the Industrial Commission she investigated the Philadelphia garment industry in 1899. She was a child-labor investigator for the Association of Neighborhood Workers of New York City in 1902, and secretary of the fledgling Pennsylvania Child Labor Commission from 1904 to 1905. In 1906 she became secretary of the Women's Trade Union League (WTUL). She resigned in 1913 to protest the dominance of the league by socialists. She led the International Ladies' Garment Workers Union (ILGWU) strike in 1909 and 1910. She was a member of the editorial board of *Masses* from 1916 to 1917. She retired in 1920 and died in New York City on June 3, 1940.

References: Helen Marot: *A Handbook of Labor Literature* (Philadelphia: Free Library of Economics & Political Science, 1899); "Salaries Paid to the Workers in Philanthropic Institutions," *Charities and the Commons* 12 (April 23, 1904): 416-20; *The Economic Position of Women* (New York: Academy of Political Science, 1910); "Women's Trade Union League," *Survey* 26 (July 1, 1911): 548-9; "Carola Woerishoffer," *Life and Labor* 1 (December 1911): 358-61; *American Labor Unions* (New York: H. Holt & Co., 1914); "Trade Unions and the Minimum Wage Boards," *American Federationist* 22 (November 1915): 966-9; *Creative Impulse in Industry* (New York: E. P. Dutton & Co., 1918); "Reconstruction at Work," *Dial* 65 (October 19, 1918): 303-5; "Labor at the Crossways," *Dial* 66 (February 22, 1919): 165-8; "Why Reform Is Futile," *Dial* 66 (March 22, 1919): 293-6; "Labor Control of Government Industries," *Dial* 66 (April 19, 1919): 411-3; "Responsible Unionism," *Dial* 67 (August 23, 1919): 131-3. *Who Was Who* 1 (1897-1942): 778. *Women in American Labor History*, Items No. 153, 254, 319, 399, and 421. *Schlesinger Library Inventory*, vol. 2, s. v. "Marot, Helen." *BDALL*, pp. 232-3. *NAW*, vol. 2, pp. 499-501.

Lupe Marshall, active 1937

Chicago social worker Lupe Marshall, a linguist, mother of three, and resident of Hull House, was active in the Republic Steel strike of 1937 and was injured in the Memorial Day Massacre.

Reference: Mary Heaton Vorse, *Labor's New Millions* (New York: Modern Age, 1938).

Lucy Randolph Mason, 1882-1959

Lucy Randolph Mason was born in an Episcopal rectory in Clarens, Virginia, on July 26, 1882, the daughter of the Reverend Landon Randolph. She worked for the Young Women's Christian Association as a stenographer from 1904 to 1914. In 1918 she was elected president of the Richmond Equal Suffrage League and the Richmond League of Women Voters. She was appointed chairman of the Committee on Women in Industry of the National Advisory Commission in Virginia by Samuel Gompers during World War I. She joined the Union Label League in Richmond in 1923; succeeded Florence Kelley (q. v.) as general secretary of the National Consumers' League in 1932; and was a founder of the League of Women Voters. She became southern director for textiles and clothing organizations in 1937 and worked for the Southern Congress of Industrial Organization's Political Action Committee. She retired in 1951 and died in Atlanta on May 6, 1959.

References: Lucy Randolph Mason: *The Shorter Day and Women Workers* (Richmond: Virginia League of Women Voters, 1922); *To Win These Rights* (New York: Harper, 1952); "Work and Color," *Nation* 175 (September 27, 1952): 263-5; *Standards for Workers in Southern Industry* (New York: National Consumers' League, n.d.). "Miss Lucy, Southern Blue Blood for the CIO," *Business Week*, February 15, 1947, p. 104. Lawrence Lader, "Lady and the Sheriff," *New Republic* 118 (January 5, 1948): 17-19. Obituary, *New York Times*, May 8, 1959, p. 1. *Schlesinger Library Inventory*, vol. 2, s. v. "Mason, Lucy Randolph." *BDALL*, pp. 236-7.

Joyce Maupin, 1914-

Joyce Maupin, coordinator of Union Women's Alliance to Gain Equality (Union W.A.G.E.), was born in 1914. Her father was a farmer, and her mother a teacher, journalist, and suffragist. Maupin left school at the age of seventeen to become self-supporting and worked as a waitress, textile worker, machinist, and office worker. She was active in the five-month strike of the International Machinists against Boeing Aircraft, and was a shop steward of Local 29 of the Office and Professional Employees. On March 8, 1971, she became a founding member of Union W.A.G.E. She received the California Woman of the Year award in 1975.

References: Joyce Maupin: "Health & Safety: Writing & Negotiating Your Union Contract," *Union W.A.G.E.*, May-June 1975, p. 6; "Legal Secretaries Keep Union Shops," *Union W.A.G.E.*, July-August, 1975, p. 8; *Labor Heroines: Ten Women Who Led The Struggle* (Berkeley, California: Union W.A.G.E., n. d.); *Working Women and Their Organizations* (Berkeley, California: Union W.A.G.E., n. d.).

Carmen Rosa Maymi, 1938-

Carmen Rosa Maymi, director of the federal Women's Bureau, was born in Puerto Rico on March 17, 1938. She received a B.A. and an M.A. from DePaul University, and attended the University of Illinois and the University of Chicago. Prior to 1965 she served as an employment counselor, community organizer, and regional supervisor of education and community organization for the Migration Division of the Commonwealth of Puerto Rico in Chicago. She became the assistant director of the Montrose Urban Progress Center of the Chicago Committee on Urban Opportunity in 1965; was a community services specialist in the Great Lakes Region of the Office of Economic Opportunity (OEO) from 1966 to 1968; and directed OEO-funded services to Indian reservation and migrant programs. In 1972 she worked with the president's cabinet committee on Opportunities for the Spanish Speaking and was the associate director of Program Development in the Women's Bureau. In 1973 Maymi was appointed director of the federal Women's Bureau by President Richard M. Nixon. She is the U.S. Department of Labor liaison on the International Women's Year.

Mary McDaniel

Mary McDaniel is vice president of the International Union of Electrical, Radio and Machine Workers of America.

Grace Burnham McDonald, 1889-

Journalist and health researcher Grace Burnham McDonald was born in New England in 1889. Her father was a neurologist at Yale Medical School; her stepmother, a social worker who had worked at Hull House, introduced Grace to Jacob Riis's photographs of child labor and tenements. After living in Louisville, Kentucky, with her first husband, McDonald moved to New York and attended the New School for Social Research. She later worked as an inspector for the Joint Board of Sanitary Control, which had been established after the Triangle Shirtwaist Fire. In 1920, with Harriet Silverman, she formed the Workers Health Bureau (WHB), an independent research organization which gathered information on occupational and safety codes to be included in union contracts. After the demise of the WHB in 1928, she continued to work for union protection until 1936 when she moved to California and shifted her attention to farm issues. She is still active in the Occupational Safety and Health legislation, and publishes the *California Farmer Consumer Reporter*. Two inviews with McDonald have been recorded by the Feminist History Research Project.

Reference: "Grace Burnham McDonald — Biographical Sketch," mimeographed (Topanga, California: Feminist History Research Project, 1973).

Mary Eliza McDowell, 1854-1936

"Fighting Mary" Eliza McDowell was born in Cincinnati on November 30, 1854, the eldest of six children of Malcolm McDowell and Jane Welch Gordon. She was educated in public schools in Ohio and Chicago. In 1890 she became a resident of Hull

House, the Chicago settlement of Jane Addams (q. v.) and Ellen Gates Starr (q. v.). Her interest in American labor was stimulated by the Pullman strike of 1894. That same year she assumed direction of the newly established University of Chicago Settlement outside the stockyards. During the 1904 stockyard strike she established the first female packinghouse union. In 1903 she cofounded the National Woman's Trade Union League (WTUL), serving as president of the Chicago WTUL from 1904 to 1907. In 1923 she was appointed commissioner of public welfare in Chicago. She was active in the Chicago branch of the National Association for the Advancement of Colored People; the Committee on International Cooperation for the Prevention of War; and the Executive Committee on Women in Industry, a subdivision of the Advisory Council of National Defense. She died on October 14, 1936, in Chicago and was buried in Arlington Cemetery, Drexel Hill, Pennsylvania. Her papers are in the archives of the Chicago Historical Society.

References: Mary Eliza McDowell: "Struggle in Family Life," *Charities and the Commons* 13 (December 3, 1904): 196-7; "For a National Investigation of Women," *Independent* 62 (January 3, 1907): 24-5; "Field Houses of Chicago and Their Possibilities," *Charities and the Commons* 18 (August 3, 1907): 535-8; "Activities of the University of Chicago Settlement," *University Record* 12 (January 1908): 111-5; "Girl's Bill," *Survey* 22 (July 3, 1909): 509-13; "National Women's Trade Union League," *Survey* 23 (October 16, 1909): 101-7; "Settlement Worker," *American Magazine* 71 (January 1911): 326-7; "House of Social Service in the Chicago Stockyards District," *Survey* 31 (December 27, 1913): 344-5. William Hard, "Chicago's Five Maiden Aunts," *American Magazine* 62 (September 1906): 481-9. Howard Eugene Wilson, *Mary McDowell, Neighbor* (Chicago: University of Chicago Press, 1928). Obituary, *New York Times,* October 15, 1936, p. 3. A. M. Rich, "Mary E. McDowell," *Survey* 72 (November 1936): 332. Caroline Hill, *Mary McDowell and Municipal Housekeeping* (Chicago: Millar, 1938). Elsie Reif Ziegler, *Light and Little Lamp* (New York: John Day Co., 1961). *Who Was Who* 1 (1897-1942): 809. *Women in American Labor History,* Item No. 419. *Schlesinger Library Inventory,* vol. 2, s. v. "McDowell, Mary Eliza." *NAW,* vol. 2, pp. 462-4.

Eula Mae McGill, 1911-

Organizer Eula Mae McGill was born on May 15, 1911, in Dalton, Georgia, the daughter of Mary Sue and Joseph Hamilton McGill, a carpenter. In 1933 she joined the United Textile Workers of America, which she served as an organizer. In 1938 she joined the Amalgamated Clothing Workers of America. By 1946 she was the national representative of Local 95, located in La Follette, Tennessee.

Reference: "Women's Collections in the Archives of Labor History and Urban Affairs," *Wayne State University Archives of Labor History and Urban Affairs Newsletter* 2 (Summer 1972).

Barbara Ann Mikulski, 1936-

Councilwoman and senatorial candidate Barbara

Ann Mikulski was born in Baltimore on July 20, 1936, the daughter of William Mikulski and Christina Kutz. She graduated from Notre Dame High School in Baltimore in 1954; received a B.A. from Mt. St. Agnes College in 1958; studied at Loyola College in Baltimore; and received a M.S.W. from the University of Maryland in 1965. Before forming the coalition of ethnic minorities with which she won election to the Baltimore City Council from District 1 in 1971, Mikulski was a teacher and social worker. She taught at Mount Saint Mary's Seminary and the Community College of Baltimore, was an administrator for the Baltimore Department of Social Services, and a caseworker for the Associated Catholic Charities of Baltimore and the York, Pennsylvania, Family Service Agency. As a councilwoman she has spearheaded legislation for senior citizens and consumer protection. In 1974 she waged a strong senatorial campaign against Charles Mathias, the popular Republican incumbent.

References: Barbara Ann Mikulski: "The Mikulski Papers: How We Lost the Election But Won the Campaign," *Ms.* 4 (July 1975): 59-61. James B. Rowland, "Mikulski Challenging Mathias," *Washington Star-News,* June 28, 1974, p. B-2. "Mikulski: War Turned Melting Pot Into Sizzling Cauldron," *Washington Star-News,* April 30, 1975, p. A-21. *Who's Who in American Women (1975–1976):* 609.

Frieda S. Miller

Frieda S. Miller, former director of the federal Women's Bureau, was born in La Crosse, Wisconsin. She received a B.A. from Milwaukee-Downer College in Wisconsin in 1911 and did graduate work at the University of Chicago. She was a research assistant in the Department of Social Economy at Byrn Mawr College; secretary of the Philadelphia Women's Trade Union League; delegate to the International Congress of Working Women held in Vienna in 1923; and a factory inspector for the Joint Board of Sanitary Control of the women's garment industry in New York in 1924. In 1927 she conducted a study of chronic sickness among social dependents for the New York City Welfare Council. She later directed the Women in Industry and Minimum Wage divisions of the New York State Labor Department. From 1938 to 1943 she was industrial commissioner of New York State. Miller was a delegate to the Pan-American Labor Conference in Santiago, Chile, in 1935, and attended the International Labor Conferences in 1936, 1938, 1941, and 1944.

Joyce D. Miller

Joyce D. Miller, East Coast vice president, Coalition of Labor Union Women (CLUW), received a B.A. in 1950 and an M.A. in 1951 from the University of Chicago. She has taught psychology and sociology at Wilkes College in Wilkes-Barre, Pennsylvania; served as education director of the Pittsburgh Joint Board of the Amalgamated Clothing Workers of America (ACWA); and was a member of the staff of the Cleveland National Consumers' League. From 1962 to 1972 she was the administrative assistant and director of social services of the ACWA Chicago Joint Board. She became executive assistant to the General Officers and director of social services of the ACWA in 1972. She is a trustee of the Amalgamated Chicago Group Employees Pension Plan and a member of the Labor Advisory Committee of the Trade Union Women's Studies Program, Cornell University Institute of Labor and Industrial Relations. She belongs to the American Civil Liberties Union, the Adult Education Association, the Industrial Relations Research Association, the International Press Association, the NAACP, the American Federation of Teachers, the National Organization for Women, and the National Women's Political Caucus. She has three children.

Josephine Sykes Morgenthau, 1863-1953

Josephine Sykes Morgenthau, philanthropist wife of an ambassador to Turkey and mother of a secretary of the treasury, was born in 1863. She established the music department of Bronx House, a settlement house founded by her husband in 1912. She died on February 19, 1953.

Lucretia Coffin Mott, 1793-1880

Lucretia Coffin Mott, abolitionist, feminist, and laborite, was born January 3, 1793, the second of seven children of Thomas Coffin and Anna Folger, in Nantucket, Massachusetts. She was educated in private and public schools in Boston and at the Friends' boarding school at Nine Partners, New York. She later taught at Nine Partners, and, on April 10, 1811, married James Mott, a fellow teacher. Between 1812 and 1828 she bore six children; her firstborn son, Thomas, died in 1817, and she turned to the Quaker ministry ·shortly thereafter. Distraught because the 1833 Anti-Slavery Convention in Philadelphia did not admit women to membership, she established the Philadelphia Female Anti-Slavery Society. Declaring with Elizabeth Cady Stanton (q. v.) that "all men and women are created equal," she opened the first feminist convention in Seneca Falls, New York, in 1848. In 1850 Mott and Elizabeth Oakes Smith (q. v.) financially supported a cooperative sewing shop organized by a union of Philadelphia seamstresses. She died on November 11, 1880, and was buried in the Fair Hill Friends Cemetery in Germantown, Pennsylvania.

References: Lucretia Coffin Mott: *Discourse on Women* (Philadelphia: T. B. Peterson, 1850). Obituary, *New York Times,* November 12, 1880, p. 4. Anna Hallowell, ed., *James and Lucretia Mott* (New York: Houghton, Mifflin & Co., 1884). "Portrait of Lucretia Coffin Mott," *New England Magazine* 28 (June 1903): 486. I. M. Tarbell, "Influential Woman," *American Magazine* 69 (January 1910): 370-3.

O. G. Villard, "Anti-Slavery Saint," *Nation* 145 (September 18, 1937): 299-300. M. O. Whitton, ed., "At Home With Lucretia Mott," *American Scholar* 20 (April 1951): 175-84. Otelia Cromwell, *Lucretia Mott* (Cambridge: Harvard University Press, 1958). Constance Burnett, *Lucretia Mott* (Indianapolis: Bobbs-Merrill, 1963). Dorothy Sterling, *Lucretia Mott* (Garden City, New York: Doubleday, 1964). Doris Faber, Lucretia Mott, *Foe of Slavery* (Champaign, Illinois: Garrard, 1971). Gerald Kurland, *Lucretia Mott* (New York: Sam Har Press, 1972). *Who Was Who*, Historical Volume (1607-1896): 441. *Schlesinger Library Inventory*, vol. 2, s. v. "Mott, Lucretia Coffin." *NAW*, vol. 2, pp. 592-5.

Mary Moultrie, 1942-

On March 17, 1969, Mary Moultrie, a twenty-seven-year-old, soft-spoken nurse's aide at the Medical College Hospital in Charleston, South Carolina, led a walkout and strike of more than 400 hospital workers and was subsequently fired by hospital officials. The strike, which was supported by District 1199 of the National Union of Hospital and Health Care Employees, the United Auto Workers of America, and the Southern Christian Leadership Conference, led to a successful settlement with hospital officials.

References: Ronald Sarro, "Charleston's Civil Rights Battleground," *Washington Evening Star*, May 21, 1969. Jules Loh, "Charleston Alliance: Labor, Rights Groups," *Richmond Times-Dispatch,* August 24, 1969.

Maud Nathan, 1862-1946

Social reformer Maud Nathan was born in New York City on October 20, 1862, the second of four children of Robert Weeks Nathan and Ann Augusta Florance. Ann Nathan Meyer, her sister, was the founder of Barnard College. She was educated at Mrs. Ogden Hoffman's school and at the Gardiner Institute in New York and in the public schools of Green Bay, Wisconsin. She married her broker cousin, Frederick Nathan, on April 7, 1880; the couple had one child, Annette Florance, who died in 1895 at age eight. Concerned about the working conditions of New York City shopgirls, Nathan helped Josephine Shaw Lowell (q. v.) to establish the New York Consumers' League in 1890. She served as the league's New York president from 1897 to 1917, was chairman of the Industrial Committee of the General Federation of Women's Clubs from 1902 to 1904, and in 1908 was a delegate to the International Congress for Labor Legislation. After 1917 she turned her attention to women's suffrage. She died in New York City on December 15, 1946, and was buried in Cypress Hills Cemetery in Queens.

References: Maud Nathan: "Woman's View of Christianity's Millstone," *North American Review* 162 (February 1896): 252-5; "Consumers' Label," *North American Review* 166 (February 1898): 250-5; "Women Who Work and Women Who Spend," *Annals of the American Academy of Political and Social Science* 27 (May 1906): 646-50; "Woman Suffrage An Aid to Social Reform," *Annals of the American Academy of Political and Social Science* 35 (May 1910): 33-5; *The Story of an Epoch-Making Movement* (New York: Doubleday, Page & Co., 1926); *Once Upon a Time and Today* (New York: G. P. Putnam's Sons, 1933). *Who Was Who* 2 (1943-1950): 393. *Schlesinger Library Inventory*, vol. 2, s. v. "Nathan, Maud." *NAW*, vol. 2, pp. 608-9.

Agnes Nestor, 1880-1948

During the spring of 1898 future labor leader Agnes McEwen Nestor, then an eighteen-year-old worker at the Eisendrath Glove Factory in Chicago, participated in her first strike. Its most memorable moment, she later recounted, was a speech by Sophie Tucker of the Boot and Shoe Workers Union. "I was so thrilled with her speech that as she left the hall I leaned over just to touch her. Then I leaned back satisfied because I had got that close to her." Agnes Nestor was born in Grand Rapids, Michigan, on June 24, 1880. Her father, Thomas Nestor, who as a child had come from Ireland to America, was a machinist by trade and a politician by avocation. Her mother, Anna McEwen, was from New York, and as a child had worked in a cotton mill. Only five feet tall and frail, Agnes nevertheless went to work in a factory when she was fourteen, putting in a ten-hour day and a six-day week. At the age of eighteen she led her fellow glove workers out on strike, and after ten days on the picket line secured her first victory. There followed a life of work as a union leader, official, and organizer, in which she fulfilled her natural talents as an administrator, tactician, and determined bargainer. She attended the organizational meeting of the International Glove Workers Union (IGWU) in 1902; was IGWU secretary-treasurer from 1906 to 1913; and was elected IGWU president in 1913. From 1913 to 1948 she was president of the Chicago Women's Trade Union League. She was appointed the Illinois representative to the Industrial Survey Commission in 1918. Nestor died on December 8, 1948, and was buried in Mount Carmel Cemetery in Chicago. Her papers are in the archives of the Chicago Historical Society and in the National Women's Trade Union League papers of the Library of Congress.

References: Agnes Nestor: "Day's Work Making Gloves," *Charities and the Commons* 20 (September 5, 1908): 659-61; "Eight-hours Day," *Survey* 37 (December 30, 1916): 369; "The Trend of Legislation Affecting Women's Hours of Labor," *Life and Labor* 7 (May 1917): 81-2; "Ushering in the New Day," *Life and Labor* 11 (June 1921): 168-171; "Workers' Education for Women in Industry," *National Conference of Social Work Proceedings* (1924): 345-8; "The Woman's Industrial Conference," *American Federationist* 33 (March 1926): 296-304; "The Experiences of a Pioneer Woman Trade Unionist," *American Federationist* 36 (August 1929): 926-32; *Brief History of the International Glove* "Workers' Education for Women in Industry," *National Glove Workers Union, 1942*); *Woman's Labor Leader, An Autobiography* (Rockford, Illinois: Bellevue Books, 1954). Octavia Roberts, "Lobbyist," *American Magazine* 73 (February 1912): 422-5. Obituary, *New York Times,* December 29, 1948, p. 3. *Who Was Who* 2 (1943-1950): 394. *Women in American Labor History*, Items No. 18, 203, 350, 400, 401, and 425. *Schlesinger Library Inventory*, vol. 2, s. v. "Nestor, Agnes." *NAW*, vol. 2, pp. 615-7.

Pauline Newman, 1891-

Pauline Newman, since 1918 health educational director of the International Ladies' Garment Workers Union (ILGWU), was born in Russian Lithuania on October 18, 1891, the daughter of Meyer and Theresa Newman. She immigrated to the United States in 1901. In 1902 she went to work in a garment factory; in 1909 she became an ILGWU organizer. She was an inspector for the Joint Board of Sanitary Control in the ladies' garment industry from 1913 to 1918. Newman was president and organizer of the Philadelphia Women's Trade Union League from 1918 to 1923 and served on the advisory committee of the federal Women's Bureau from 1943 to 1953. She is a member of the Center for the Study of Democratic Institutions and the Euthanasia Educational Council.

References: Pauline Newman: "From the Battlefield," *Life and Labor* 1 (October 1911): 292-6; "The Need of Cooperation Among Working Girls," *Life and Labor* 4 (October 1914): 312-3; "Out of the Past—Into the Future," *Life and Labor* 11 (June 1921): 171-4; "Difficulties With Sister," *Labor Age* 11 (April 1922): 18; "Women in the Labor Movement of the U.S.," *Free Labor World* 75 (September 1956): 15-20. *Women in American Labor History,* Items No. 104, 176, 320, 351, and 426. *BDALL*, pp. 269-70.

Gwen Newton, 1930-

Gwen Newton, business manager and financial secretary of Local 30, Office and Professional Employees International Union, was born on November 11, 1930. She was educated at San Diego State College, Los Angeles City College, and the University of California at Los Angeles. She has been a union member for twenty-two years, an executive board member of Local 30 for eighteen years. During this time she has served Local 30 as a steward, business representative, and vice president. She was international vice president for nine years and a vice president and member of the executive board of the Los Angeles County Federation of Labor, the second largest AFL-CIO federation in the United States. She was a delegate to the founding convention of the Coalition of Labor Union Women. She is a member of the Western Labor Press Association; the Industrial Welfare Commission, Department of Industrial Relations, the State of California; and the NAACP.

Elizabeth Nord, 1902-

Elizabeth Nord was born on May 16, 1902, in Lancashire, England, the daughter of Richard Nord, a miner, and Elizabeth Jackson, a weaver. A skilled weaver, she attended evening school in Pawtucket, Rhode Island; Bryn Mawr Summer School for Women Workers in Industry in 1923 and 1924; Barnard College Summer School; and the Vineyard Shore School for Women Workers in 1930. In 1928 she

joined the United Textile Workers Union, becoming an organizer in 1934. In addition to organizing in New England and Virginia, Nord was the union's legislative representative in Washington, D.C. She became an organizer for the Textile Workers Union of America (TWUA) in 1937, working in New England. In 1939 she was elected to the TWUA's executive board, on which she served until 1946. She was appointed assistant to the director of labor for Rhode Island in 1946, a position she resigned in 1947, when she became assistant manager of the TWUA's Joint Board. Nord was elected a trustee of the TWUA in 1947 and served in this capacity until 1956. In 1955 she was appointed to her present position of Member Representing Labor, Board of Review, Rhode Island Department of Employment Security.

Stella Nowicki, 1916-

Rank-and-file labor organizer Stella Nowicki was raised on a farm, the daughter of a Polish miner and a devout Catholic mother. In 1933 she left home because of the depression and went to Chicago. There she spent twelve years working in the meat-packing industry, agitating for the establishment of a trade union on behalf of the Packinghouse Workers Organizing Committee. Because of her participation in a sit-down strike in 1934 over unsafe working conditions, she was fired and blacklisted. She joined the Young Communist League and continued her organizational efforts. In 1936 she received a scholarship from the YWCA Industrial Division for six weeks of study at the School for Workers in Industry of the University of Wisconsin in Madison. She returned to work in the meat-packing industry at Swift & Company, where she helped compile *Swift Flashes,* a CIO newsletter. At Swift, she became the educational director of Packinghouse District Number 1, giving classes in public speaking and labor history, as well as serving as a member of the grievance committee and the Swift nationwide negotiating team. She participated in the unionization of Swift during World War II. She left work in the packing industry in 1945. Married after World War II, Nowicki has three children and is active in the women's movement. In 1971 Nowicki participated in the Labor History Workshop in Gary, Indiana.

Reference: Stella Nowicki, "Back of the Yards," in Alice Lynd and Staughton Lynd, eds., *Rank and File* (Boston: Beacon Press, 1973), pp. 67-88.

Diana Nunes, 1926-

Diana Nunes, since 1972 vice president of the Amalgamated Clothing Workers of America (ACWA), was born in 1926. At sixteen she began working in the Shelburn Shirt Company as a collar stitcher in Fall River, Massachusetts. During World War II she was employed by the Fall River Kay Sportswear plant, where she became vice president of Local 177. She joined the staff of the ACWA in 1953, serving as business agent for the New Bedford local. She was appointed assistant New England regional director of ACWA in 1964.

Reference: *Advance*, December 1972, p. 11.

Leonora O'Reilly, 1870-1927

Leonora O'Reilly, rank-and-file organizer, was born on February 16, 1870, in New York City, the youngest of two children of John O'Reilly, a printer, and Winifred Rooney, a garment worker. Her brother died in childhood. After her father's death in 1871, the eleven-year-old girl went to work in a collar factory. In 1886 she joined the Knights of Labor and organized the Working Women's Society. O'Reilly organized a woman's local of the United Garment Workers of America in 1897. She graduated from Pratt Institute in Brooklyn in 1900 and taught at the Manhattan Trade School for Girls from 1902 to 1909. In 1907 she adopted a daughter, Alice, who died in 1911. O'Reilly was a member of the executive board of the National Women's Trade Union League (WTUL) from 1903 to 1905 and became vice president of the New York WTUL in 1909. She participated in the New York City garment workers' strike of 1909 and 1910. In 1911 she investigated the causes of the Triangle Shirtwaist Company fire, agitating for safety protection and building codes. She was one of the founders of the National Association for the Advancement of Colored People and chairman of the industrial committee of the New York City Woman Suffrage Party in 1912. In 1914 she retired from the WTUL. She died on April 3, 1927. Her papers are in the Schlesinger Library, Radcliffe College.

References: Leonora O'Reilly: "The Story of Kalamazoo," *Life and Labor* 2 (August 1912): 228-30. Frances H. Howe, "Leonora O'Reilly, Socialist and Reformer" (Honors thesis, Radcliffe College, 1952). Eric L. Sandquist, "Leonora O'Reilly and the Progressive Movement" (Honors thesis, Harvard University, 1966). *Women in American Labor History*, Item No. 322. *NAW*, vol. 2, pp. 651-3.

Mary Kenney O'Sullivan, 1864-1943

Factory inspector and labor leader Mary Kenney O'Sullivan was born on January 8, 1864, in Hannibal, Missouri, the daughter of Michael Kenney and Mary Kelly. She was a delegate to the Chicago Trades and Labor Assembly in the 1880s. She met Samuel Gompers, president of the American Federation of Labor in 1891, and in 1892 he appointed her the AFL's first female general organizer. She lobbied in Springfield, Massachusetts, for the first state factory law, which was passed in 1893. She married John F. O'Sullivan, an editor for the *Boston Globe*, in 1894. She was a cofounder of the National Women's Trade Union League in 1903 and served as its first vice president.

She was a prohibitionist and a member of the Women's International League for Peace and Freedom. From 1914 to 1934 O'Sullivan was a factory inspector for the Massachusetts Department of Labor and Industries. She died on January 18, 1943. Her papers are in the Schlesinger Library, Radcliffe College.

References: Mary Kenney O'Sullivan: "Labor War at Lawrence," *Survey* 28 (April 6, 1912): 72-4. Obituary, *Boston Globe*, January 19, 1943. *NAW*, vol. 2, pp. 655-6.

Carrie Burton Overton

Carrie Burton Overton was the secretary of Mary White Ovington (q. v.), cofounder of the NAACP, and secretary to Julian D. Rainey, head of the Colored Division of the National Democratic Committee from 1932 to 1940. Her papers, covering 1936 to 1969, are in the Wayne State University Archives of Labor History and Urban Affairs.

Reference: "Women's Collections in the Archives of Labor History and Urban Affairs." *Wayne State University Archives of Labor History and Urban Affairs Newsletter* 2 (Summer 1972).

Mary White Ovington, 1865-1951

Mary White Ovington, a founder of the National Association for the Advancement of Colored People (NAACP), was born on April 11, 1865, in Brooklyn, New York, the daughter of Unitarians Theodore Tweedy Ovington and Louise Ketcham. She attended Brackett School, Parker Institute, and, from 1891 to 1893, Radcliffe College. In 1894 she became registrar at Pratt Institute in Brooklyn. Assisted by Frederick B. Pratt and the Pratt students, she established the Greenpoint Settlement, where she worked from 1896 to 1903. From 1904 to 1905 she was a fellow of the Greenwich House Committee on Social Investigations; as such, she began her documentation of the particular problems of transplanted black workers in New York City. The fruit of her investigation, *Half a Man*, appeared in 1911. In 1909 she became a cofounder of the NAACP, in which she remained active until 1947.

References: Mary Ovington: "Negro in the Trade Unions in New York," *Annals of the American Academy of Political and Social Science* 27 (May 1906): 551-8; "Atlanta Riots," *Outlook* 84 (November 17, 1906): 684; "Closing the Little Black Schoolhouse," *Survey* 24 (May 28, 1910): 343-5; *Half A Man* (New York: Longmans, Green & Co., 1911); "New-Time Negro," *Century* 83 (January 1912): 476-7; *Hazel* (New York: Crisis Publishing Co., 1913); "Conference on Negro Advancement," *Survey* 30 (June 7, 1913): 322. *The Shadow* (New York: Harcourt, Brace, & Howe, 1920); *Portraits in Color* (New York: Viking Press, 1927); *The Walls Came Tumbling Down* (New York: Harcourt, Brace, 1947). Obituary, *New York Times*, July 16, 1951, p. 4. Obituary, *Newsweek* 38 (July 30, 1951): 49. *Who Was Who* 3 (1951-1960): 658. *Schlesinger Library Inventory*, vol. 2, s. v. "Ovington, Mary."

Lucy Eldine Gonzalez Parsons, active 1886-1914

The widow of Haymarket martyr Albert R. Parsons, Lucy Eldine Gonzalez Parsons sought for years after her beloved husband's execution to clear his name, writing a biography and apologia in 1889. Her commitment to the American labor movement, however, was not bounded by personal tragedy. She, along with Mother Mary Harris Jones (q. v.) and Elizabeth Gurley Flynn (q. v.), was a founding member of the International Workers of the World.

References: Lucy Eldine Gonzalez Parsons: *Life of Albert R. Parsons* (Chicago: L. E. Parsons, 1889); comp., *Famous Speeches of the Eight Chicago Anarchists* (New York: Arno Press, 1969).

Hildegard E. Peplau, 1909-

Educator and nurse Hildegard Peplau was born in Reading, Pennsylvania, on September 1, 1909. She received a diploma in nursing from Pottstown Hospital in 1931, a B.A. from Bennington College in 1943, an M.A. in teaching and supervision of psychiatric nursing from Columbia University in 1947, an Ed.D. in curriculum from Columbia University in 1954, and a Certificate of Psychoanalysis Applied for Teachers from the William Alanson White Institute in 1954. She practiced nursing from 1931 to 1936, when she became executive officer of the College Health Services at Bennington College. She did a study of Child Care Agencies in 1937, was employed by Bellevue Psychiatric Department in 1941, served as the educational director of Highland Hospital in Ashville, North Carolina, in 1948, and in 1952 was employed by the National League for Nursing. In 1954 she became a faculty member of the College of Nursing at Rutgers University, where she is now a Professor Emeritus. Peplau was director of the New Jersey State Nurses' Association from 1965 to 1967. She was executive director of the American Nurses' Association from September 1969 to May 1970, president of the association from 1970 to 1972, and second vice president from 1972 to 1974. In 1972 she served on the editorial boards of *Nursing* and *Nursing Digest*. She is active in the National League for Nursing, the United States Public Health Service, the World Health Organization, the American Psychiatric Association, the National Association for Mental Health, the Veterans Administration Research Study Group, and the Nursing Education Advisory Committee to the New Jersey Board of Higher Education.

Frances Perkins, 1880-1965

Frances Perkins, secretary of labor during the administration of President Franklin D. Roosevelt, was born in Boston on April 10, 1880, the daughter of Frederick and Susan Perkins. She received a B.A. from Mt. Holyoke College in 1902 and an M.A. from Columbia University in 1910. On March 25, 1911, she witnessed the tragic holocaust at the Triangle Shirtwaist Company, on the eighth floor of a ten-story building in New York City. The doors of the sweatshop had been locked to keep union organizers out. Attempting to escape, employees jumped from windows; 143 died. Perkins later recalled: "I felt I must sear it not only on my mind but on my heart as a never-to-be-forgotten reminder of why I had to spend my life fighting conditions that would permit such a tragedy." Perkins served as an investigator of the New York State Factory Commission from 1912 to 1913 and was the executive secretary of the Committee on Safety in New York from 1912 to 1917. She was the executive director of the New York Council of Organization for War Service from 1917 to 1919; commissioner of the New York State Industrial Commission from 1919 to 1921; a member of the State Industrial Board in New York in 1923 and chairman of the board from 1926 to 1929; and industrial commissioner of the state of New York from 1929 to 1933. President Franklin D. Roosevelt appointed Perkins U.S. secretary of labor in 1933, and reappointed her three times thereafter. She died on May 14, 1965, and was buried in Newcastle, Maine.

References: Frances Perkins: "Do Women in Industry Need Special Protection?" *Survey* 55 (February 15, 1926): 529-31; "Should Women Take Men's Jobs?" *Woman's Journal* 15 (April 1930): 7-9; *People at Work* (New York: John Day Co., 1934); "Unemployment and Relief," *American Journal of Sociology* 39 (May 1934): 768-75; "National Labor Policy," *Annals of the American Academy of Political and Social Science* 184 (March 1936): 1-3; "Child Labor," *Review of Reviews* 95 (May 1937): 44-5; "Women in Industry," *Independent Woman* 16 (May 1937): 133; "Eight Years as Madame Secretary," *Fortune* 24 (September 1941): 76-9; "Women's Work in Wartime," *Monthly Labor Review* 56 (April 1943): 661-5; *The Roosevelt I Knew* (New York: Viking Press, 1946); "Methods of Moral Progress," *New Republic* 128 (June 8, 1953): 18; "Franklin Roosevelt's Apprenticeship," *New Republic* 132 (April 25, 1955): 19-21; "Rise of the New Deal," *Atlantic Monthly* 203 (March 1959): 72-4; *Two Views of American Labor* (Los Angeles: Institute of Industrial Relations, University of California, 1965). A. W. Hinshaw, "Story of Frances Perkins," *Century* 114 (September 1927): 596-605. "Frances Perkins: Industrial Crusader," *World's Work* 59 (April 1930): 64-7. "Portrait," *Woman Citizen* 10 (February 1926): 31. "Portrait," *Ladies' Home Journal* 47 (January 1930): 17. "Frances Perkins of New York," *Review of Reviews* 81 (May 1930): 109. "Political Woman," *Commonweal* 13 (November 26, 1930): 87. "Mr. Roosevelt's New Deal for Women," *Literary Digest* 115 (April 15, 1933): 22. "To Make Miss Perkins the Big Boss of Industry," *Literary Digest* 115 (April 29, 1933): 5-6. "Miss Perkins Does Man-Sized Job in Labor's Behalf," *Newsweek* 1 (July 29, 1933): 16. P. W. Ward, "Madame Secretary and the Consumers' Division," *Nation* 142 (March 11, 1936): 303. "Strikes: Enter Madame Secretary," *Literary Digest* 123 (February 6, 1937): 3-5. H. R. Whitely, "Madame la Secretary Perkins," *American Mercury* 42 (December 1937): 416-26. Helen Essary, "What the Government Wants for Labor," *Good Housekeeping* 106 (March 1938): 28-9. Heywood Broun, "Miss Perkins Reconsidered," *New Republic* 94 (April 13, 1938): 302. "Miss Perkins Accused," *Time* 33 (February 6, 1939): 8. "House Is Asked to Impeach First Woman Cabinet Officer," *Scholastic* 34 (February 11, 1939): 10. "Woman with a Cause," *Newsweek* 25 (June 4, 1945): 37. "Goodby to Perkins," *Life* 19 (July 9, 1945): 32. "Lady Returns," *Time* 48 (September 23, 1946): 25. "Portrait," *Publishers' Weekly* 151 (January 25, 1947): 416.

"Last of the New Dealers," *Nation* 176 (April 4, 1953): 278. Obituary, *New York Times*, May 16, 1965: 6. "Lady Secretary," *Newsweek* 65 (May 24, 1965): 37. Don Lawson, *Frances Perkins, First Lady of the Cabinet* (New York: Abelard-Schuman, 1966). Elisabeth P. Myers, *Madam Secretary* (New York: J. Messner, 1972). *Who Was Who* 4 (1961-1968): 744. *Women in American Labor History*, Items No. 107 and 157. *Schlesinger Library Inventory*, vol. 2, s. v. "Perkins, Frances."

Rose Pesotta, 1896-

Union organizer Rose Pesotta was born in Dera-zhyna, Russia, on November 20, 1896, the second of the seven children of Isaak and Marsha Peisoty. In 1913 Pesotta, accompanied by her grandmother, immigrated to the United States, reuniting with her older sister, Esther, in New York City. Pesotta found work in a shirtwaist factory. She joined Waistmakers Local 25 of the International Ladies' Garment Workers Union (ILGWU) in 1914. As a scholarship student, Pesotta attended the newly established Bryn Mawr College Summer School for Women in Industry, founded by M. Carey Thomas (q. v.) and directed by Hilda Smith (q. v.), in 1921, 1922, and 1923; Brookwood Labor College, a resident school established by Fannia Cohn (q. v.) in Katonah, New York, from 1924 to 1926; and the University of Wisconsin Summer School for Industrial Workers in 1930. From 1934 to 1944 Pesotta became national vice president of the ILGWU and was a general organizer for the United States, Puerto Rico, and Canada. Among the numerous labor campaigns in which Pesotta participated were the 1937 rubber workers' sit-down in Akron, Ohio, and the 1937 United Auto Workers' sit-down in Flint, Michigan. In 1942 she voluntarily returned to the rank and file, working as a sewing-machine operator on the production line in a New York City garment factory. At the 1944 convention of the ILGWU she declined to accept a fourth term on the General Executive Board, protesting the rule that only a single woman could so serve.

References: Rose Pesotta: *Bread Upon the Waters* (New York: Dodd, Mead & Co., 1944); *Days of Our Lives* (Boston: Excelsior, 1958); "Women in the Labor Movement," Rose Pesotta Papers, New York Public Library, n. d.; "The Shop," Rose Pesotta Papers, New York Public Library, n. d. *Women in American Labor History*, Items No. 64, 204, and 403. *Schlesinger Library Inventory*, vol. 2, s .v. "Pesotta, Rose." *Who's Who in Labor*, p. 277.

Esther Peterson, 1906-

Esther Peterson, assistant secretary of labor under President John F. Kennedy, was born in Provo, Utah, on December 9, 1906, the youngest of six children of Lars Eggertson and Ann Nielson. She received a B.A. from Brigham Young University in 1927 and an M.A. from Columbia in 1930. She was a physical education teacher at Branch Agricultural College in Cedar City, Utah, from 1927 to 1929; taught at Windsor School in Boston in 1930; and was an in-

structor in the industrial section of Boston's Young Women's Christian Association. She taught economics at Bryn Mawr Summer School for Women Workers and at the Hudson Shore Labor School from 1932 to 1939. In 1936 she became an organizer for the American Federation of Teachers. Before being appointed director of education for the Amalgamated Clothing Workers of America (ACWA) in 1939, Peterson served as the New England educational director of the International Ladies' Garment Workers Union, and in 1945 became the ACWA legislative representative. She went to Sweden and worked with the Women's Committee of the Swedish Confederation of Trade Unions from 1948 to 1952. She served as a delegate to the founding conference of the International Confederation of Free Trade Unions in 1949. In 1961 she was appointed head of the federal Women's Bureau and vice chairman of the President's Commission on the Status of Women. She was named assistant secretary of labor that same year. In 1964 President Lyndon B. Johnson appointed her to the newly created post of special assistant to the President for consumer affairs; she also served as chairman of the President's Committee on Consumer Interests. In 1970 she became the vice president of consumer programs for Giant Food, Inc., a Washington, D.C.-based supermarket chain.

References: Esther Peterson: "Importance of the Homemaker," *Vital Speeches of the Day* 28 (August 15, 1962): 662-5; "Mrs. Roosevelt's Legacy," *McCall's* 91 (October 1963): 84; "Do Shoppers Need Help From the Government?" *Changing Times* 18 (August 1964): 7-12; "How Much Federal Protection Do Consumers Want?" *Consumer Bulletin* 50 (May 1967): 26-8; "Consumerism as a Retailer's Asset," *Harvard Business Review* 52 (May 1974): 91-101. "Consumer Specialist," in *Women and Success*, R. B. Knudson, ed. (New York: William Morrow & Co., 1973): 78-80. "Esther Peterson Appointed Assistant Secretary of Labor," *Advance*, September 1, 1961. "Lady Watchdog," *Newsweek* 63 (January 20, 1964): 64. "Mrs. Consumer," *Newsweek* 64 (November 2, 1964): 78. "So Far, Just A Sympathetic Ear," *Business Week* February 15, 1964, p. 32. "New Era in Consumer Affairs," *Consumer Reports* 29 (March 1964): 143-4. "Consumer's Voice in Washington," *Consumer Reports* 30 (January 1965): 8. "Truly a Consumer Council," *Consumer Reports* 30 (September 1965): 456. "USDA's Role as the Consumer's Adviser," *Consumer Bulletin* 48 (November 1965): 39-40. *Schlesinger Library Inventory*, vol. 2, s. v. "Peterson, Esther." *BDALL*, pp. 285-6.

Cornelia Elizabeth Bryce Pinchot, 1881-1960

Cornelia Elizabeth Bryce Pinchot, the wife of Gifford Pinchot, Republican governor of Pennsylvania from 1923 to 1927 and 1931 to 1935, was a staunch supporter of child-labor legislation. She participated in the 1934 strike of New York City garment and laundry workers; was a close friend of Eleanor Roosevelt (q. v.); and in 1949 attended as a delegate the United Nations Scientific Conference on Conservation and Utilization of Resources. She died on September 9, 1960.

References: Cornelia Elizabeth Bryce Pinchot: "Women Who Work," *Survey* 62 (April 15, 1929): 138-9. Elizabeth Frazer, "Mrs. Gifford Pinchot, Housewife and Politician," *Saturday*

Evening Post 195 (August 26, 1922): 8-9. "Mrs. Pinchot, Candidate," *Woman's Journal* 13 (April 1928): 28. "They Stand Out From the Crowd," *Literary Digest* 116 (August 19, 1933): 11. "Mrs. Pinchot Backs the Baby Strikers of Allentown and Northampton, Pennsylvania," *Literary Digest* 115 (May 20, 1933): 9. "Governor's Wife, Picket and Politician," *Newsweek* 3 (February 3, 1934): 18. "Portrait," *Literary Digest* 117 (March 10, 1934): 5. "Portrait," *Newsweek* 3 (March 17, 1934): 26. Obituary, *New York Times*, September 10, 1960, p. 5. *Women in American Labor History*, Item No. 353.

Yvonne Porter

United Steel Workers of America (USWA) recording secretary Yvonne Porter attended Lincoln Grade School in Gary, Indiana; Froebel High School in Gary, from which she graduated in 1960; Indiana University; and the Chicago School of Dental Nursing. On October 12, 1966, she was hired by the Inland Steel Company in East Chicago, Indiana, where she quickly distinguished herself as a member of the USWA. The first black female member of Local 1010's executive board and the first woman to serve on the USWA negotiating team, Porter was named by Mayor Richard Hatcher to the Gary Commission on the Status of Women on July 17, 1974. She is the mother of one, and an active member of the NAACP.

Pearl O. Rasin

Pearl O. Rasin, president of the Licensed Practical Nurses of New York, Inc., and the first vice president of the National Federation of Licensed Practical Nurses, was trained at Lincoln Hospital School of Professional Nursing, New York. Rasin began work as a practical nurse at the Third Avenue YWCA. She left the YWCA to work privately, and then went to work at Elmhurst City Hospital, where she remained for thirty years. In 1966 she attended the Cornell University School of Industrial and Labor Relations in Manhattan, and in 1968 became a field representative in the Department of Labor Relations for the city of New York. She was elected president of the Licensed Practical Nurses of New York in 1972. A longtime advocate of professional status for LPN's, Rasin has worked to promote the passage of state laws which would permit them collective bargaining. She is a member of the Urban League and the NAACP. She is married to Walter M. Rasin; the couple have one daughter.

References: Sylvia Federman, "She Takes A Practical Approach To Nursing," *Long Island Press*, January 16, 1972. "Nursing Officials Urge Collective Bargaining," *Omaha World-Herald*, May 30, 1974. "Pearl Rasin Talks About Collective Bargaining," *Nursing Care*, February 1975, pp. 14-5.

Jeanne M. Rasmussen

Labor photojournalist Jeanne M. Rasmussen has recorded the verbal and visual history and culture of the Appalachian coalfields. She was the West Virginia press representative of the late Joseph A. ("Jock") Yablonski during his campaign for the presidency of the United Mine Workers (UMW). She also served the Yablonski campaign as a national treasurer of the Committee for a Responsible UMW. In 1974 she was named "Contributor of the Year" by Morris Harvey College Publications and received the Gold Medallion Award. She is a member of the National Federation of Press Women and the National Free Lance Photographers' Association.

Bertha Rembaugh, 1876-1950

Bertha Rembaugh, lawyer for the Women's Trade Union League (WTUL), was born in Philadelphia in 1876, the daughter of Alonzo C. Rembaugh and Martha B. Crum. She received a B.A. from Bryn Mawr in 1897, an M.A. in 1898, and an LL.B. from New York Law School in 1904. She was a member of the Progressive party in New York from 1912 to 1913 and ran as the Republican candidate for Justice of the Municipal Court from the first district of Manhattan in 1919. She was a member of the New York County Lawyers' Association and the Women Lawyers' Association. She died January 31, 1950.

References: Bertha Rembaugh: *The Political Status of Women in the United States* (New York: Putnam, 1911); *Woman Suffrage* (Chicago: Civics Society, 1913). *Who Was Who* 3 (1951-1960): 719. *Schlesinger Library Inventory*, vol. 2, s. v. "Rembaugh, Bertha."

Matilda Rabinowitz Robbins

Matilda Rabinowitz Robbins, an organizer for the Industrial Workers of the World, emigrated from Russia in 1900. She participated in the 1912 strike of Lawrence, Massachusetts, textile workers. A prolific writer, Robbins investigated the particular problems of the working mother. Her 1927 manuscript, "From the Life of a Wage-Earning Mother," and other unpublished writings are in the Wayne State University Archives of Labor History and Urban Affairs.

Reference: "Women's Collections in the Archives of Labor History and Urban Affairs," *Wayne State University Archives of Labor History and Urban Affairs Newsletter* 2 (Summer 1972).

Margaret Dreier Robins, 1868-1945

Margaret Dreier Robins, the first of five children of Theodor Dreier and Dorothea Adelheid, was born in Brooklyn, New York, on September 6, 1868. She served as chairman of the legislative committee of the Women's Municipal League in New York from 1903 to 1904; was president of the New York Association for Household Research from 1904 to 1905; and became president of the New York Women's Trade

Union League (WTUL) in 1905. She married Raymond Robins, a Chicago settlement worker, on June 21, 1905. She was president of the Chicago WTUL from 1907 to 1914 and president of the National WTUL from 1907 to 1922. As such, she participated in the garment strikes of 1910 and 1911. She chaired the Industrial Committee of the Illinois Federation of Women's Clubs from 1907 to 1908; from 1908 to 1917 she served on the executive board of the Chicago Federation of Labor. Robins was a member of the American Federation of Labor and the Cook County Central Committee of the Progressive party. She was chairman of the Committee on Women in Industry of the League of Women Voters. In 1919 she was elected president of the First International Congress of Working Women in Washington. She was appointed to the Planning Committee of the White House Conference on Child Health and Protection by President Herbert Hoover in 1922. In 1934 she was elected to the executive board of the WTUL and in 1937 was appointed chairman of its regional southern committee. Her papers are in the University of Florida Library in Gainesville, the Wisconsin Historical Society, the Library of Congress, and the Schlesinger Library, Radcliffe College.

References: Margaret Dreier Robins: "Movement To Organize Women Industrial Workers into a Labor Union," *American Magazine* 70 (August 1910): 464-5; "How To Take Part in Meetings," *Life and Labor* 1 (June 1911). "Women in American Industry," *Life and Labor* 1 (November 1911): 324-325; "Self Government in the Workshop, the Demand of the Women's Trade Union League," *Life and Labor* 2 (April 1912): 108-10; "The Minimum Wage," *Life and Labor* 3 (June 1913): 168-72; "Need of a National Training School for Women Organizers" (presidential address delivered at the Fourth Biennial Convention of the National Women's Trade Union League, St. Louis, Missouri, June 2, 1913); "Women in Industry," *Survey* 31 (December 27, 1913): 351; *Woman and the Larger Citizenship* (Chicago: Civics Society, 1914); "Educational Plans of the National Women's Trade Union League," *Life and Labor* 4 (June 1914): 164-7. "Portrait," *Survey* 23 (October 16, 1909): 103. "Wealthy Worker for Workers," *Hampton's Magazine* 26 (March 1911): 367-8. Floyd Dell, *Women as World Builders* (Chicago: Forbes, 1913). "Portrait," *Outlook* 123 (November 12, 1919): "Appreciation," *Survey* 48 (July 1, 1922): 477. Obituary, *Survey* 81 (March 1945): 93. Mary E. Robins, *Margaret Dreier Robins, Her Life, Letters and Work* (New York: Island Press, 1950). *Who Was Who* 2 (1943-1950): 452-3. *Women in American Labor History*, Items No. 158, 208, 265, 372, 373 and 438. *Schlesinger Library Inventory*, vol. 2, s. v. "Robins, Margaret Dreier," *BDALL*, pp. 308-9. *NAW*, vol. 3, pp. 179-81.

Dollie L. Robinson

Educator and administrator Dollie L. Robinson was educated at Brooklyn College, the Hudson Shore Labor School, and the Wellesley Institute for Social Progress, and received her LL.B. from New York Law School. From 1941 to 1951 she was the international representative of the Amalgamated Clothing Workers of America and educational director of the Laundry Workers' Joint Board; from 1956 to 1958, secretary of the New York State Department of Labor; from 1961 to 1963, director of Voluntary

Hospitals, Local 144, Building Service Employees Union. Robinson was director of the Department of Educational Affairs of the A. Philip Randolph Educational Fund from 1968 to 1970. She also served as director of Political Education and Voter Registration for Minorities for the New York State COPE (AFL-CIO) and participated in the 1970 gubernatorial campaign of Arthur Goldberg. She is a member of the executive board of the NAACP, the American Labor Education Service, and the Hudson Shore Labor School, and is the recipient of the Sojourner Truth Award of the Association of Business and Professional Women. She resides in Brooklyn, New York.

References: Dolly Robinson: "Role of Trade Unions on Women Workers" (paper delivered at Sarah Lawrence College, Bronx, New York, 1951); "Urban Politics" (paper delivered at Syracuse University, Syracuse, New York, 1968); "Black Politics" (paper delivered at Bernard Baruch College, 1971); "What Vocational Guidance Counselors Should Know About the Labor Movement" (paper delivered at Cornell University, Ithaca, New York, 1971).

Harriet Jane Hanson Robinson, 1825-1911

Harriet Jane Hanson Robinson, textile worker, was born in Boston on February 8, 1825, one of four children of William Hanson and Harriet Browne. In 1831 her father died and the family moved to Lowell, Massachusetts, where her mother supervised a boardinghouse for millworkers. She entered the mill as a bobbin-tender at age ten, and became a contributor to the *Lowell Offering*. On November 30, 1848, she married William Stevens · Robinson, an itinerant journalist and staunch abolitionist; the couple had four children. In 1882 Robinson and her daughter, Harriette R. Shattuck, organized the National Woman Suffrage Association of Massachusetts. In 1898 she published *Loom and Spindle*, the story of her life as a factory operative. She died on December 22, 1911, and was buried in Concord's Sleepy Hollow Cemetery. Her papers are in the Schlesinger Library, Radcliffe College.

References: Harriet Jane Robinson: *Captain Mary Miller* (Boston: W. H. Baker, 1887); *Early Factory Labor in New England* (Boston: Wright & Potter, 1889); *The New Pandora* (New York: G. P. Putnam's Sons, 1889); *Loom and Spindle* (New York: Crowell & Co., 1898); "Loom and Spindle, A Review," *Dial* 26 (February 16, 1899): 127. *Women in American Labor History*, Item No. 209. *Schlesinger Library Inventory*, vol. 2, s. v. "Robinson, Harriet Jane." *NAW*, vol. 3, pp. 181-2.

Betty P. Rocker

Betty P. Rocker, legislative affairs specialist for the Seafarers International Union (SIU) from 1970 to 1974, is one of two children of Eugene Hamilton Pugh, an employee of the Army Corps of Engineers, and Thelma Anderson. She received a B.A. from American University and an M.A. from George Washington University. Rocker represented SIU on the AFL-CIO Council for Scientific, Professional and Cultural Employees; was an SIU delegate to COPE, AFL-CIO; and a delegate to the Women's Auxiliary of the AFL-CIO. Now employed by the Transportation Institute, she is the mother of four.

Elizabeth Flynn Rodgers, 1847-1939

Labor organizer Elizabeth Flynn Rodgers was born on August 25, 1847, the daughter of Robert Flynn and Bridget Campbell. She married George Rodgers, an iron molder; the couple settled in Chicago. A member of the Knights of Labor, she headed women's Local Assembly No. 1789. She represented the local at the State Trades' Assembly of Illinois and at District Assembly No. 24 of the Knights of Labor. In 1886 she became master workman of District Assembly No. 24. Accompanied by her two-week-old infant, she attended the 1886 convention of the Knights of Labor. She organized the Women's Catholic Order of Foresters, an insurance society, and served as the High Chief Ranger until 1908. She died on August 27, 1939, and was buried in Mount Olivet Cemetery in Chicago.

Reference: *NAW*, vol. 3, pp. 187-8.

Anna Eleanor Roosevelt, 1884-1962

First Lady Anna Eleanor Roosevelt was born on October 11, 1884. She was the niece of President Theodore Roosevelt. Her parents, Elliott Roosevelt and Anna Hall, died when she was eight years old. On March 17, 1905, she married Franklin Delano Roosevelt, a distant cousin. In 1921 she joined the League of Women Voters and the Women's Trade Union League. On March 4, 1933, her husband was inaugurated President of the United States. As First Lady, Eleanor Roosevelt established a weekly conference attended by women journalists. In 1939 she resigned from the D.A.R. when it refused black contralto Miriam Anderson the use of Constitution Hall for a concert. President Harry Truman appointed Mrs. Roosevelt a delegate to the General Assembly of the United Nations in 1947, and President John Kennedy named her a delegate to the General Assembly's Fifteenth Session in 1961. She died on November 7, 1962.

References: Anna Eleanor Roosevelt: *When You Grow Up To Vote* (New York: Houghton, Mifflin Co., 1932); "Today's Girl and Tomorrow's Job," *Woman's Home Companion* 59 (June 1932): 11-12; *It's Up to the Women* (New York: Frederick A. Stokes, 1933); "State's Responsibility for Fair Working Conditions," *Scribner's Magazine* 93 (March 1933): 140; *This Is My Story* (New York: Harper & Brothers, 1937); "Should Wives Work?" *Good Housekeeping* 105 (December 1937): 28-9; *My Days* (New York: Dodge, 1938); *This Troubled World* (New York: H. C. Kinsey & Co., 1938); *The Moral Basis of Democracy* (New York: Howell, Soskin & Co., 1940); *This Is America* (New York: G. P. Putnam's Sons, 1942); "American Women in the War," *Reader's Digest* 44 (January 1944): 42-4; "Women

at the Peace Conference," *Reader's Digest* 44 (April 1944): 48-9; "Promise of Human Rights," *Foreign Affairs* 26 (April 1948): 470-7; *This I Remember* (New York: Harper, 1949); "Women Have Come a Long Way," *Scholastic* 57 (October 11, 1950): 13; *Ladies of Courage* (New York: G. P. Putnam, 1954); *It Seems To Me* (New York: W. W. Morton, 1954); *On My Own* (New York: Harper, 1958); *Autobiography* (New York: Harper, 1961). I. M. Tarbell, "Portrait," *Delineator*, 119 (October 1931): 19. Ruby Black, *Eleanor Roosevelt* (New York: Duell, Sloan & Pearce, 1940). Sally Knapp, *Eleanor Roosevelt* (New York: Crowell, 1949). Jeanette Eaton, *The Story of Eleanor Roosevelt* (New York: Morrow, 1956). Lena Hickok, *The Story of Eleanor Roosevelt* (New York: Grosset & Dunlap, 1959). Alfred Steinberg, *Eleanor Roosevelt* (New York: Putnam, 1959). George Johnson, *Eleanor Roosevelt* (Derby, Connecticut: Monarch Books, 1962). Obituary, *New York Times*, November 8, 1962: 2. Robert Wallace, "Great Lady is Dead," *Life* 53 (November 16, 1962): 50. Archibald MacLeish, "Eleanor Roosevelt: 1884-1962," *Nation* 195 (November 17, 1962): 317. "Eleanor Roosevelt: 1884-1962," *Look* 26 (December 18, 1962): 124-5. Obituary, *Publishers' Weekly* 182 (November 19, 1962): 33. Obituary, *Christian Century* 79 (November 21, 1962): 1408. Helen Douglas, *The Eleanor Roosevelt We Remember* (New York: Hill & Wang, 1963). Margaret Mead, "Mrs. Roosevelt," *Redbook* 120 (January 1963): 6. R. C. Smith, "Miner's First Lady," *Christian Century* 80 (January 9, 1963): 53. Esther Peterson, "Mrs. Roosevelt's Legacy," *McCall's* 91 (October 1963): 84. Joseph Lash, *Eleanor Roosevelt* (Garden City, N.Y.: Doubleday, 1964). Robin McKown, *Eleanor Roosevelt's World* (New York: Grosset & Dunlap, 1964). Archibald MacLeish, *The Eleanor Roosevelt Story* (Boston: Houghton, Mifflin, 1965). Ann Weil, *Eleanor Roosevelt* (Indianapolis: Bobbs-Merrill, 1965). Wyatt Blasingame, *Eleanor Roosevelt* (New York: Putnam, 1968). Tamara K. Hareven, *Eleanor Roosevelt* (Chicago: Quadrangle Books, 1968). James R. Kearney, *Anna Eleanor Roosevelt* (Boston: Houghton, Mifflin, 1968). Margaret Davidson, *The Story of Eleanor Roosevelt* (New York: Four Winds Press, 1969). Jane Goodsell, *Eleanor Roosevelt* (New York: Crowell, 1970). Stella Hershan, *The Woman of Quality* (New York: Crown Publishers, 1970). Joseph Lash, *Eleanor and Franklin* (New York: Norton, 1971). Joseph Lash, *Eleanor: the Years Alone* (New York: Norton, 1972). Elliott Roosevelt, *An Untold Story* (New York: Putnam, 1973). *Who Was Who* 4 (1961-1968): 809. Schlesinger Library Inventory, vol. 2, s. v. "Roosevelt, Anna Eleanor."

Sarah Rozner, 1893-

Labor organizer Sarah Rozner was born in Hungary in 1893, the daughter of a rabbi. She immigrated to the United States when she was sixteen and worked in the garment trades. As an employee of Hart, Schaffner & Marx, Rozner participated in the 1910 men's clothing strike in Chicago. During the 1915 garment workers' strike she coordinated strike activities for the Amalgamated Clothing Workers of America (ACWA). The only woman officer in her local, she established in 1920 a separate local, Local 275, to provide a training ground for female labor leaders. From 1920 to 1924 she was business agent of Local 275. She attended Brookwood Labor College from 1924 to 1926, and agitated for a women's bureau within the ACWA. In 1938 she moved to Los Angeles, where she was one of the chief organizers of the 1938 laundry workers' strike. Upon retirement in 1959, she established a scholarship fund to be used for women workers' education. Three interviews with Sarah Rozner have been recorded by the Feminist History Research Project.

Reference: "Sarah Rozner—Biographical Sketch," mimeographed (Topanga, California: Feminist History Research Project, 1973).

Kelly Rueck

Kelly Rueck, president of the Association of Flight Attendants (AFA), was born in Monroe, Louisiana, and received her B.A. and B.S. from the Louisiana State University in Baton Rouge. Before her election as AFA president, Rueck was master chairperson of United Airlines' flight-attendant group, having earlier served as secretary, vice president, and grievance chairperson. She is a member of the secretary of labor's Advisory Committee on Women and serves on the Steering Committee and National Coordinating Committee of the Coalition of Labor Union Women.

Mamie Santora

Mamie Santora, business agent of Amalgamated Clothing Workers of America (ACWA), retired in 1956 after forty years as a unionist. She began her union activities in Baltimore and served on the general executive board of the ACWA from 1920 to 1934.

Reference: *Advance,* January 1956, p. 11.

Rose Schneiderman, 1882-1972

Rose Schneiderman was born on April 6, 1882, in Savin, Russian Poland, the daughter of Samuel Schneiderman and Deborah Rothman. She immigrated to the United States in 1890, and entered the garment trades in 1899. She helped establish Local 23 of the United Cloth Hat and Cap Makers of North America (UCHCM) in 1903 and was a delegate to the Central Federated Union of New York City. She joined the Women's Trade Union League (WTUL) in New York in 1905; was elected vice president in 1907; became a member of the executive board in 1911; and was elected WTUL president in 1917. She was vice president of the National WTUL from 1919 to 1926 and president from 1926 to 1947. Schneiderman was a trustee of Brookwood Labor College from 1924 to 1929. She was the only woman appointed to the Labor Advisory Board of the National Recovery Administration and was secretary of the New York State Department of Labor from 1933 to 1944. She died on August 11, 1972, in New York City.

References: Rose Schneiderman: "Cap Maker's Story," *Independent* 58 (April 27, 1905): 935-8; "The White Goods Workers of New York," *Life and Labor* 3 (May 1913): 132-6; "Up From the Ranks," *Scholastic* 30 (April 17, 1937): 20; "Is Woman Suffrage Failing?" *Woman Citizen* 8 (March 22, 1924): 9; *All for One* (New York: Paul S. Eriksson, 1967). "Portrait," *Review of Reviews* 59 (April 1919): 425. "Solidarity," *New Republic* 19 (June 14, 1919): 202-3. "Portrait," *Woman Citizen* 11 (August 1926): 34. "They Stand Out From the Crowd," *Literary Digest* 116 (August 12, 1933): 9. "Portrait," *Independent Woman* 13 (March 1934): 66. "Portrait," *Good Housekeeping* 102 (January 1936): 38. *Women in American Labor History,* Items No. 324, 405, and 455. *Schlesinger Library Inventory,* vol. 2, s. v. "Schneiderman, Rose." *BDALL,* pp. 321-2.

Vida Dutton Scudder, 1861-1954

Author and educator Vida Dutton Scudder, an active member of the Women's Trade Union League, was born on December 15, 1861, in Madura, India, the daughter of Harriet L. Dutton and David Coit Scudder, a minister. Her uncle, Horace Scudder, edited the *Atlantic Monthly*. She received a B.A. from Smith College in 1884 and an M.A. from Wellesley in 1889. Among the strikes in which Scudder participated as a member of the WTUL was that of the Lawrence, Massachusetts, textile workers in 1912. From 1892 to 1933 she taught at Wellesley. Scudder was one of the founders of the college settlement movement in the United States. She died on October 9, 1954, and was buried in Newton Cemetery in Massachusetts.

References: Vida Dutton Scudder: "Women's Toynbee Hall," *Review of Reviews* 2 (July 1890): 46; "College Settlements and College Women," *Outlook* 70 (April 19, 1902): 973-6; "Hidden Weakness in Our Democracy," *Atlantic Monthly* 89 (May 1902): 638-44; "Socialism and Sacrifice," *Atlantic Monthly,* June 1910, pp. 836-49; "Christianity in the Socialist State," *Living Age* 265 (June 18, 1910): 707-17; "Class-Consciousness," *Atlantic Monthly,* 107 (March 19, 1911): 320-30; *Socialism and Character* (Boston: Houghton, Mifflin, 1912); *The Christian Attitude Toward Private Property* (Milwaukee: Morehouse, 1934). Obituary, *New York Times,* October 11, 1954, p. 6. *Who Was Who* 3 (1951-1960): 769. *Schlesinger Library Inventory,* vol. 2, s. v. "Scudder, Vida Dutton."

Fannie Sellins, 1872-1919

Labor organizer Fannie Mooney Sellins was born in New Orleans in 1872. After the death of her husband, Charles Sellins, a garment worker, she went to work in a garment shop in St. Louis to support herself and four children. Moving to Chicago, Sellins became the secretary of a garment workers' local. She later was an organizer for the United Mine Workers of America (UMW) in West Virginia; as such, she was imprisoned on a charge of inciting to riot, but was pardoned by President Woodrow Wilson after serving six months of her sentence. She then went to Allegheny County, Pennsylvania, where she worked as an organizer for District 5 of the UMW, and as secretary of the Allegheny Trades' Council. In July 1919 miners at Brackenridge struck the Allegheny Coal and Coke Company, and the coal operators immediately brought in strikebreakers and private police. On August 26, 1919, Sellins was shot to death by company guards as she led a group of protesting striking miners to the Brackenridge mine.

Rose Pastor Stokes. (Courtesy New York University, Tamiment Library)

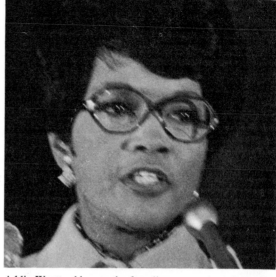

Addie Wyatt addresses the founding convention of CLUW. (Courtesy CLUW)

Margaret Dreier Robins. (Courtesy Library of Congress)

Myra Wolfgang. (Courtesy Catering Industry Employee)

Dolores Huerta. (Courtesy Archives of Labor History and Urban Affairs, Wayne State University)

Linda Tarr-Whelan. (Courtesy Linda Tarr-Whelan)

According to several accounts, she was slain while attempting to protect strikers' children. She is buried in Union Cemetery in New Kensington, Pennsylvania.

References: *Chronicle Telegraph*, August 27, 1919, p. 2. *Pittsburgh Gazette Times*, August 27, 1919, p. 1. *Pittsburgh Leader*, August 27, 1919, p. 1. *Pittsburgh Post*, August 27, 1919, p. 1. *Pittsburgh Press*, August 27, 1919, p. 1. *Pittsburgh Sun*, August 27, 1919, p. 20. *Valley Daily News*, Tarentum, Pennsylvania, August 27, 1919. Philip Murray to John L. Lewis, August 29, 1919, files of United Mine Workers of America. *Pittsburgh Leader*, September 26, 1919. George Korson, *Coal Dust on the Fiddle* (Philadelphia: University of Pennsylvania, 1943).

Mary Septek, active 1897

Community organizer Mary Septek, known as "Big Mary," was active in the organization of immigrant Slavic workers in the eastern Pennsylvania coalfields. She was the operator of a boardinghouse near the Lattimer company store. On September 16, 1897, she organized the men and women of the Slavic community near Hazelton, Pennsylvania, to successfully drive out scab workers who were returning to the mines. Authorities were at a loss as to how to deal with Septek's "Amazon" army, wielding clubs, rolling pins, and pokers. The *Wilkes-Barre Record* of September 22, 1897, commented: "Those who have made themselves so conspicuous the past week in . . . the Hazelton region were the wives, mothers, and sisters of the Hungarian, Polish and Italian strikers, and it is assumed that they had the sanction of their husbands, sons and brothers in their ill-advised and unwomanly demonstrations."

References: *Daily Miners' Journal*, September 18, 1897, p. 2. *Wilkes-Barre Record*, September 18, 1897, p. 21. *Wilkes-Barre Record*, September 22, 1897, p. 1. Victor R. Greene, *The Slavic Community on Strike: Immigrant Labor in the Pennsylvania Anthracite* (Notre Dame, Indiana: University of Notre Dame, 1968).

Lillian Sherwood

Lillian Sherwood worked for the Kent County, Michigan, and National Congress of Women's Auxiliaries of the Congress of Industrial Organizations. Her papers, covering 1943 to 1955, are in the Wayne State University Archives of Labor History and Urban Affairs.

Reference: "Women's Collections in the Archives of Labor History and Urban Affairs," *Wayne State University Archives of Labor History and Urban Affairs Newsletter* 2 (Summer 1972).

Karen Gay Silkwood, 1946-1974

Union activist Karen Silkwood was born on February 19, 1946, in Longview, Texas. Her grandfather worked in a Texas oil refinery and was a member of the Oil, Chemical, and Atomic Workers Union (OCAW). In 1972 she moved to Oklahoma City and began to work as a laboratory technician at the Cimarron plutonium fuel plant of the Kerr-McGee Corporation. She joined OCAW and walked picket lines when the union went on strike in the fall of 1972. In the spring of 1974 she was elected one of three governing committee members of the OCAW local. She began to document hazardous conditions at the Cimarron facility in 1974. On November 13, 1974, en route to a meeting with a *New York Times* reporter and an official of OCAW to discuss health and safety conditions at Cimarron, she was killed in an automobile accident under mysterious circumstances.

Reference: B. J. Phillips, "The Case of Karen Silkwood," *Ms.*, April 1975, pp. 59-66.

Edith Barksdale Sloan

Lawyer Edith Barksdale Sloan, executive director of the National Committee on Household Employment, received a B.A. from Hunter College and a J.D. from Catholic University School of Law in 1974. She worked for the U. S. Commission on Civil Rights, served in the Peace Corps, and was an Eleanor Roosevelt Human Relations Intern. Sloan was a student delegate to the World Conference on Peace through Law in 1973. She received the Adam Clayton Powell Award for Contributions to Minority Citizens from the Congressional Black Caucus in 1974. She received special recognition for contributions to labor standards from the National Consumers' League in March 1975, and was a delegate to the National Black Economic Caucus in September 1975. Sloan is a member of the Women's Advisory Board of the Center on Law and of the Black Women's Community Development Foundation. She is married to Ned Sloan, a lawyer; the couple have one son.

Hilda Worthington Smith, 1888-

Educator Hilda Worthington Smith, sometimes called Jane Smith, was the daughter of a New York businessman and a teacher. She graduated from Bryn Mawr College in 1910 and attended the New York School of Social Work. In 1921, while Dean at Bryn Mawr College, she was asked by president M. Carey Thomas (q. v.) to direct the newly established Summer School for Women in Industry. Among the future labor leaders attending was Rose Pesotta (q. v.). Smith came to Washington, D. C., in 1933 to become director of Workers' Service Programs in the Works Progress Administation (WPA). She established the Hudson Shore Labor School on her family's estate. In 1965 she joined the Office of Economic Opportunity, from which she retired in 1972.

References: Hilda Worthington Smith: *Castle of Dream* (New York: H. W. Smith, 1910); "Bryn Mawr Summer School of 1927," *American Federationist* 34 (October 1927): 1217-23; "Bryn Mawr Summer School of 1928," *American Federationist* 35 (October 1928): 1498-1500; *Women Workers at the Bryn Mawr Summer School* (New York: American Association for Adult Education, 1929); "Bryn Mawr Summer School of 1929," *American Federationist* 36 (September 1929): 1107-10; "Federal Training Schools for Household Employment," *Journal of Home Economics* 27 (April 1935): 215-17; "Workers' Education As Determining Social Control," *Annals of the American Academy of Political and Social Science,* 182 (November 1935): 82-92; "What's Next on the Labor Extension Bill?" *Opportunity* 26 (October 1948): 126-7. Jean Ogden, *Education and the Worker-Student* (New York: Affiliated Schools for Workers, 1934). Anne Crutcher, "OEO Honors a Long-Liberated Woman," *Washington Daily News,* May 25, 1972. "Hilda Smith, 84, Honored by OEO for Exceptional Contributions to Programs Which Serve Nation's Disadvantaged," mimeographed (Washington, D.C.: Office of Economic Opportunity, May 25, 1972). John Carmody, "Jane Smith's Retired," *Washington Post,* May 26, 1972. Patsy Sims, "Programs Train Women for Labor Union Leadership," *Philadelphia Inquirer,* February 3, 1974. David Wessel, "Hilda Smith '10: The Spirit of the Worker," *Bryn Mawr-Haverford College News,* January 24, 1975. *Women in American Labor History,* Items No. 375, 376, and 377. *Schlesinger Library Inventory,* vol. 2, s. v. "Smith, Hilda Worthington."

Elizabeth Cady Stanton, 1815-1902

Feminist Elizabeth Cady Stanton was born on November 12, 1815, in Johnstown, New York, the fourth of six children of Margaret Livingston and Daniel Cady, a New York judge. In 1832 she graduated from Troy Female Seminary. While attending anti-slavery rallies she met Henry Brewster Stanton, an abolitionist, journalist, and orator, whom she married on May 10, 1840. With Lucretia Mott (q. v.), she sponsored the first feminist convention in Seneca Falls, New York, in 1848. She was a contributor to the *New York Tribune* and *Una,* a woman's magazine published by Pauline Wright Davis, and co-editor of Susan B. Anthony's *The Revolution.* In 1868 she was a delegate to the National Labor Union's convention. She became president of the National Woman Suffrage Association in 1869, a position she retained for twenty-one years. She died October 26, 1902. Her papers are in the Library of Congress, the Vassar College Library, the Henry E. Huntington Library, New York Public Library, Smith College, and the Schlesinger Library, Radcliffe.

References: Elizabeth Cady Stanton: *The Slave's Appeal* (Albany: Weed, Parsons & Co., 1860); "Where Must Lasting Progress Begin?" *Arena* 4 (August 1891): 293-8; "Woman's Bible," *Critic* 28 (March 28, 1896): 218; "Progress of the American Woman," *North American Review* 171 (December 1900): 904-7. John Willis Abbot, *Women of History* (Philadelphia: J. C. Winston Co., 1913). Elmer C. Adams and Warren D. Foster, *Heroines of Modern Progress* (New York: Sturgis & Walton, 1913). I. H. Harper, "Suffrage and a Woman's Centenary," *North American Review* 202 (November 1915): 730-5. H. S. Blatch, "Glimpses of Three Pioneers," *Woman's Journal* 14 (December 1929): 22-3. Allan Seager, *They Worked for a Better World* (New York: Macmillan, 1939). Ramona Barth, "Feminist Crusade," *Nation* 167 (July 17, 1948): 71-3. Peter Lyon, "Herald Angels of Woman's Rights," *American Heritage* 10 (October 1959): 18-21. Esther Winifred Wise, *Rebel in Petticoats* (Philadelphia: Chilton Co., 1960). Mary Ann Oakley, *Elizabeth Cady Stanton* (New York: Feminist Press, 1972). Barbara Salsini, *Elizabeth Stanton* (New York: Sam Har Press, 1973). Barbara Welter, *The Original Feminist Attack on the Bible* (New York: Arno Press, 1974). *Women in American History,* Item No. 9. *Schlesinger Library Inventory,* vol. 2, s. v. "Stanton, Elizabeth Cady," *NAW,* vol. 3, pp. 343-7.

Ellen Gates Starr, 1859-1940

Ellen Gates Starr, cofounder of Hull House, was born in Laona, Illinois, in 1859, the third of four children of Caleb Allen Starr and Susan Childs. She was a close friend of Jane Addams (q. v.), whom she met while attending school in Rockford, Illinois, and with whom she established Hull House in 1889. In 1903 she joined the Illinois Women's Trade Union League. She participated in the garment strikes of 1910 and 1915. In 1916 she was an unsuccessful candidate for alderman from the Nineteenth Ward of Chicago. She converted to Catholicism in 1920. In 1929 she was paralyzed below the waist during an operation. She entered the Convent of the Holy Child in Suffern, New York, where she died on February 10, 1940. Her papers are in the Sophia Smith Collection of Smith College.

References: Ellen Gates Starr: "Efforts to Standardize Chicago Restaurants, the Henrici Strike," *Survey* 32 (May 23, 1914): 214-5; "The Chicago Clothing Strike," *New Review,* March 1916. "Portrait," *Survey* 67 (February 1, 1932): 480. Obituary, *New York Times,* February 11, 1940, p. 3. Obituary, *Catholic World* 150 (March 1940): 751. "Portrait," *Survey Graphic* 29 (March 1940): 206. E. G. Clark, "Ellen Gates Starr, 1859-1940, Life of the Co-Foundress of Hull House," *Commonweal* 31 (March 15, 1940): 444-7. *NAW,* vol. 3, pp. 351-3.

Marjorie Stern, 1918-

Marjorie Stern, a member of the steering committee of the Coalition of Labor Union Women (CLUW), was born on September 2, 1918, in Chicago. She received a B.A. from San Francisco State College in 1958, an M.A. in sociology in 1965, and has done graduate work in industrial relations at the University of Illinois, the Universities of California at Berkeley and Los Angeles, and the AFL-CIO Center for Labor Studies in Washington, D. C. From 1937 to 1954 Stern was a secretary; in 1959 she joined the faculty of San Francisco Community College. She organized at the State Universities of New York at Buffalo and Albany and at the University of Hawaii in 1971. She helped organize the Seattle Federation of Teachers in 1972 and the Washington State Federation of Teachers in 1973. Stern has been a member and secretary of Local 61 of the San Francisco Federation of Teachers since 1959. She was chief negotiator for the Tacoma Federation of Teachers and chairwoman of the Women's Rights Committee of the American Federation of the Teachers from 1971 to 1974.

Alzina Parsons Stevens, 1849-1900

Alzina Parsons Stevens was born on May 27, 1849, in Parsonsfield, Maine, the youngest of seven children of Enoch Parsons, a farmer, and Louise Page. After her father's premature death, the thirteen-year-old girl went to work in a textile factory, where she lost her right index finger in an industrial accident. She entered a short-lived early marriage. In 1872 she became a newspaper proofreader and typesetter in Chicago, where she joined the Typographical Union Number 16. She organized and was the first president of the Working Woman's Union Number 1. In Ohio she worked as a compositor, contributor, and editor of the *Toledo Bee* from 1882 to 1891. She organized the Joan of Arc assembly of the Knights of Labor, and in 1890 was elected master workman of District Assembly 72. In 1892 she represented labor at a national convention of the People's party. Returning to Chicago in 1892, she resided at Hull House and became coeditor of the *Vanguard,* a journal of industrial reform. She was appointed assistant factory inspector in 1893; with Florence Kelley (q. v.) she documented the industrial abuse of children. She died on June 3, 1900; her ashes were buried in Graceland Cemetery, Chicago. Her partial correspondence is in the Henry D. Lloyd Papers of Wisconsin State Historical Society.

References: Alzina Parsons Stevens: "Some Chicago Tenement Houses," *Arena* 9 (April 1894): 662-8; "Child Slavery in America," *Arena* 10 (June 1894): 117-35; "Life in a Social Settlement—Hull House," *Self Culture,* March 1899, pp. 42-51. Obituary, *Chicago Tribune,* June 4, 1900. *NAW,* vol. 3, pp. 368-9.

Rose Harriet Pastor Stokes, 1879-1933

Rose Pastor Stokes was born in Augustow, Russian Poland, on July 18, 1879, the daughter of Jacob Wieslander and Anna Lewin. The family immigrated to London, where from 1887 to 1889 she attended the Jewish Free School. Her father died when she was an infant, and her mother married a cigarmaker named Pastor. After coming to the United States in 1890, Stokes worked to support her six siblings as a cigarmaker in Cleveland until 1893. In 1903 her family moved to the Bronx, where Stokes became assistant editor of the *Jewish Daily News.* On July 18, 1905, she married J. G. Phelps Stokes, a reputed millionaire, who divorced her in 1925. In 1917 she renounced her membership in the Socialist party in protest of its antiwar stand; in 1919 she joined the Communist party and was a delegate to the Fourth Congress of the Communist International in Moscow. She was a frequent contributor to *Pravda* and the *Daily Worker.* In 1927 she married Isaac Romaine. Stokes died on June 20, 1933. She left only a small estate, having refused alimony. Her papers are in the Tamiment Library of New York University.

References: Rose Pastor Stokes: "The Condition of Working Women, From the Working Women's Point of View," *Annals of the American Academy of Political and Social Science* 27 (May 1906): 165-175; "New Democracy," *Everybody's Magazine* 14 (May 1906): 607; *The Woman Who Wouldn't* (New York: G. P. Putnam's Sons, 1916). Lillian Baynes Griffin, "Mrs. J. G. Phelps Stokes at Home," *Harper's Bazaar* 40 (September 1906): 794-9. "Portrait," *World To-Day* 18 (March 1910): 268. Seymour Stedman, *Rose Pastor Stokes* (Chicago: Champlin Law Printing Co., 1918). "Scott Nearing and Mrs. Stokes Arrested," *Survey* 39 (March 30, 1918): 711-2. Obituary, *New York Times,* June 21, 1933, p. 3. Obituary, *Nation* 137 (July 5, 1933): 3. Robert D. Reynolds, Jr., *Rose Pastor Stokes* (New York: Tamiment Library, 1974). *Who Was Who* 1 (1897-1942): 1191. *Women in American Labor History,* Item No. 211. *BDALL,* p. 339. *NAW,* vol. 3, pp. 384-6.

Anna Louise Strong, 1885-1970

Author Anna Louise Strong, the daughter of Sydney Strong and Ruth Maria Tracy, was born in Friend, Nebraska, on November 24, 1885. She studied at Bryn Mawr in 1903, received a B.A. from Oberlin College in 1905, and a Ph.D. from the University of Chicago in 1908. She set up child welfare exhibits in New York and Chicago in 1911. She later organized similar exhibits in Rochester, St. Louis, Kansas City, Louisville, Providence, Montreal, and Dublin. She worked as an exhibits expert for the U. S. Children's Bureau in Washington, D. C., from 1914 to 1916; was a member of the Seattle School Board from 1916 to 1918; and was the feature editor of the *Seattle Union Record* from 1918 to 1921. She served as a correspondent to the American Friends Relief Mission in Russia from 1921 to 1922. In 1922 she was employed as a correspondent by Heart's *International Magazine* for central and eastern Europe, and in 1925 worked as a correspondent in Russia for the North American Newspaper Alliance. In 1930 she organized the *Moscow Daily News,* the first English newspaper in Russia. In 1932 she married Joel Shubin. From 1958 to 1970 she was a Peking correspondent. She died in China in March 1970.

References: Anna Louise Strong: "Tenement Back Yards," *Nation* 84 (February 28, 1907): 199; "Everett's Bloody Sunday," *Survey* 37 (January 27, 1917): 475-6; "Verdict at Everett," *Survey* 38 (May 19, 1917): 160-2; "Woman Speaks," *Current Opinion* 63 (August 1917): 123; "When the Reds Get Down to Business," *Collier's* 73 (February 16, 1924): 10; "Women of Nationalist China," *Woman Citizen* 12 (November 1927): 18-9; "Women Citizens of the Soviet Union," *Asia,* 28 (April 1928): 294-9; "Free Women," *Asia,* 36 (May 1936): 326-31. "Portrait," *Review of Reviews,* 83 (April 1931): 6. "Portrait," *Newsweek* 9 (January 23, 1937): 29. "Expelled from the Soviet Union," *Publishers' Weekly* 155 (February 26, 1949): 1074. "Case of Anna Louise Strong," *New Republic* 120 (March 21, 1949): 21. "Anna Louise Strong," *Nation* 168 (April 9, 1949): 402. Nym Wales, "Anna Louise Strong," *New Republic* 162 (April 25, 1970): 17-19. *Who Was Who* 5 (1969-1973): 702.

Dorothy Swanson, 1937-

Dorothy Swanson, librarian and archivist at the Tamiment Library at New York University, was born on August 7, 1937, the daughter of Emil Swanson and Marie Wick. She received a B.A. in 1960, an M.L.S. in 1961 from the University of Minnesota, and an M.A. in 1968 from New York University. From 1961 to 1964 she was a reference librarian at the Newark Public Library in Newark, New Jersey. She is a member of the Society of American Archivists.

Maud O'Farrell Swartz, 1879-1937

Maud O'Farrell Swartz, former secretary of the New York State Department of Labor, was born May 3, 1879, in County Kildare, Ireland, one of fourteen children of William J. O'Farrell and Sarah Matilda Grace. She immigrated to the United States in 1901, and in 1902 she worked as a proofreader in New York City. In 1905 she married Lee Swartz, a printer from whom she separated shortly thereafter. For thirty years she was a member of the Women's Trade Union League (WTUL). She served as executive secretary of the New York WTUL from 1916, and president of the National WTUL from 1922. In 1931 she became secretary of the New York State Department of Labor. She died on February 22, 1937, and was buried in St. John's Cemetery in Brooklyn, New York.

References: "Portrait," *Woman Citizen* 9 (February 7, 1925): 4. Obituary, *New York Times*, February 23, 1937, p. 1. *BDALL*, p. 345. *NAW*, vol. 3, pp. 413-5.

Nelle Swartz, 1882-1952

Social reform advocate Nelle Swartz was born in 1882. She graduated from Wells College in 1904. In 1911 she investigated the Triangle Shirtwaist Fire, a holocaust which occurred on March 25 of that year when fire broke out on the eighth floor of a ten-story building in New York City. The doors had been locked to keep union organizers out and employees in. Attempting to escape, workers jumped from windows; 143 died in the blaze. Swartz's investigation of the tragedy helped to bring about the enactment of protective legislation which led to the sweatshop's demise and inspired building codes. She was a social worker for the Brooklyn Bureau of Charities and the superintendent of the Charity Organization Society of Elizabeth, New Jersey, a post she resigned in 1913. She succeeded Frances Perkins (q. v.) as the executive secretary of the Consumers' League of New York. She helped found the bureau for working women in the U. S. Department of Labor and was its director from 1919 to 1929. Swartz succeeded Frances Perkins on the State Industrial Board, which administered workman's compensation. She remained on the Workman's Compensation Board until her retirement in March 1951. She was appointed a member of the Regional Loyalty Board of the Second U. S. Civil Service Region. She died on March 5, 1952.

References: Nelle Swartz: "Commercial Organizations Can Aid the Early Shopping Movement," *American City* 13 (November 1915): 406-7; "The Cost of Clean Clothes in Terms of Health," (New York: Department of Health, 1917); "Help Wanted," *Survey* 39 (March 23, 1918): 677-8; "Women Workers in the 5 and 10," *Survey* 47 (November 12, 1921): 244-5; "Women Who Work," *Survey* 48 (May 13, 1922): 243-4; "Women in Industry," *Woman Citizen* 10 (August 8, 1925): 19-20; "The Trend in Women's Wages," *Annals of the Academy of Political and Social Science* 143 (May 1929): 104-8. *Women in American Labor History*, Item No. 269.

Gertrude L. Sweet, 1890-

Gertrude Sweet, since 1973 vice president of the Eighth District, Hotel and Restaurant Employees' and Bartenders' International Union (HREU), was born on February 23, 1890, the daughter of Adelbert Belknap, a carpenter, and Lillian Lake. From 1919 to 1924 she worked as a waitress; in 1920 she became the recording secretary of the Waiters' and Waitresses' Union Local 189, and was elected president of the newly chartered Waitresses' Local 305 in 1921, a post she retained until 1924 when she was elected secretary of the Portland, Oregon, Local Joint Executive Board. In 1938 she resigned that office to accept an appointment as an international organizer, a position she retained until 1957. Since 1973 she has also been administrative assistant to general president Edward T. Hanley. She is the mother of two sons and two daughters.

Reference: "Nomination and Election of Vice President for Ninth District," *Catering Industry Employee* 47 (October 12, 1938): 149.

Linda Tarr-Whelan, 1940-

Linda Tarr-Whelan, national secretary of the Coalition of Labor Union Women (CLUW), was born on May 24, 1940, in Springfield, Massachusetts, the daughter of Jane Lillian Zack, a librarian, and Albert Joseph Zack, director of public relations for the AFL-CIO. She received a diploma from Johns Hopkins School of Nursing in 1960, a B.S.N. from Johns Hopkins in 1963, and an M.S. from the University of Maryland in 1967. She worked as acting department head of Maternal and Infant Health in the Washington Hospital Center School of Nursing from 1964 to 1965, and was instructor and project coordinator for the University of Maryland School of Nursing from 1967 to 1968. In 1969 she became technical consultant to the Hospital Career Development Program of the American Federation of State, County, and Municipal Employees (AFSCME) and in 1973 the union's director of program development. Since 1974 she has been AFSCME International Union Director. She is married to Keith Tarr-Whelan and has two children.

Martha Carey Thomas, 1857-1935

Educator Martha Carey Thomas was born in Baltimore on January 2, 1857, the eldest of ten children of Dr. James Carey Thomas and Mary Whitall, Quaker philanthropists. In 1877 she received a B.A. from Cornell University, and became the school's first woman trustee. She studied Greek at Johns Hopkins University from 1877 to 1879. Because the school was open only to men, she was forced to sit silently behind a screen at the back of the classroom. In 1882 she became the first female and first foreign student to obtain a Ph.D. from the University of Zurich *summa cum laude*. Denied admission as a regular student to medical school, Thomas was to devote her life to women's education, first as professor of English and dean of Bryn Mawr (1885-1894), then as Bryn Mawr's second president (1894-1922). In 1889 she helped raise $500,000 for the establishment of the Johns Hopkins Medical School on condition that women should henceforth be admitted. Although she opposed protective legislation as restrictive, she founded the Bryn Mawr Summer School for Women Workers in Industry in 1921. She died on December 5, 1935. Her papers are in the archives of Bryn Mawr College.

References: Martha Thomas Carey: *Education of Women* (New York: J. B. Lyon Co., 1900); "Should the Higher Education of Women Differ From That of Men?" *Educational Review* 21 (January 1901): 1-10; "College," *Educational Review* 29 (January 1905): 62-84; "Present Tendencies in Women's Education," *Educational Review* 35 (January 1908): 64-85; "Upheaval at Bryn Mawr," *Nation* 102 (April 27, 1916): 451; "Conditions at Bryn Mawr," *School and Society* 3 (June 10, 1916): 864-6. "Portrait," *Outlook* 71 (August 2, 1902): 828. Clarence Wellford, "College President and the Suffrage," *Harper's Weekly* 53 (February 13, 1909): 32. E. S. Martin, "Woman's Part in the Future," *Ladies' Home Journal* 30 (February 1913): 21. Sarah Comstock, "Master-Mistress of Education," *World's Work* 26 (September 1913): 579-87. "Portrait," *Literary Digest* 74 (June 8, 1922): 38. "M. Carey Thomas of Bryn Mawr," *Woman Citizen* 9 (August 9, 1924): 13. Obituary, *Publishers' Weekly* 128 (December 7, 1935): 2087. Edith Finch, *Carey Thomas of Bryn Mawr* (New York: Harper, 1947). "Portrait," *Newsweek* 38 (October 15, 1951): 48. *Who Was Who* 1 (1897-1942): 1230. *NAW*, vol. 3, pp. 446-50.

Mary Williams Thomas

Labor organizer Mary Williams Thomas was born in Wales. In 1913 she traveled with her two children to the United States in search of her miner husband, who had deserted her. After settling in Colorado she became involved in the United Mine Workers of America's (UMWA) organizational campaign. She was the only woman in the mining community to be arrested after the Ludlow Massacre of April 1914. She toured the eastern United States exposing the Ludlow atrocities. In Salt Lake City she worked as a waitress, later managing a restaurant and dance hall in Nevada. Thomas's labor activities ended after her remarriage and move to Los Angeles. The Feminist History Research Project has recorded two interviews with Thomas.

Reference: "Mary Williams Thomas O'Neal Biographical Sketch," mimeographed (Topanga, California: Feminist History Research Project, 1974).

Augusta Lewis Troup, 1848-1920

Typographer, journalist, and labor leader Augusta Lewis Troup was born in New York City in 1848, the daughter of Charles Lewis and Elizabeth Rowe. In 1866 she worked as a printer and reporter for the *New York Sun*. She later worked at *The Revolution*, a paper devoted to women's rights founded by Susan B. Anthony (q. v.). With Anthony and Elizabeth Cady Stanton (q. v.), she established the New York Working Women's Association in 1868. That same year, she became president of Women's Typographical Union No. 1. In 1868 Anthony discharged Lewis from *The Revolution*. Lewis's cause was taken up at the 1869 convention of the National Labor Union, members of which refused to seat Anthony as a delegate, forcing her withdrawal from the arena of organized labor. In 1870 Lewis was elected corresponding secretary of the International Typographical Union. In 1874 she became a reporter for the *New Haven Union*, a newspaper published by her husband, Alexander Troup. Her skill as a compositor was such that she was chosen to test the Alden, one of the first typesetting machines. She died on September 14, 1920, and is buried in Evergreen Cemetery in New Haven, Connecticut.

References: Obituary, *New York Times*, September 15, 1920, p. 1. *NAW*, vol. 3, pp. 478-9.

Rosemary Trump, 1944-

Rosemary Trump, president of Local 585, Service Employees' International Union (SEIU), was born in Smithfield, Pennsylvania, on August 23, 1944, the daughter of Ralph Hugh, a storekeeper, and Mary Almeda, a school secretary. She received a B.A. from American University in 1966 and worked as a social worker for the Department of Public Welfare of the Commonwealth of Massachusetts from 1967 to 1969. She is a member of the Coalition of Labor Union Women, the National Organization for Women, the Pennsylvania Labor History Society and the American Civil Liberties Union. Her husband, Thomas Trump, is a college instructor.

Bee Tumber, ca. 1894-1968

Labor organizer Bee Tumber was born in Los Angeles ca. 1894. From 1932 to 1950 she was international vice president of the Hotel, Restaurant Employees' and Bartenders' Union. Her successor was Myra Wolfgang (q. v.). She died on January 26, 1968.

References: Bee Tumber: "Women in Industry," *American Federationist* 35 (July 1928): 824-5. "Bee Tumber Resigns

Board Membership," *Catering Industry Employee*, January 1950, p. 19. "Bee Tumber Schmidt Dies," *Catering Industry Employee*, March 1968, p. 10. *Women in American Labor History*, Item No. 272.

Mary Van Kleeck, 1883-1972

Industrial sociologist Mary Van Kleeck was born in Glenham, New York, on June 26, 1883, the daughter of Reverend Robert Boyd Van Kleeck and Elizabeth Mayer. She received a B.A. from Smith College in 1904. She was director of industrial studies for the Russell Sage Foundation from 1908 to 1948; director of the women's industrial service section of the Ordnance Department in 1918; and director of the Woman in Industry Service of the U. S. Department of Labor from 1918 to 1919. From 1918 to 1919 she served as a member of the War Policies Board; from 1928 to 1948 she was associate director of the International Industrial Relations Institution. She died on June 8, 1972 in Woodstock, New York.

References: Mary Van Kleeck: "Working Hours of Women in Factories," *Charities and the Commons* 17 (October 6, 1906): 13-21; "Child Labor in New York City Tenements," *Charities and the Commons* 19 (January 18, 1908): 1405-20; "Child Labor in Home Industries," *Annals of the American Academy of Political and Social Science* 35 (March 1910): 145-9; "How Girls Learn the Millinery Trade," *Survey* 24 (April 16, 1910): 105-13; "Women and Children Who Make Men's Clothes," *Survey* 26 (April 1, 1911): 65-9; *Artificial Flower Makers* (New York: Survey Associates, 1913); *Women in the Bookbinding Trade* (New York: Survey Associates, 1913); "Working Conditions in New York Department Stores," *Survey* 31 (October 11, 1913): 50-1; *Facts About Wage-Earners in the United States* (New York: School of Philanthropy, 1915); "Effect of Unemployment on the Wage Scale," *Annals of the American Academy of Political and Social Science* 61 (September 1915): 90-102; "For Women in Industry," *Survey* 37 (December 23, 1916): 327-9; *A Seasonal Industry* (New York: Russell Sage Foundation, 1917); "Trade Union Women," *New Republic* 17 (November 16, 1918): 74-5; "The Government and Women in Industry," *American Federationist* 25 (September 1918): 788-90; "Federal Policies for Women in Industry," *Annals of the American Academy of Political and Social Science* 81 (January 1919): 87-94; "The Working Woman and the New Social Vision," *Life and Labor* 9 (December 1919): 320-3; "Women and Machines," *Atlantic Monthly* 127 (February 1921): 250-60; *What Industry Means to Women Workers* (Washington, D.C.: Government Printing Office, 1923); *Employees' Representation in Coal Mines* (New York: Russell Sage Foundation, 1924); "Employees' Representation in Steel and Coal," *New Republic* 42 (February 25, 1925): 9-12; "Place of the City in Stabilizing Employment," *American City* 35 (October 1926): 535-6; *Miners and Management* (New York: Russell Sage Foundation, 1934); "About the Women's Charter," *Independent Woman* 16 (March 1937): 72-3; *Social Work, Peace and the People's Well-Being* (New York: Social Work Today, 1941); *Technology and Livelihood* (New York: Russell Sage Foundation, 1944). "Industrial Citizenship for Women: Appointment of Mary Van Kleeck as a Member of the National War Policies Board," *New Republic* 15 (July 13, 1918): 304-5. "Portrait," *Survey* 74 (May 1938): 151. *Who Was Who* 5 (1969-1973): 741. *Women in American Labor History*, Items No. 31, 32, 52, 67, 68, 114, and 229.

Mary Marvin Heaton Vorse, 1874-1966

Journalist Mary Marvin Heaton Vorse was born in 1874 in New York City, the daughter of Hiram Heaton and Ellen Cordelia Blackman. Twice widowed, she was married to writer Albert White Vorse in 1898, to journalist Joseph O'Brien in 1912, and to artist Robert Minor in 1920. On March 25, 1911, she witnessed the fire at the Triangle Shirtwaist Company, which claimed the lives of 143 women workers. Vorse subsequently participated in the 1912 strike of Lawrence, Massachusetts, textile workers; the steel strike of 1919; the 1926 strike of Passaic, New Jersey, mill workers; the 1929 United Textile Workers' strike in Gastonia, North Carolina; and the steel strikes of 1937. She died in Provincetown, Massachusetts on June 25, 1966. Her papers are in the Wayne State Archives of Labor History and Urban Affairs.

References: Mary Marvin Heaton Vorse: "Casting Vote," *Everybody's Magazine* 14 (January 1906): 22-30; "Heart of the House," *Everybody's Magazine* 15 (December 1906): 724-35; "Confessions of a Young Mother," *Harper's Bazaar* 41 (March 1907): 210-9; "Undoing of Man," *Everybody's Magazine* 16 (March 1907): 403-10; *Breaking In of a Yachtsman's Wife* (New York: Houghton, Mifflin & Co., 1908); "Destroyer of Homes," *Atlantic Monthly* 104 (October 1909): 501-10; "Hidden World," *Woman's Home Companion* 37 (January 1910): 12-3; "Country of Paradoxes," *Outlook* 95 (May 28, 1910): 197-206; *Autobiography of an Elderly Woman* (New York: Houghton, Mifflin & Co., 1911); *The Very Little Person* (New York: Houghton, Mifflin & Co., 1911); "Is the American Man a Failure?" *Woman's Home Companion* 39 (January 1912): 10; "Trouble at Lawrence," *Harper's Weekly* 56 (March 16, 1912): 10; "Their Martyrdom," *Woman's Home Companion* 39 (July 1912): 16-7; *The Heart's Country* (New York: Houghton, Mifflin & Co., 1914); "Freedom of Self-Expression," *Woman's Home Companion* 41 (May 1914): 4; "Woman Who Was," *Good Housekeeping* 59 (August 1914): 168-76; "Devastation of Dennisport," *Atlantic Monthly* 114 (November 1914): 646-54; "Making Over Mother," *Woman's Home Companion* 41 (November 1914): 14-5; "Independence of Sarah," *Woman's Home Companion* 42 (September 1915): 14-5; "Mining Strike in Minnesota," *Outlook* 113 (August 30, 1916): 1036; "Man Eater," *Woman's Home Companion* 43 (December 1916): 21-2; *I've Come To Stay* (New York: Century Co., 1918); *The Prestons* (New York: Boni & Liveright, 1918); "Bridgeport and Democracy," *Harper's Magazine* 138 (January 1919): 145-54; "Through Sheffield Smoke," *Harper's Magazine* 138 (May 1919): 766-74; "Box Stall," *Harper's Magazine* 139 (August 1919): 399-407; "Civil Liberty in the Steel Strike," *Nation* 109 (November 15, 1919): 633-5; *Growing Up* (New York: Boni & Liveright, 1920); *Men and Steel* (New York: Boni & Liveright, 1920); *The Ninth Man* (New York: Harper & Brothers, 1920); "Milorad," *Harper's Magazine* 140 (January 1920): 256-62; "Behind the Picket Line," *Outlook* 124 (January 21, 1920): 107-9; "True Talisman," *Woman's Home Companion* 47 (August 1920): 11; "Amalgamated Clothing Workers in Session," *Nation* 110 (May 22, 1920): 684-5; "Counter Revolutionists," *Unpartizan Review* 14 (October 1920): 255-69; "Derelicts of the Steel Strike," *Survey* 45 (December 4, 1920): 355-7; "Men Are Beasts," *Woman's Home Companion* 48 (September 1921): 19-20; "Halfway House," *Harper's Magazine* 143 (October 1921): 557-66; *Fraycar's Fist* (New York: Boni & Liveright, 1924); *Wreckage* (New York: Appleton & Co., 1924); "Elizabeth Gurley Flynn," *Nation* 122 (February 17, 1926): 175-6; "War in Passaic," *Nation* 122 (March 17, 1926): 280-1; *Second Cabin* (New York: Liveright, 1928); *Strike!* (New York: Liveright, 1930); "Rebellion in the Cornbelt," *Harper's Magazine* 166 (December 1932): 1-10; "Farmer's Relief Conference," *New Republic* 73 (December 28, 1932): 183-5; "Illinois Miners," *Scribner's Magazine* 93 (March 1933): 169-72; "Consumers' Strike," *New Republic*

75 (June 28, 1933): 178-80; "Perkins, This Way!" *New Republic* 78 (February 21, 1934): 44-5; "On the Detroit Front," *New Republic* 78 (April 4, 1934): 204-6; "Canners, Women, and Workers," *Scribner's Magazine* 96 (September 1934): 185-7; "New England on Strike," *New Republic* 80 (September 19, 1934): 147-8; *A Footnote to Folly: Reminiscences of Mary Heaton Vorse* (New York: Farrar & Rinehart, 1935); "Ten-Hour Day, Seven-Day Week," *New Republic* 81 (January 9, 1935): 242-3; "Organizing the Steel Workers," *New Republic* 88 (August 12, 1936): 13-15; "Year of the CIO," *New Republic* 89 (November 25, 1936): 106-7; "Emergency Brigade at Flint," *New Republic* 90 (February 17, 1937): 38-9; "Detroit Has the Jitters," *New Republic* 90 (April 7, 1937): 256-8; "Steel Signs Up," *New Republic* 90 (May 5, 1937): 375-6; "Steel Strike," *New Republic* 91 (June 16, 1937): 154-6; "Tories Attack Through Steel," *New Republic* 91 (July 7, 1937): 246-8; "Farm Workers Meet," *New Republic* 91 (July 28, 1937): 327-8; *Labor's New Millions* (New York: Modern Age Books, 1938); "Steel Faces the Depression," *New Republic* 93 (January 5, 1938): 250; "Transport Workers Organize," *New Republic* 95 (June 22, 1938): 181-2; *Time and the Town* (New York: Dial, 1942); "Women Don't Quit If—," *Independent Woman* 23 (January 1944): 8-9; "Conference at Chapultepec," *Independent Woman* 24 (May 1945): 122-4; "South Has Changed," *Harper's Magazine* 199 (July 1949): 27-33; "Altogether Different Strike," *Harper's Magazine* 200 (February 1950): 50-7; "Trouble in Tennessee," *New Republic* 123 (July 10, 1950): 9-11; "UAW Convention," *Nation* 172 (April 14, 1951): 342-3; "Leave Us Old Ladies Alone," *Woman's Home Companion* 78 (May 1951): 8; "Pirates' Nest of New York," *Harper's Magazine* 204 (April 1952): 27-37; "Big Steel and the Little Man," *Nation* 174 (June 21, 1952): 603-5; "America's Submerged Class: the Migrants," *Harper's Magazine* 206 (February 1953): 86-93. "Portrait," *Bookman* 27 (April 1908): 157. "Portrait," *Woman's Home Companion* 40 (November 1913): 9. "Men and Steel," *Bookman* 62 (April 1922): 36. "Portrait," *Time* 26 (December 23, 1935): 51. "Biographical Sketch," *Scholastic* 29 (October 24, 1936): 4. Malcolm Cowley, "Tribute to Mary Vorse," *New Republic* 107 (July 13, 1942): 59-60. Obituary, *New York Times*, June 15, 1966, p. 4. *Who Was Who* 4 (1961-1968): 973. BDALL, pp. 364-5.

Lillian D. Wald, 1867-1940

Lillian Wald was born in Ohio on March 10, 1867, the third of four children of Max D. Wald and Minnie Swartz. She graduated from the New York Hospital Training School for Nurses in 1891 and attended the Women's Medical College in New York in 1893. Also in 1893 she established the Henry Street Settlement House in which she pioneered public health nursing. In 1904 Wald and Florence Kelley (q. v.) established the National Child Labor Committee. In 1905 she suggested to President Theodore Roosevelt a federal Children's Bureau, created by an act of Congress in 1908. She died on September 1, 1940, and her ashes were buried in Rochester, New York. Her papers are in the New York Public Library, Columbia University, and the American Jewish Archives in Cincinnati.

References: Lillian Wald: "Medical Inspection of Public Schools," *Annals of the American Academy of Political and Social Science* 25 (March 1905): 290-8; "Henry Street Settlement," *Charities and the Commons* 16 (April 7, 1906): 35-41; "Organization Amongst Working Women," *Annals of the American Academy of Political and Social Science* 27 (May 1906): 638-45; "Feeding of the School Children," *Charities and the Commons* 20 (June 13, 1908): 371-4; "Need for a Federal Children's Bureau," *Annals of the*

*American Academy of Political and Social Scienc*e 33 (March 1909): 23-8; "Construction Camps of the People," *Survey* 23 (January 1, 1910): 449-65; "Put Responsibility on the Right Shoulders," *Survey* 25 (November 26, 1910): 315-6; "Taking Stock in New York's Factories," *Survey* 27 (March 16, 1912): 1928-9; *The House on Henry Street* (New York: H. Holt & Co., 1915); "House on Henry Street," *Atlantic Monthly* 115 (March 1915): 289-300; "Fifty Years of Child Welfare," *Survey* 50 (May 1, 1923): 181-3; "Helping the Workers," *Outlook* 156 (September 24, 1930): 158; *Windows on Henry Street* (Boston: Little, Brown & Co., 1934). "Portrait," *Survey* 29 (February 1, 1913): 559. J. A. Riis, "Real Story of Miss Wald," *Survey* 30 (July 26, 1913): 551-2. Elizabeth Wallace, "Three Pioneer Women," *Outlook* 112 (February 9, 1916): 346-7. Paul Kellogg, "Settler and Trailblazer," *Survey* 57 (March 15, 1927): 777-80. "Angel of Tenements," *Literary Digest* 121 (February 1, 1936): 34. Jerome Beatty, "She Never Gave Up," *Forum* 96 (August 1936): 70-3. Robert Luther Duffus, *Lillian Wald, Neighbor and Crusader* (New York: Macmillan, 1938). Obituary, *New York Times*, September 2, 1940, p. 1. Obituary, *Survey* 76 (September 1940): 264. Obituary, *Newsweek* 16 (September 9, 1940): 6. Obituary, *Time* 36 (September 9, 1940): 38. Obituary, *Nation* 151 (September 14, 1940): 203. "Portrait," *Survey* 81 (October 1945): 263. Beryl Epstein, *Lillian Wald, Angel of Henry Street* (New York: J. Messner, 1948). Sally Rogow, *Lillian Wald, the Nurse in Blue* (Philadelphia: Jewish Publication Society of America, 1966). Irvin Block, *Neighbor to the World* (New York: Crowell, 1969). *Who Was Who* 1 (1897-1942): 1287. *Women in American Labor History*, Item No. 162. *NAW*, vol. 3, pp. 526-9.

Jean Y. Webber

Jean Y. Webber heads the AFL-CIO Library in Washington, D. C.

Barbara Mayer Wertheimer

The prolific labor historian Barbara Mayer Wertheimer, a founding member of the Coalition of Labor Union Women, received a B.A. from Oberlin College in 1946 and an M.A. from New York University in 1960. From 1946 to 1958 she worked for the Amalgamated Clothing Workers of America (ACWA) as an organizer, associate national education director, and acting national education director. In 1959 she received the Leadership Training Award from the Ford Foundation; in 1961 she became a writer and consultant for the American Labor Service. Wertheimer was a community services consultant for the New York State Division of Housing and Community Renewal from 1961 to 1966 and senior extension associate at Cornell University's School of Industrial and Labor Relations from 1966 to 1972. From 1972 to 1973 she conducted a study of obstacles to female participation in labor unions. Wertheimer has been Director of Trade Union Women's Studies for Cornell University's New York State School of Industrial and Labor Relations since 1973. She has received two awards from the National University Extension Association: the Creative Programming Award in 1969 and the American College Testing Program Award for Innovative Untested Ideas in Adult Education in 1973. Wertheimer is a member of the Adult Education Association, the American Civil Liberties

Union, the National Organization for Women, the University and College Labor Education Association, the Industrial Relations Research Association, the American Federation of Teachers, and the Labor History Society. She is on the Board of Directors for the Settlement Housing Fund; on the Advisory Committee of Essex County Community College; on the Advisory Committee on Women Workers, Region II, of the U. S. Department of Labor; and is cochairperson of the Task Force for Trade Union Women of the University and College Labor Education Association.

References: Barabara Mayer Wertheimer: "Labor Educators Analyze Values and Objectives in U.S. Society," *Journal of Educational Sociology,* March 1961; "Blueprint for Community Action," *Adult Leadership,* December 1961; "Labor Explores the Arts," *Adult Leadership,* May 1968; *Exploring the Arts: A Handbook for Trade Union Program Planners* (New York: New York State School of Industrial and Labor Relations, 1970); *Handbook for Consumer Counselors: A Resource and Training Manual* (New York: New York State School of Industrial and Labor Relations, 1971); *Handbook for Conducting a Pre-Retirement Program* (Washington, D.C.: International Association of Machinists, 1971); "A Pilot Center for Workers at Mid-Career," *Industrial Gerontology,* Spring 1973; "The American Woman at Work," *Personnel Management,* March 1974; with Anne H. Nelson, *Trade Union Women: A Study of Their Participation in Seven New York City Locals,* 1975; "Focus on Women Unionists," *Labor Education Viewpoints,* June 1975; "Women in Unions: Search for a Partnership Role," in *Economic Independence For Women: The Foundation for Equal Rights* (Sages Press, forthcoming); *We Were There: The Story of Working Women in America* (Pantheon, forthcoming).

Mollie Wexler, 1896-

Labor organizer Mollie Wexler was born in 1896 in Brest-Litovsk, Russia, the third child of an orthodox Jewish family. At the age of eight, she was apprenticed to a woman dressmaker. In 1906 she moved to Warsaw with a French dressmaker. Arriving in the United States in 1914 without papers or passport, she was at work three days later in the New York garment industry. In 1916 Wexler moved to Chicago, where she organized Local 100 of the International Ladies' Garment Workers Union (ILGWU). In her shop she was elected the first chairlady. After her marriage to a dental student in 1918, she continued to work and to participate in union activities. From the birth of her first child in 1922 until her move to Los Angeles and separation from her husband in 1934, her union activity was less rigorous. From 1934 to 1953 Wexler was an active union member, despite difficulty in finding jobs during the McCarthy era. Wexler's participation in the Helen Rose Shop strike of 1960 climaxed her career as a unionist, and she retired shortly thereafter. Four interviews with Wexler have been recorded by the Feminist History Research Project.

Reference: "Mollie Wexler—Biographical Sketch," mimeographed (Topanga, California: Feminist History Research Project, 1973).

Mary R. Wheeler

Mary R. Wheeler, vice president of the American Federation of Teachers, was president and executive secretary of Local 571 of the West Suburban Teachers Union in Westchester, Illinois. In 1970 she placed her papers in the Wayne State University Archives of Labor History and Urban Affairs.

Reference: "Women's Collections in the Archives of Labor History and Urban Affairs," *Wayne State University Archives of Labor History and Urban Affairs Newsletter* 2 (Summer 1972).

Agnes Burns Wieck, 1885-1966

Agnes Burns Wieck, president of the women's auxiliary of the Progressive Miners, was born in 1885 in Spillertown, Illinois. Her father operated a small grocery store, worked in the mines, and was widowed early in his marriage. She attended the Normal Teachers' College at Carbondale, Illinois, and then taught school in Johnson City, Illinois, from 1900 to 1904. Later, she became an organizer for the International Ladies' Garment Workers Union (ILGWU) in Philadelphia. She met her husband, Edward A. Wieck, in 1917 in the offices of the United Mine Workers of America in Springfield while applying for work on *The Illinois Miner.* Among her contributions to *The Illinois Miner* were articles on female participation in the labor movement. In 1932 her activities on behalf of the newly formed Ladies' Auxiliary of the Progressive Miners of America earned her the nickname "The Illinois Hellraiser." She was elected first state president of the auxiliary and served two terms. In the 1930s Wieck moved to New York City and worked in a union-endowed cooperative nursing home. She spent her last years at the home, where she died in 1966. Information on Wieck has been compiled by labor historian Barbara Herndon (q. v.).

Reference: Irene Allard, "Biography of Agnes Burns Wieck," mimeographed.

Ella May Wiggins, ca. 1900-1929

Balladeer and labor martyr Ella May Wiggins, a skilled weaver and the twenty-nine-year-old widowed mother of five, was assassinated in Gastonia, North Carolina, on September 14, 1929, while en route with other strikers to a meeting of the National Textile Workers' Union.

Reference: *Charlotte (North Carolina) Sunday Observer,* September 15, 1929.

Emma Carola Woerishoffer, 1885-1911

Social worker and philanthropist Emma Carola

Woerishoffer was born in New York City in August 1885, the youngest of two daughters of Charles Frederick Woerishoffer, a Wall Street banker, and Anna Uhl. She graduated from Bryn Mawr College, where she had been strongly influenced by M. Carey Thomas (q. v.), in 1907, and joined the board of managers of Greenwich House, a settlement in lower Manhattan. She joined the New York Women's Trade Union League in 1908, posted her property as bond for the jailed female participants in the shirtwaist strike of 1909, and was an investigator for the Bureau of Industries and Immigration in 1910. While on an inspection tour of immigrant labor camps, she was killed in an automobile accident in Canonsville, New York, on September 11, 1911. With her sizable bequest, Bryn Mawr College established the Carola Woerishoffer Graduate Department of Social Economy and Social Research in 1915.

References: Obituary, *New York Times*, September 12, 1911, p. 5. V. G. Simkhovitch, "Sketch of Carola Woerishoffer," *Survey* 26 (September 30, 1911): 902-5. Helen Marot, "Carola Woerishoffer," *Life and Labor* 1 (December 1911): 358-61. *Carola Woerishoffer, Her Life and Work* (Philadelphia: Bryn Mawr College, 1912). I. M. Tarbell, "Noble Life: The Story of Carola Woerishoffer," *American Magazine* 74 (July 1912): 281-7. "Portrait," *Review of Reviews* 46 (August 1912): 245. C. M. Syford, "Her Life and Work," *New England Magazine* 48 (October 1912): 358-9. "Carola Woerishoffer's Gift to Bryn Mawr," *Survey* 33 (March 27, 1915): 686. "College Girl's Memorial," *Outlook* 109 (March 31, 1915): 751-2. *NAW*, vol. 3, pp. 639-41.

Myra Wolfgang

Labor leader Myra Wolfgang of the Coalition of Labor Union Women, general organizer and international vice president of the Hotel and Restaurant Employees' and Bartenders' International Union (HREU), was educated in the public schools of Detroit and attended Carnegie Institute of Technology in Pittsburgh. She joined Local 705 of HREU in 1933. In 1953 Wolfgang was elected vice president of District 3. The widowed mother of two, Wolfgang is a member of the Michigan Women's Commission; the Wage Deviation Board of the Michigan Department of Labor; the Detroit Municipal Charter Revision Committee; the Advisory Committee of the Michigan Occupational Safety Standards Commission; and the National Council on Manpower Needs of the Food Service Industry.

Reference: "Young Women Who Work: An Interview with Myra Wolfgang," in Irving Howe, ed., *The World of the Blue-Collar Worker* (New York: Quadrangle Books, 1972).

Victoria Claflin Woodhull, 1838-1927

Editor Victoria Claflin Woodhull, the first female stockbroker, was born in Homer, Ohio, on September 23, 1838, the seventh of ten children of Reuben Claflin, a lawyer of dubious repute, and Roxanna Hummel, and sister of Tennessee Celeste Claflin

Cook (q. v.). Her early years were spent traveling in her family's medicine show. In 1853 she married Dr. Canning Woodhull, an abusive alcoholic to whom she bore two children: Byron, mentally retarded, and Zula Maud. She divorced Woodhull and, on July 14, 1866, married Colonel James Harvey Blood. While visiting Pittsburgh in the summer of 1868 Woodhull said that she received an apparition of Demosthenes, who instructed her to go to New York City. There, with her sister Tennessee, she opened a brokerage, Woodhull, Claflin & Co., on February 4, 1870. On March 29, 1870, she declared her candidacy for president of the United States. The first issue of *Woodhull & Claflin's Weekly* appeared on May 14, 1870. Devoted to social reform, the paper included articles exposing corporate fraud and political corruption, as well as features on labor, divorce, free love, and abortion. The positions espoused in the paper quickly earned Woodhull the nickname "Mrs. Satan." In 1871 Marx's *Communist Manifesto* was published in English for the first time in America in *Woodhull & Claflin's Weekly*. That same year the sisters assumed leadership of Section 12 of Marx's International Workingman's Party. In 1872 Woodhull was arrested by Anthony Comstock and charged with public immorality: she had published an exposé of the adulterous liaison of the Reverend Henry Ward Beecher in the November 7, 1872, issue of *Woodhull & Claflin's Weekly*. This attack on Beecher had purportedly been inspired by Harriet Beecher Stowe's unflattering portrayal of Woodhull as Audacia Dangyreyes in *My Wife and I*. In 1876 she divorced Colonel Blood. Following the death of the sisters' patron, Commodore Cornelius Vanderbilt, in 1877, Woodhull moved to London, where she lectured extensively on spiritualism. She immediately infatuated the aristocratic banker John Biddulph Martin, whom she married on October 31, 1883. Now a Hyde Park matron, Woodhull was caricatured by Henry James as the socially ambitious Mrs. Headway in his *Siege of London* (1883). In 1892 she founded, together with her daughter, the *Humanitarian*, a monthly devoted to redressing the evils caused by "unequal distribution of wealth." Widowed in 1897, she moved to Bredon's Norton, Tewkesbury, from which she continued publication of the *Humanitarian* until 1901. Woodhull died on June 10, 1927; her body was cremated.

References: Victoria Claflin Woodhull: *The Origin, Tendencies, and Principles of Government* (New York: Woodhull & Claflin, 1871); *Freedom! Equality! Justice!* (New York: Woodhull & Claflin, 1872); *The Human Body the Temple of God* (London, 1890). Pauline Davis, *A History of the National Woman's Rights Movement* (New York: Journeymen Printers' Co-operative Association, 1871). Theodore Tilton, *Victoria C. Woodhull* (New York: Golden Age, 1871). Madeleine Legge, *Two Noble Women, Nobly Planned* (Walham Green: Phelps Brothers, 1893). "The Woodhull," *Nation* 124 (June 29, 1927): 711. Freda Kirchwey, "To the Terrible Siren," *Nation* 128 (January 16, 1929): 83. "For President: Victoria Woodhull," *Literary Digest* 100 (February 16, 1929): 46-54. Beril Becker, *Whirlwind in Petticoats* (Garden City, New York: Doubleday, 1947). "That Was New York: Beecher-Tilton Case," *New Yorker* 30 (June 12, 1954): 34-6. G. W. Johnson, "Dynamic Victoria

Woodhull," *American Heritage* 7 (June 1956): 44-7. "Portrait," *Saturday Review of Literature* 40 (October 26, 1957): 30. Johanna Johnston, *Mrs. Satan* (London: Melbourne, 1967). Saul Maloff, "First Teeney Bopper," *Newsweek* 69 (April 10, 1967): 101. Marion Marberry, *Vicky* (New York: Funk & Wagnalls, 1967). Arlene Kisner, *Woodhull & Claflin's Weekly: The Lives and Writings of Notorious Victoria Woodhull and Her Sister Tennessee Claflin* (Washington, New Jersey: Times Change Press, 1972). Madeleine Stern, *The Victoria Woodhull Reader* (Weston, Massachusetts: M & S Press, 1974); *We the Women* (New York: Burt Franklin Reprints, 1974). *Who Was Who* 4 (1961-1968): 1031-2. *Women in American Labor History,* Item No. 9. *Schlesinger Library Inventory,* vol. 2, s. v. "Martin, Victoria Claflin Woodhull," *NAW,* vol. 3, pp. 622-5.

Sylvia Woods, 1909-

Sylvia Woods was born on March 15, 1909, in New Orleans, one of three children of a union roofer, and a domestic worker. As a child Woods witnessed her parents' enthusiastic participation in the Marcus Garvey movement. At age sixteen Woods married and moved to Chicago. While working in a succession of laundries, she agitated for equal pay and promotion for black employees. She was later employed by Wilson Jones, a stationary manufacturer, and during World War II, by Bendix Aviation, where she worked on an assembly line. At Bendix she joined the United Auto Workers and was quickly elected shop steward, shop committeewoman, and financial secretary. When Bendix Aviation closed after the war, Woods continued her union activities. She was active in the campaign to free Angela Davis.

Reference: Sylvia Woods: "You Have to Fight for Freedom," in Alice Lynd and Staughton Lynd, eds., *Rank and File* (Boston: Beacon Press, 1973).

Addie Wyatt

Addie Wyatt, vice president of the Coalition of Labor Union Women (CLUW), is the present director of the Women's Affairs Department of the Amalgamated Meat Cutters & Butcher Workmen of North America, a post she assumed in February 1974. She is married to Reverend Claude S. Wyatt, Jr., and has two sons. She was appointed by Eleanor Roosevelt to serve on the Protective Labor Legislation Committee of President Kennedy's Commission on the Status of Women, and is a past president of Local P-56. In 1972 she was appointed to the International Executive Board Advisory Council of Amalgamated. She is active in the Illinois State AFL-CIO Committee on Political Education and the Jewish Labor Committee. A brilliant orator, she was keynote speaker at the founding convention of CLUW in 1974.

References: "Addie Wyatt Appointed Director of Women's Affairs Department," *Butcher Workman,* March, 1974, p. 12. "Women Unionists Form Coalition," *Butcher Workman,* May, 1974, p. 6.

Bibliography

Entries are listed in chronological order.

Books and articles referring to or authored by a particular worker or ally are listed at the end of her individual biographical entry.

Books

Willett, Mabel H. *Employment of Women in the Clothing Trade*. New York: Columbia University Press, 1902.

Van Vorst, Bessie, and Van Vorst, Marie. *The Woman Who Toils*. New York: Doubleday, 1903.

Herron, Belva M. *The Progress of Labor Organization Among Women*. Urbana: University of Illinois Press, 1905.

Abbott, Edith. *Women in Industry*. New York: Appleton & Co., 1910.

Butler, Elizabeth Beardsley. *Women and the Trades*. New York: Russell Sage Foundation, 1910.

MacLean, Annie Marion. *Wage Earning Women*. New York: Macmillan, 1910.

Andrews, John B., and Bliss, W. D. P. *History of Women in Trade Unions*. Vol. 10 of *Report on Conditions of Women and Child Wage Earners in the United States*, U.S. Senate Document No. 645, 61st Congress, 2d Sess., 1911.

Schreiner, Olive. *Women and Labor*. New York: Frederick A. Stokes Co., 1911.

Wolfe, F. E. *Admission to American Trade Unions*. Baltimore: Johns Hopkins Press, 1912.

Matthews, Lillian L. *Women in Trade Unions in San Francisco*. Berkeley: University of California Press, 1913.

Andrews, Irene. *Minimum Wage Legislation*. Albany, New York: J. B. Lyon Co., 1914.

Marot, Helen. *American Labor Unions*. New York: H. Holt & Co., 1914.

Beard, Mary. *Women's Work in Municipalities*. New York: Appleton, 1915.

Henry, Alice. *The Trade Union Woman*. New York: Appleton, 1916.

Kelley, Florence. *Women in Industry*. New York: National Consumers' League, 1916.

MacLean, Annie Marion. *Women Workers and Society*. Chicago: A. C. McClurg, 1916.

U.S. Bureau of Labor Statistics. *Summary of the Report on Conditions of Women and Child Wage Earners in the United States*. Washington, D.C.: Government Printing Office, 1916.

Commons, John Rodgers. *History of Labor in the United States*. New York: Macmillan, 1918.

Mann, Annette. *Women Workers in Factories*. Cincinnati: Consumers' League of Cincinnati, 1918.

Delzell, Ruth. *Early History of Women Trade Unionists of America*. Chicago: National Women's Trade Union League, 1919.

Hutchinson, Emilie J. *Women's Wages*. New York: Columbia University Press, 1919.

National Women's Trade Union League of America. *Women in Trade Unions in the United States*. Chicago: National Women's Trade Union League, 1919.

Budish, Jacob M., and Soule, George. *The New Unionism in the Clothing Industry*. New York: Harcourt, Brace & Howe, 1920.

U.S. Women's Bureau. *The New Position of Women in American Industry*. Washington, D.C.: Government Printing Office, 1920.

Adams, Elizabeth K. *Women Professional Workers*. New York: Macmillan, 1921.

Winslow, Mary Nelson. *Health Problems of Women in Industry*. Washington, D.C.: Government Printing Office, 1921.

———. *Some Effects of Legislation Limiting Hours of Work for Women*. Washington, D.C.: Government Printing Office, 1921.

Carroll, Mollie Ray. *Women and the Labor Movement in America*. Washington, D.C.: National League of Women Voters, 1923.

Van Kleeck, Mary. *What Industry Means to Women Workers*. Washington, D.C.: Government Printing Office, 1923.

Winslow, Mary Nelson. *The Share of Wage-Earning Women in Family Support*. Washington, D.C.: Government Printing Office, 1923.

Beard, Mary. *A Short History of the American Labor Movement*. New York: George H. Doran, 1924.

Galster, Augusta E. *The Labor Movement in the Shoe Industry*. New York: Ronald Press Co., 1924.

Levine, Louis. *The Women's Garment Workers: A History of the International Ladies' Garment Workers' Union*. New York: B. W. Huebsch, Inc., 1924.

Winslow, Mary Nelson. *Married Women in Industry*. Washington, D.C.: Government Printing Office, 1924.

Baker, Elizabeth F. *Protective Labor Legislation, With Special Reference to Women in the State of New York*. New York: Columbia University Press, 1925.

Gompers, Samuel. *Seventy Years of Life and Labor*. New York: Dutton, 1925.

U.S. Women's Bureau. *Facts About Working Women*. Washington, D.C.: Government Printing Office, 1925.

Wolfson, Theresa. *The Woman Worker and Trade Unions*. New York: International Publishers, 1926.

Hopkins, Mary D. *The Employment of Women at Night*. Washington, D.C.: Government Printing Office, 1928.

Winslow, Mary Nelson. *A Summary: The Effects of Labor Legislation on the Employment Opportunities of Women*. Washington, D.C.: Government Printing Office, 1928.

Beyer, Clara Mortenson. *History of Labor Legislation for Women in Three States*. Washington, D.C.: Government Printing Office, 1929.

National Women's Trade Union League. *How To Organize: A Problem*. Chicago: National Women's Trade Union League, 1929.

U.S. Women's Bureau. *History of Labor Legislation for Women in Three States and Chronological Development of Labor Legislation for Women in the United States*. Washington, D.C.: Government Printing Office, 1929.

Ware, Norman J. *The Labor Movement in the United States*. New York: Appleton, Century & Crofts, Inc., 1929.

Beard, Mary. *On Understanding Women*. New York: Longmans, Green & Co., 1931.

Beyer, Clara Mortenson. *Children of Working Mothers in Philadelphia*. Washington, D.C.: Government Printing Office, 1931.

U.S. Women's Bureau. *Industrial Experience of Women Workers at the Summer Schools, 1928-1930*. Washington, D.C.: Government Printing Office, 1931.

———. *Chronological Development of Labor Legislation for Women in the United States*. Washington, D.C.: Government Printing Office, 1931.

Beard, Mary. *America Through Women's Eyes*. New York: Macmillan Co., 1933.

Breckinridge, Sophonisba Preston. *Women in the Twentieth Century*. New York: McGraw-Hill, 1933.

U.S. Women's Bureau. *The Occupational Progress of Women*. Washington, D.C.: Government Printing Office, 1933.

Hutchins, Grace. *Women Who Work*. New York: International Publishers, 1934.

Beard, Mary. *A Changing Political Economy As It Affects Women*. Washington, D.C.: Government Printing Office, 1934.

Wolfson, Theresa. *Labor and the N.R.A.* New York: Affiliated Schools for Workers, 1934.

Best, Ethel. *Technological Changes in Relation to Women's Employment*. Washington, D.C: Government Printing Office, 1935.

Brophy, Loire. *If Women Must Work*. New York: Appleton-Century Co., 1936.

Hourwich, Andria T., and Palmer, Gladys L., eds. *I Am A Woman Worker: A Scrapbook of Autobiographies*. New York: Affiliated Schools for Workers, 1936.

Yellen, Samuel. *American Labor Struggles*. New York: Harcourt, Brace, 1936.

Wolfson, Theresa. *Industrial Unionism in the American Labor Movement*. New York: League for Industrial Democracy, 1937.

Pidgeon, Mary Elizabeth. *Women in Industry: A Series of*

Papers To Aid Study Groups. Washington, D.C.: Government Printing Office, 1938.

Benham, Elizabeth D. *The Woman Wage Earner: Her Situation Today*. Washington, D.C.: Government Printing Office, 1939.

U.S. Women's Bureau. *Women at Work: A Century of Industrial Change*. Washington, D.C.: Government Printing Office, 1939.

Beard, Mary. *Women Take Stock of Themselves*. New York: Women's Press, 1941.

Schneider, Florence H. *Patterns of Workers' Education: The Story of Bryn Mawr Summer School*. Washington, D.C.: American Council on Public Affairs, 1941.

Boone, Gladys. *Women's Trade Union Leagues in Great Britain and the United States of America*. New York: Columbia University Press, 1942.

U.S. Department of Labor. *The Women Worker*. Washington, D.C.: Government Printing Office, 1921-1942.

Baker, Laura Nelson. *Wanted: Women in War Industry*. New York: E. P. Dutton & Co., 1943.

Burstein, Herbert. *Women in War*. New York: New York Service Publishing Co., 1943.

Hamilton, Alice. *Exploring the Dangerous Trades*. Boston: Little, Brown, 1943.

Blood, Kathryn. *Negro Women War Workers*. Washington, D.C.: Government Printing Office, 1945.

Bryn Mawr College. *Women During the War and After*. Philadelphia: Curtis, 1945.

Beard, Mary. *Women as Force in History*. New York: Macmillan, 1946.

McLean, Ethel. *Women and the International Labor Organization*. Washington, D.C.: International Labor Office, 1946.

Wolfson, Theresa. *Labor's Coming Age*. New York: Society for Ethical Culture, 1946.

Anderson, Margaret Kay. *Women's Wartime Hours of Work*. Washington, D.C.: Government Printing Office, 1947.

Waggaman, Mary Theresa. *Women Workers in Wartime and Reconversion*. New York: Paulist Press, 1947.

Beyer, Sylvia Sternoff. *Women's Jobs, Advance, and Growth*. Washington, D.C.: Government Printing Office, 1949.

Josephson, Hannah. *Golden Threads: New England's Mill Girls and Magnates*. New York: Duel, Sloan & Pearce, 1949.

Dexter, Elizabeth Williams. *Career Women of America, 1776-1840*. Clifton, New Jersey: A. M. Kelley, 1950.

Erickson, Ethel. *Maternity Protection of Employed Women*. Washington, D.C.: Government Printing Office, 1952.

Pidgeon, Mary Elizabeth. *Changes in Women's Occupations, 1940-1950*. Washington, D.C.: Government Printing Office, 1954.

Foner, Philip Sheldon. *History of the Labor Movement in the United States*. 3 vols. New York: International Publishers, 1947-55.

National Manpower Council. *Womanpower*. New York: Columbia University Press, 1957.

Thorne, Florence Calvert. *Samuel Gompers, American Statesman*. New York: Philosophical Library, 1957.

Daniels, Walter Machray. *The American Labor Movement*. New York: H. W. Wilson, 1958.

Haber, S. *Female Labor Force Participation and Economic Development*. Santa Monica, California: Rand Corp., 1958.

Flexner, Eleanor. *Century of Struggle: The Women's Rights Movement in the United States*. Cambridge, Massachusetts: Harvard University Belknap Press, 1959.

Price, Hazel Marie. *Women's Contributions to Industrial Development in America*. Fort Hays: Kansas State College, 1962.

Baker, Elizabeth Faulkner. *Technology and Women's Work*. New York: Columbia University Press, 1964.

Foner, Philip. *The Industrial Workers of the World*. Vol. 4 in *History of the Labor Movement in the United States*. New York: International Publishers, 1962-64.

Turner, Marjorie B. *Women and Work*. Los Angeles: University of California, 1964.

Winter, Elmer. *Women at Work: Every Woman's Guide to Successful Employment*. New York: Simon & Schuster, 1967.

Harbeson, Gladys Evans. *Choice and Challenge for the American Woman*. Cambridge, Massachusetts: Schenkman Publishing Co., 1967.

Herbert, Robert. *Laws Affecting the Employment of Women*. Columbus, Ohio: Legislative Service Commission, 1967.

U.S. Women's Bureau. *Underutilization of Women Workers*. Washington, D.C.: Government Printing Office, 1967.

Bird, Caroline. *Born Female*. New York: D. McKay Co., 1968.

Scoresby, William. *American Factories and Their Female Operatives*. New York: B. Franklin, 1968.

Astin, Helen S. *The Woman Doctorate in America*. New York: Russell Sage Foundation, 1969.

Ely, Richard Theodore. *The Labor Movement in America*. New York: Arno, 1969.

O'Neill, William L. *Everyone Was Brave: The Rise and Fall of Feminism in America*. Chicago: Quadrangle, 1969.

U.S. Department of Labor. *1969 Handbook on Women Workers*. Washington, D.C.: Government Printing Office, 1969.

Wolfe, Helen Bickel. *Women in the World of Work*. Albany: University of the State of New York, 1969.

Clover, Vernon. *Changes in Differences in Earnings and Occupational Status of Men and Women*. Lubbock: Texas Technological University, 1970.

Oppenheimer, Valerie Kincade. *The Female Labor Force in the United States*. Berkeley: University of California, 1970.

Wells, Jean A. *Automation and Women Workers*. Washington, D.C.: Government Printing Office, 1970.

Eastwood, Mary. *Fighting Job Discrimination*. Washington, D.C.: Today Publications & News Service, 1971.

Epstein, Cynthia Fuchs. *Woman's Place: Options and Limits in Professional Careers*. Berkeley: University of California Press, 1971.

Killian, Ray. *The Working Woman*. New York: American Management Association, 1971.

Kreps, Juanita Morris. *Sex in the Marketplace*. Baltimore: Johns Hopkins Press, 1971.

Swartz, Eleanor Brantley. *The Sex Barrier in Business*. Atlanta: Georgia State University, 1971.

Smuts, Robert W. *Women and Work in America*. New York: Schocken Books, 1971.

Bulwik, Helen. *Affirmative Action for Women: Myth and Reality*. Berkeley: University of California Press, 1972.

Cahn, William. *A Pictorial History of American Labor*. New York: Crown Publishers, 1972.

O'Neill, William. *Women at Work*. Chicago: Quadrangle, 1972.

Schnapper, Morris Bartel. *American Labor: A Pictorial Social History*. Washington, D.C.: Public Affairs Press, 1972.

Soltow, Martha Jane; Forché, Carolyn; and Massre, Murray. *Women in American Labor History, 1825-1935*. East Lansing: Michigan State University Press, 1972.

Hoskins, Dalmer. *Women and Social Security*. Washington, D.C.: Government Printing Office, 1973.

Lyle, Jerolyn. *Affirmative Action Programs for Women*. Washington, D.C.: Equal Employment Opportunity Commission, 1973.

_____. *Women in Industry*. Lexington, Massachusetts: Lexington Books, 1973.

Graham, Ellen. *What Do Women Really Want?* Chicopee, Massachusetts: Dow Jones Books, 1974.

San Francisco Woman's History Group. *What Have Women Done?* San Francisco: United Front Press, 1974.

Hoffman, Lois Wladis, and Nye, F. Ivan. *Working Mothers*. San Francisco: Jossey-Bass Publishers, 1974.

Cook, Alice Hanson. *The Working Mother*. Ithaca, New York: Cornell University, 1975.

Garson, Barbara. *All the Livelong Day*. New York: Doubleday, 1975.

Kenneally, James J. *Women in the American Labor Movement*. Washington, D.C.: Public Affairs Press, forthcoming.

Wertheimer, Barbara Mayer. *We Were There: The Story of Working Women in America.* New York: Pantheon, forthcoming.

Articles and Papers

Campbell, Helen. "The Working Women of Today." *Arena* 4 (1891): 329-39.

Webb, Sidney. "The Alleged Differences in the Wages Paid to Men and to Women for Similar Work." *Economic Journal* 1 (1891): 635-662.

DeGraffenreid, Claire. "Conditions of Wage Earning Women." *Forum* 15 (1893): 68-82.

Phillips, E. M. "Progress of Women's Trade Unions." *Fortnightly Review* 54 (1893): 92-104.

Toph, Olla Perkins. "Women and Work." *American Federationist* 1 (1894): 1.

Woodbridge, Alice L. "Woman's Labor." *American Federationist* 1 (1894): 66.

Foster, E. P. "Women's Work in the Labor Movement." *American Federationist* 2 (1895): 86-7.

Stephens, Kate. "Women's Wages." *North American Review* 162 (1896): 377-9.

Valesh, Eva McDonald. "Women and Labor." *American Federationist* 2 (1896): 221-3.

MacLean, Annie Marion. "Factory Legislation for Women in the United States." *American Journal of Sociology* 3 (1897): 183-205.

O'Donnell, Edward. "Women as Bread Winners." *American Federationist* 4 (1897): 186-7.

Kelley, M. E. J. "Women and the Labor Movement." *North American Review* 166 (1898): 408-17.

"Women's Labor Resolution." *American Federationist* 4 (1899): 219-20.

Holmes, Lizzie M. "Not by Bread Alone." *American Federationist* 9 (1902): 11-14.

"Women in Economics." *American Federationist* 9 (1902): 366-7.

Grant, Lake. "Women in Trade Unions." *American Federationist* 10 (1903): 655-6.

Roberts, Peter. "Employment of Girls in Textile Industries of Pennsylvania." *Annals of the American Academy of Political and Social Science* 23 (1904): 434-4.

Yudelson, Sophie. "Women's Place in Industry and Labor Organizations." *Annals of the American Academy of Political and Social Science* 24 (1904): 343-43.

Bretell, Mamie. "Woman's Union Label League." *American Federationist* 12 (1905): 276.

Holmes, Lizzie. "Women Workers of Chicago." *American Federationist* 12 (1905): 507-10.

Falling, William English. "Field of Organization for Women Workers." *American Federationist* 12 (1905): 625-7.

Davis, Philip. "Women in the Cloak Trade." *American Federationist* 12 (1905): 745-7.

Filene, Edward A. "The Betterment of the Conditions of Working Women." *Annals of the American Academy of Political and Social Science* 27 (1906): 613-23.

Yudelsohn, Sophie. "Women in Unions." *American Federationist* 13 (1906): 19-21.

Tabee, Esther. "Women in Unions." *American Federationist* 13 (1906): 85-6.

Teller, Charlotte. "Women in Unions." *American Federationist* 13 (1906): 222-4.

Valesh, Eva McDonald. "Wage Working Women." *American Federationist* 13 (1906): 363-67.

Commons, John R. "Women in Unions." *American Federationist* 13 (1906): 382-4.

"Women Wage Earners." *Nation* 82 (February 22, 1906): 152-3.

"Women and Children in Industry." *Outlook* 85 (May 5, 1906): 12.

"May the Legislation Protect Women and Children." *Outlook* 83 (August 11, 1906): 823.

Mies, Frank P. "Statutory Regulation of Women's Employment." *Journal of Political Economy* 14 (1906): 109-18.

Darr, Rheta Childe. "Bullying the Woman Worker." *Harper's Weekly* 51 (March 30, 1907): 458-9.

"American Women at Men's Work." *Harper's Weekly* 51 (June 8, 1907): 831.

Hard, W. I., and Dorr, Rheta Childe. "Women's Invasion." *Everybody's Magazine* 19 (1908).

"A Women's Strike." *Outlook* 93 (December 11, 1909):

Leupp, Constance D. "Shirtwaist Makers Strike." *Survey* 23 (December 18, 1909): 383-6.

Mailly, William. "The Working Girls Strike." *Independent* 67 (December 23, 1909): 1416-30.

Comstock, S. C. "Uprising of the Girls." *Collier's* 44 (December 25, 1909): 14-6.

Tarbell, Ida M. "The Shirtwaist Strikers." *American Federationist* 17 (1910): 209-10.

Hauser, Elizabeth J. "Women Workers and the Labor Movement." *American Federationist* 17 (1910): 305-6.

Gompers, Samuel. "Good Work for Women by Women." *American Federationist* 17 (1910): 685-6.

"Female Labor Arouses Hostility and Apprehension in Union Ranks." *Current Opinion* 64 (1910): 292-4.

Davis, Philip. "The Shirtwaist Makers' Strike." *Chautaquan* 59 (1910): 99-105.

Stewart, Jane A. "National Women's Trade Union League." *Chautauquan* 59 (1910): 116-20.

"Shirt Shops After the Strike." *Survey* 25 (October 1, 1910): 7-8.

Gompers, Samuel. "The Shirtwaist Strike." *American Federationist* 18 (1911): 44-5.

Women's Trade Union League. "What New York Is Doing To Organize Women." *American Federation* 18 (1911): 141-2.

Mailly, William. "The Triangle Trade Union Relief." *American Federationist* 18 (1911): 544-7.

Potter, Francis Squire. "The Educational Value of the Woman's Trade Union." *Life and Labor* 1 (1911): 36-40.

"The Organization of Women Workers." *Life and Labor* 1 (1911): 342-3.

O'Toole, Kitty. "Protective Legislation for Women." *Life and Labor* 1 (1911): 356-7.

Delzell, Ruth. "1828—First Woman's Strike in America." *Life and Labor* 2 (1912): 82-4.

Andrews, Irene Osgood. "The Courts and Woman's Work." *Life and Labor* 2 (1912): 123.

Delzell, Ruth. "1847—First Ten Hour Law for Women in America." *Life and Labor* 2 (1912): 184-5.

_____. "1825-1851—Organization of Tailoresses and Seamstresses." *Life and Labor* 2 (1912): 242-4.

Crawford, Caroline. "The Hello Girls of Boston." *Life and Labor* 2 (1912): 260-4.

Delzell, Ruth. "1886—Laundry Workers' Union, Troy, New York." *Life and Labor* 2 (1912): 333.

Dell, Margery. "The National Trade Union League of America." *Life and Labor* 2 (1912): 345-6.

Wells, E. L. "Women and Child Wage Earners in the United States." *American Economic Review* 2 (1912): 436-42.

Gannett, Alice. "Bohemian Women in New York." *Life and Labor* 3 (1913): 49-52.

"Uprising in the Needle Trades in New York." *Life and Labor* 3 (1913): 69-71.

"On the Picket Line." *Life and Labor* 3 (1913): 71-3.

Bruere, Martha Bensley. "The White Goods Strikes." *Life and Labor* 3 (1913): 73-5.

Carr, Lillian. "Women of the World Unite, the Lesson of the Washington Parade." *Life and Labor* 3 (1913): 112-6.

Baine, C. L. "Women in the Shoe Industry." *Life and Labor* 3 (1913): 164-7.

"The Candy Workers of Boston." *Life and Labor* 3 (1913): 261-3.

Steghagen, Emma. "A Summer of Strikes in Cincinnati." *Life and Labor* 3 (1913): 333-5.

Gompers, Samuel. "The Struggles in the Garment Trades." *American Federationist* 20 (1913): 185-202.

_____. "Women's Wages and Morality." *American Federationist* 20 (1913): 465-7.

_____. "Woman's Work, Rights and Progress." *American Federationist* 20 (1913): 624-7.

_____. "Working Women Organize." *American Federationist* 21 (1914): 231-4.

"Eight Hours for Women." *American Federationist* 21 (1914): 238-9.

Gompers, Samuel. "Mother Jones Causes a Military Nightmare." *American Federationist* 21 (1914): 405-6.

"Protest of Working Women of New York." *Survey* 31 (February 14, 1914): 605-6.

"Women on the Night Shift." *Life and Labor* 4 (1914): 377-9.

"Women's Right to a Living Wage." *Independent* 81 (January 4, 1915): 4-5.

Andrews, Irene Osgood. "Relation of Irregular Employment to the Living Wage for Women." *American Labor Legislation Review* 5 (1915): 287-418.

MacLean, Annie Marion. "Trade Unionism Versus Welfare Work for Women." *Popular Science Monthly* 87 (1915): 50-5.

O'Brien, Agnes. "Suffrage and the Woman in Industry." *Life and Labor* 5 (1915): 132-3.

Gompers, Samuel. "Coming Into Her Own." *American Federationist* 22 (1915): 517-9.

Fitzgerald, Anna. "Women's International Union Label League and Trade Union Auxiliary." *American Federationist* (1915): 731.

Scott, Melinda. "The Way to Freedom." *American Federationist* 22 (1915): 729-31.

Field, Amy Walker. "More About Herzog Strike." *Life and Labor* 5 (1915): 157-8.

Walsh, Frank P. "Women and Labor." *Life and Labor* 5 (1915): 165.

Field, Amy Walker. "Victory for the Springfield Corset Workers." *Life and Labor* 5 (1915): 168-9.

"Working Hours of Women in Chicago." *Life and Labor* 5 (1915): 171-2.

Obenauer, Marie L. "What Is the United States Bureau of Labor Statistics Doing for Women in Industry?" *Life and Labor* 6 (1916). 67-70.

"The Boot and Shoe Industry in Massachusetts as a Vocation for Women." *Life and Labor* 6 (1916): 88-9.

Taussig, F. W. "Minimum Wages for Women." *Quarterly Journal of Economics* 30 (1916): 411-2.

Gompers, Samuel. "Women Workers Organize and Win." *American Federationist* 23 (1916): 199-201.

_____. "Garment Workers' Heroic Struggle." *American Federationist* 23 (1916): 683-4.

_____. "Ladies' Garment Workers' Victory." *American Federationist* 23 (1916): 847-8.

Holcombe, A. N. "The Effects of the Legal Minimum Wage for Women." *Annals of the American Academy of Political and Social Science* 69 (1917): 34-41.

Wolman, Leo. "Extent of Trade Unionism." *Annals of the American Academy of Political and Social Science* 69 (1917): 125-6.

Thorne, Florence C. "Trend Toward Equality." *American Federationist* 24 (1917): 120-1.

_____. "Women's War Service." *American Federationist* 24 (1917): 455-6.

Gompers, Samuel. "Don't Sacrifice Womanhood." *American Federationist* 24 (1917): 640-1.

Morrison, Harry L. "Trade Organizations and War Problems." *American Federationist* 24 (1917): 732-3.

"Are Many Women Replacing Soldiers in Industrial Work?" *Current Opinion* 64 (1918): 60-1.

"Women in the Industries." *Scientific American* 116 (February 3, 1917): 127.

"Position of the Trade Union Women." *Survey* 38 (June 23, 1917): 277.

Burns, Agnes. "Shirt Makers Win." *Life and Labor* 7 (1917): 63.

Sullivan, Olive M. "One League's Gift to the Nation's Service." *Life and Labor* 7 (1918): 27-8.

_____. "The Women's Part in the Stockyard's Organization Work." *Life and Labor* 7 (1918): 102.

Smith, Ethel M. "At Last—A National Women's Labor Bureau." *Life and Labor* 7 (1918): 159-60.

Aldrich, Amey. "New York's New Women in Industry Bureau." *Life and Labor* 7 (1918): 182-3.

Fawcett, M. E. "Equal Pay for Equal Value." *Contemporary Review* 114 (1918): 387-90.

"Women in Industry." *New Republic* 16 (October 26, 1918): 365-6.

"Regulation of Women's Working Hours in the United States." *American Labor Legislation Review* 8 (1918): 339-54.

"Gravity of the Woman Labor Problem After the War." *Current Opinion* 66 (1919): 61-2.

"What Shall Be Done With Women Who Have Replaced Men in Industry?" *Current Opinion* 66 (1919): 124-5.

Currey, Margery. "The Labor Party for Women." *Life and Labor* 8 (1919): 64-6.

Funk, Bertha. "The Girl in the Gas Mask Plant." *Life and Labor* 8 (1919): 90-1.

Waggaman, Mary T. "National Women's Trade Union League." *Monthly Labor Review* 8 (1919): 1183-90.

"Solidarity." *New Republic* 19 (June 14, 1919): 202-3.

Best, Harry. "Extent of Organization in the Women's Garment Making Industries of New York." *American Economic Review* 9 (1919): 776-92.

Johnson, Agnes. "What the Boot and Shoe Workers' Union Means to Women Members." *Life and Labor* 10 (1920): 102-3.

Bronson, Charlotte. "Because I Am A Women." *Life and Labor* 10 (1920): 173-4.

Campbell, Margaret N. "Organization and the Southern Worker." *Life and Labor* 10 (1920): 312-3.

Huntzinger, Leona. "Why I Joined My Union and What It Has Done for Me." *Life and Labor* 10 (1920): 312-3.

Gompers, Samuel. "Labor and Woman Suffrage." *American Federationist* 27 (1920): 937-9.

Kanka, Mabel. "Women's Struggle for Emancipation." *One Big Union Monthly* 12 (1920): 22-3.

Lape, Esther. "Women in Industry." *New Republic* 25 (January 26, 1921): 251-3.

Gilson, Mary B. "Wages of Women in Industry." *Industrial Management* 61 (June 1, 1921): 427-31.

Fisher, Katherine. "Women Workers and the American Federation of Labor." *New Republic* 27 (August 3, 1921): 265-7.

"The Strike in the New York Garment Industry." *Industrial and Labor Information* (1922): 446.

Wolfson, Theresa. "Education During a Strike." *Survey* 48 (August 15, 1922): 626.

Sigman, Morris. "Ladies' Garment Workers Gain." *American Federationist* 30 (1923): 742-3.

_____. "Garment Workers' Problems." *American Federationist* 30 (1923): 831-2.

"Trade Union Organization Among Woman Workers." *Industrial and Labor Information* 7 (1923): 12.

"Women in Trade Unions." *Monthly Labor Review* 19 (1924): 124-6.

Maher, Amy G. "Women Trade Unionists in the United States." *International Labour Review* 11 (1925): 366-80.

Stewart, Ethelburt. "Trend of Employment of Men and Women in Specified Industries." *Monthly Labor Review* 20 (1925): 739-50.

Miller, Spencer, Jr. "Summer Schools for Workers." *American Federationist* 32 (1925): 569-71.

Perkins, George W. "Women in the Cigar Industry." *American Federationist* 32 (1925): 808-10.

Wolfson, Theresa. "Wages of Organized Women Workers." *American Federationist* 32 (1925): 811-3.

Troxell, John P. "Wisconsin's Summer School for Working Women." *American Federationist* 32 (1925): 943-5.

Carroll, Mollie Ray. "Women Workers and the Minimum Wage." *American Federationist* 32 (1925):1155-8.

Cook, Cara. "Women Who Work for Wages." *American Federationist* 33 (1926): 454-9.

Johnson, Ethel M. "The Problem of Women in Industry." *American Federationist* 33 (1926): 974-7.

Wolfson, Theresa. "Schools the Miners Keep." *Survey* 56 (June 1, 1926): 308-10.

Craton, Ann Washington. "Working the Woman Workers." *Nation* 124 (March 23, 1927): 311-3.

Witte, E. E. "The Effects of Special Labor Legislation for Women." *Quarterly Journal of Economics* 42 (1927):

153-64.

Carmer, Lucy. "Shorter Hours for Women Workers." *American Federationist* 35 (1928): 1246-9.

Johnson, Ethel M. "Fifteen Years of Minimum Wage in Massachusetts." *American Federationist* 35 (1928): 1469-77.

Winslow, Mary N. "The Effects of Labor Legislation on Women's Work." *Annals of the American Academy of Political and Social Science* 143 (1929): 280-300.

Wolfson, Theresa. "Trade Union Activities of Women." *Annals of the American Academy of Political and Social Science* 143 (1929): 120-31.

Herstein, Lillian. "Women Discuss Wages." *American Federationist* 36 (1929): 949-59.

Trouland, Belle. "The Women's Local." *American Federationist* 36 (1929): 970-1.

Lindsay, Matilda. "Southern Women in Industry." *American Federationist* 36 (1929): 973-5.

Andrews, Nellie. "Organizing Women." *American Federationist* 36 (1929): 976-7.

Katzor, Clara. "Shoemaker's Story." *American Federationist* 36 (1929): 976-7.

Lowther, Mrs. R. J. "The Typographical Woman's International Auxiliary." *American Federationist* 36 (1929): 980-3.

Geisinger, Anna. "What the Union Has Accomplished." *American Federationist* 36 (1929): 983.

Hohn, Gertrude. "Why the Union." *American Federationist* 36 (1929): 1060-1.

Hochman, Julius. "Organizing the Dressmakers." *American Federationist* 36 (1929): 1462-7.

Nagler, Isidore. "Wages, Hours and Employment." *American Federationist* 36 (1929): 1468-71.

Kotchin, Morris. "The Ladies' Garment Industry." *American Federationist* 36 (1929): 1472-7.

"Hosiery Workers Open Campaign." *American Federationist* 38 (1931): 745-8.

Maher, A. G. "Employment of Women." *Social Service Review* 5 (1931): 28-36.

Anderson, Mary. "Women in Industries." *American Federationist* 39 (1932): 182-7.

Miller, Frieda S. "Women's Place—What Will Determine It?" *American Federationist* 39 (1932): 287-90.

Anderson, Mary. "With Women Workers in the Stockyards." *American Federationist* 39 (1932): 556-60.

———. "What Canneries Mean to Women." *American Federationist* 39 (1932): 1375-81.

Rosinos, Jean E. "Marching Women of Illinois." *Labor Age* 21 (1932): 6-7.

Kula, Anna. "The Dress Strike." *Labor Age* 21 (1932): 12.

———. "Local 66 Proves It Can Be Done." *Labor Age* 21 (1932): 12.

Ogden, Jean. "Organizing the Food Workers." *Labor Age* 21 (1932): 13.

Krupskaya, N. K. "March 8th, 1932, International Women's Day." *Labour Monthly* 14 (1932): 158-61.

Anderson, Mary. "Unemployed Women and Public Works." *American Labor Legislation Review* 24 (1932): 38-40.

Pell, Orlie. "A Workers' School for the Office Worker." *American Federationist* 42 (1935): 622-4.

"Nineteenth Session of the International Labor Conference; Employment on Underground Work in Mines of All Kinds." *International Labour Review* 32 (1935): 302-4.

Loughlin, Ann. "Women Trade Unionists." *American Federationist* 42 (1935): 1178-9.

Starr, Mark. "Trade Union Pioneers in Education." *American Federationist* 43 (1936): 54-60.

Pruette, Lorine. "Women Workers Have Come Through." *American Scholar* 5 (1936): 328-36.

Wolfson, Theresa. "Should White Collar Workers Organize?" *Independent Woman* 15 (1936): 356.

MacDonald, A. H. "Lowell: A Commercial Utopia." *New England Quarterly* 10 (1937): 37-62.

Newman, Pauline M. "Equal Rights Amendment." *American Federationist* 45 (1938): 815-7.

"Employment of Women in U.S. Defense Industries." *International Labour Review* 43 (1941): 98-100.

Davis, Allen F. "The Women's Trade Union League: Origins and Organization." *Labor History* 5 (1964): 3-17.

"Women in Defense Industry." *American Federationist* 48 (1941): 6-8.

Vernon, H. M. "Women in Industry." *New Statesman and Nation* 22 (December 13, 1941): 488.

Anderson, Mary. "Women in War Industry." *American Federationist* 48 (1942): 18-9.

Punke, H. H. "Democracy and the Employment of Women." *South Atlantic Quarterly* 41 (1942): 425-6.

Perkins, Frances. "Women War Workers Must East." *Social Service Review* 17 (1943): 372-3.

Anderson, Mary. "Industry, Women, Safety, and Health." *American Journal of Nursing* 43 (1943): 275-8.

Shackleton, Peggy. "Women in Industry." *Labour Monthly* 25 (1943): 218-21.

Leevy, J. R. "Modern Industrial Working Woman." *American Sociological Review* 8 (1943): 720-2.

"Post-War Employment of Women in the United States." *International Labour Review* 49 (1944): 224.

Campbell, Mary. "Women Workers—A Challenge." *American Federationist* 51 (1944): 31.

"Women's Employment in the United States." *International Labour Review* 51 (1945): 638-9.

Miller, F. S. "Female Worker." *American Federationist* 52 (1945): 20.2.

Merrill, L. T. "Mill Town on the Merrimack." *New England Quarterly* 19 (1946): 19-31.

Wolfbein, S. L., and Jaffe, A. J. "Demographic Factors in Labor Force Growth." *American Sociological Review* 11 (1946): 392-6.

Green, William. "Women Who Work and Trade Unions." *American Federationist* 55 (1948): 19.

"One Hundred Years After Seneca Falls, 1848-1948." *Social Service Review* 22 (1948): 254.

"Equal Pay for Equal Work in the United States." *International Labour Review* 58 (1948): 391-4.

Josselyn, I. M., and Goldman. R. S. "Should Mothers Work?" *Social Service Review* 23 (1949): 74-87.

Heffner, B. B. "Women in Trade Unionism." *American Federationist* 57 (1950): 22.

Miller, Frieda S. "They Need the Money: That's the Reason Why Women Work." *American Federationist* 57 (1950): 28-31.

"Negro Women Workers." *Social Service Review* 24 (1950): 255-6.

"Women's Wages." *Social Service Review* 24 (1950): 256.

Miller, Frieda S. "Women at Work, Then and Now." *American Federationist* 58 (1951): 10-1.

Turner, R. H. "Children and Women's Work." *Sociology & Social Research* 36 (1952): 377-81.

Lee, P. M. "Why Not More Women in Public Office?" *National Municipal Review* 43 (1954): 307-8.

Aumont, Michele. "Women in the Factory." *International Labour Review* 74 (1956): 345-62.

Muntz, E. E. "Women's Changing Role in the United States." *International Labour Review* 74 (1956): 415-36.

Pratt, Nancy. "When Women Work." *American Federationist* 64 (1957): 7-9.

"Women in the Labour Force." *International Labour Review* 77 (1958): 254-72.

"Child Care Facilities for Women Workers." *International Labour Review* 78 (1958): 91-109.

"Women at Work." *Economist* 188 (August 23, 1958): 603.

Marcus, M. R. "Women in the Labor Force." *Social Casework* 41 (1960): 298-302.

"The Woman Workers and the Labour Movement." *Labour Gazette* (November 30, 1960): 1120-2.

"Women at Work." *Economist* 201 (October 28, 1961): 343.

Solomon, B. M. "Women's Archives." *Social Service Review* 36 (1962): 325-7.

"Equal Is As Equal Earns." *Economist* 204 (August 11, 1962): 526.

"To Do a Man's Job," *Economist* 211 (April 18, 1964): 270.

Peterson, Esther. "Status of Women in the United States." *International Labour Review* 89 (1964): 447-60.

CZ

Keniston, Ellen, and Keniston, Kenneth. "American Anachronism: The Image of Women and Work," *American Scholar* 33 (1964): 355-75.

"Occupational Training of Women in the United States." *International Labour Review* 90 (1964): 573-4.

"Work-Happy Women." *Economist* 222 (January 14, 1967): 130.

Leary, J. P. "Women in American Society Today." *Thought* 42 (1967): 112-20.

Cook, Alice. "Women and American Trade Unions." *Annals of the American Academy of Political and Social Science* 375 (1968): 124-32.

Suelzle, Marijean. "Women in Labor." *Transaction* 8 (1970): 56.

Dewey, Lucretia. "Women in Labor Unions." *Monthly Labour Review* (1971): 42.

Coser, R. L., and Rokoff, Gerald. "Women in the Occupational Field: Social Disruption and Conflicts." *Social Problems* 18 (1971): 535-54.

Smichak, M. M. "Equal Pay in the United States." *International Labour Review* 103 (1971): 541-7.

Donahue, M. P. "Female Labor Force in the United States." *Geographical Review* 61 (1971): 440-2.

Goldstein, M. I. "Blue Collar Women and the American Labor Unions." *Industrial and Labor Relations Forum* 7 (1971): 1-35.

Friedman, Joel W. "Sex and the Law." *Industrial and Labor Relations Forum* 7 (1971): 36-65.

Jacobson, Carolyn. "Some Special Problems the Older Woman Encounters When Seeking Employment." *Industrial and Labor Relations Forum* 7 (1971): 66-75.

Glazer, P. M. "Organizing for Freedom." *Massachusetts Review* 13 (1972): 29-44.

Wright, Helena. "Uncommon Mill Girls of Lowell." *History Today* 23 (1973): 10-9.

Stevenson, Mary. "Women's Wages and Job Segregation." *Politics & Society* 4 (1973): 83-96.

Kenneally, James J. "Women and Trade Unions, 1870-1920: The Quandry of the Reformer." *Labor History* 14 (1973): 42-55.

Lemons, J. S. "Social Feminism in the 1920's: Progressive Women and Industrial Legislation." *Labor History* 14 (1973): 83-91.

Dreifus, Claudia. "Trade Union Women's Conference—First Time in New York." *Nation* 218 (March 30, 1974): 402-4.

Sexton, Patricia Cayo. "Workers (Female) Arise!" *Dissent* 21 (Summer 1974): 380-95.

Hudson, G. H. "Women, Too, in American History." *Crisis* 81 (1974): 229-31.

Davies, Margery. "The Feminization of White Collar Occupations." Paper read at the Second Berkshire Conference, October 26, 1974, at Radcliffe College.

Dublin, Thomas. "Women, Work and the Family: Women Operatives in the Lowell Mills, 1830-1860." Paper read at the Second Berkshire Conference, October 26, 1974, at Radcliffe College.

Harris, Alice Kessler. "Problems of Class and Culture in Organizing Women Workers; 1900-1920." Paper read at the Second Berkshire Conference, October 26, 1974, at Radcliffe College.

Hareven, Tamara K. "Women's Time, Family Time and Industrial Time: An Analysis of the Relationship of Work Careers and Family Conditions of Women Workers in Manchester, New Hampshire, 1910-1940." Paper read at the Second Berkshire Conference, October 26, 1974, at Radcliffe College.

Oates, Mary J. "Occupational Segregation: A Case Study of American Clerical Workers 1970-1930." Paper read at the Second Berkshire Conference, October 26, 1974, at Radcliffe College.

Rupp, Leila. "A Reappraisal of American Women in a Men's War, 1941-45." Paper read at the Second Berkshire Conference, October 26, 1974, at Radcliffe College.

Schramm, Sarah Slavin. "The Question of Female Consciousness as Seen in the Response to the Economy Act of 1932." Paper read at the Second Berkshire Conference, October 26, 1974, at Radcliffe College.

Seller, Maxine S. "Immigrant Women in Leadership Roles within Amrican Ethnic Communities, 1890-1924; Three Case Studies." Paper read at the Second Berkshire Conference, October 26, 1974, at Radcliffe College.

Smith, Judith. "The 'New Woman' Knows How to Type: Some Connections Between Sexual Ideology and Clerical Work, 1890-1930." Paper read at the Second Berkshire Conference, October 26, 1974, at Radcliffe College.

Vinyard, JoEllen. "From Europe to Urban America: Immigrant Women in 19th Century Detroit." Paper read at the Second Berkshire Conference, October 26, 1974, at Radcliffe, College.

Vogel, Lise. 'The Lowell Mill-Women in the 1840's: Consciousness, Ideology, and Organization." Paper read at the Second Berkshire Conference, October 26, 1974, at Radcliffe College.

Dye, Nancy Schrom. "Creating A Feminist Alliance: Sisterhood and Class Conflict in the New York Women's Trade Union League, 1903-1914." *Feminist Studies* 2 (1975): 24-38.

Niemi, Beth, and Lloyd, Cynthia. "Sex Differentials in Earnings and Unemployment Rates." *Feminist Studies* 2 (1975): 195-201.

Dye, Nancy Shrom. "The WTUL and Organized Labor." *Feminist Studies,* in press.

Jacoby, Robin. "The WTUL and American Feminism." *Feminist Studies,* in press.